API

-Fact or Fallacy?

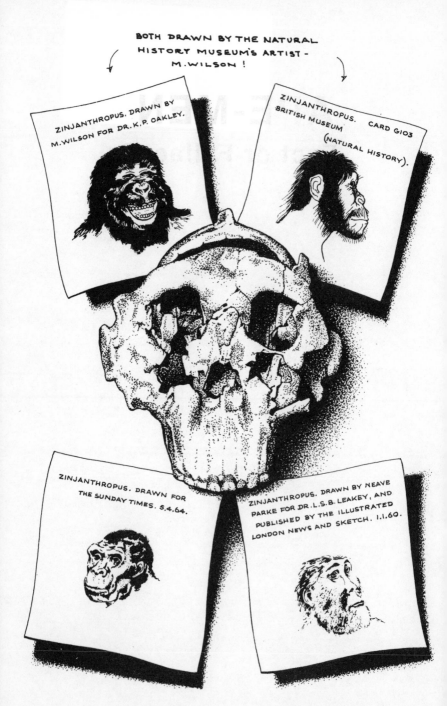

Four different artistic impressions of Zinjanthropus boisei

APE-MEN
-Fact or Fallacy?

A critical examination of the evidence
by
Malcolm Bowden.

SOVEREIGN PUBLICATIONS
P.O. Box 88
Bromley
Kent
BR2 9PF

SOVEREIGN PUBLICATIONS
P.O. Box 88, Bromley, Kent, BR2 9PF

Copyright © M. Bowden 1977

First edition 1978
Second Edition 1981
Reprinted 1988

ISBN 0 9506042 1 6

Typeset by Solo Typesetting, Maidstone, Kent
Printed in Great Britain by The Bath Press, Avon.

CONTENTS

Acknowledgements

I must record my grateful thanks to the Estate of C. S. Lewis for permission to publish his letter on p.35 and to the editors of 'Punch' for the article on p.228. Particular thanks are due to Mr. and Mrs. Taylor for the extensive and helpful notes they made on the manuscript, and to Mrs. Audrey Hooker who coped ably with the difficult task of typing the manuscript. I must also thank Mr. C. Kuss for some items included in the second edition regarding Pekin Man, dealt with on pages 95-6. I am grateful to Mr. Jan van Ijken for his extensive translation of Reck's paper dealing with the Olduvai skeleton. Finally I must express my gratitude to my wife for her patience and her assistance with the labour involved in writing this book.

Dedication

This book is dedicated to those of my readers who are prepared to accept the evidence which it presents, even though it may conflict with popular preconceptions.

Author's Note

Whilst every care has been taken in the extensive research for this book, errors may nevertheless have occurred. Correction of these and any new evidence brought to the author's notice will be incorporated in future editions.

Illustrations

The cover picture, frontispiece and Figs. 1, 2 and 3 were drawn by Mr. W. Taylor. All other illustrations were drawn by the author.

LIST OF ILLUSTRATIONS

INTRODUCTION

MISSING LINK FOUND!
MAN'S APE ANCESTRY PROVEN!

Headlines such as these in newspapers throughout the world have heralded the discovery of a variety of fossil bones, ever since the publication of Darwin's *Origin of Species* in 1859.

With so much publicity surrounding these fossils, scientists specialising in this subject, and the general public, assume the evidence supporting the ape-man links to be so substantial as to establish them beyond any reasonable doubt.

But are they right?

In this book I have examined the 'credentials' of those fossil discoveries which are said to be the main links between man and that animal ancestor which he has in common with the apes. Except for one letter (p35), only published works have been used, and a series of composite pictures have been built up, in which many conflicting factors become apparent. Whether there is room for doubt regarding the far reaching claims made for many of these fossils will be left for the reader to judge as the evidence is laid before him.

It can doubtless be argued that the study of fossil bones is an advanced and highly technical science, and criticism by one whose qualifications are not in this particular field is of no value. To this I would reply that no matter how technically involved a field of enquiry may be, in order to be entitled a 'science' it must be seen clearly to conform with the basic principles of scientific investigation. These would include such fundamental considerations as:

(i) the presentation of *all* the relevant evidence,
(ii) the interpretation should encompass all the available evidence and as far as possible be free from any preconceptions,
(iii) the rejection of any hypothesis which is contradicted by any of the evidence.

I have endeavoured to show that the interpretation, which has been superimposed upon many fossil remains, does not comply with one or more of the basic criteria given above. Assessment of whether the evidence and theories conform with these fundamental requirements does not need any special scientific expertise, and the layman's judgement can be as valid as that of the expert. Much research is condensed and summarised for presentation in popular works, but when criticising any particular aspect, it is often necessary to refer to the original papers, sometimes in detail. I have tried, however, to set out any complex issues as clearly as possible, so that the reader is easily able to grasp the various points being discussed.

I have only the highest regard for eminent scientists of undoubted integrity, who study fossils, write reports, and carry out very highly skilled tests in the course of their work. However, in the particular field of fossil man, I do question the very speculative assumptions made, and the far-reaching conclusions based upon very meagre evidence. It must be remembered that the 'fossil hunter' has often a subconscious desire to fit his discoveries to his preconceptions, whether or not they are in line with current expert opinion. On this, I can do no better than quote Vayson de Pradenne, who was Director of the École des Hautes Études, and Professor at the École d'Anthropologie. In his book *Fraudes Archéologiques*, published 1925, he gives a hypothetical instance of an archaeologist finding two types of artefacts, coarse and highly finished, in the same excavation. Assuming that the coarser articles were earlier, and at a lower level, he will class them according to type and not by the stratum in which they were found. Finding an advanced implement at a low level, he will assume that it reached there accidentally, and he will class it with the others at the higher level. De Pradenne concludes:

> He will end with real trickery in the stratigraphic presentation of his specimens; trickery in aid of a pre-conceived idea, but more or less unconsciously done by a man of good faith whom no one would call fraudulent. The case is often seen, and if I mention no names it is not because I do not know any.

Introduction to Second Edition

Subsequent to the publication of the first edition, further revelations concerning the Piltdown hoax were made in November 1978. In the same year, 'humanoid' footprints were reported to have been discovered at Laetolil and information on the 'Ten skeletons' of Pekin was obtained. Whilst incorporating these, the opportunity was taken of making a full investigation of the discoveries of Richard Leakey at East Rudolf, and of D. C. Johanson at Hadar in Ethiopia. It is therefore hoped that this work now includes all the main fossils discovered up to the present time, which purport to link man with an ape-like ancestor.

NOTES

1   All emphasis in italics in quoted passages are by the author of this book, unless otherwise noted.
2   Reference numbers of publications are given in the bibliography.
3   As an indication of the scale of illustrations of fossils, a distance of 10 cm. is indicated by two vertical marks, and 5 cm. by two dots.

SECTION I

THE PILTDOWN FORGERY

Ever since the publication of the fraudulent nature of the fossil remains discovered at Piltdown in 1912, various efforts have been made to unravel the mystery of the identity of the hoaxer. Despite several publications being produced on this topic, no convincing solution has been provided so far, and the whole affair has remained an enigma to this day.

The conjunction, however, of a few small, but vital, pieces of evidence, hitherto virtually unnoticed, focuses considerable suspicion upon one person who has hardly been considered seriously by previous investigators. Furthermore, they raise a number of questions which reach beyond that quiet corner of the Sussex Downs, which was the centre of interest that excited our forefathers over sixty years ago.

Unravelling the intricate strands of evidence is far from easy, and several digressions have to be made in order to examine particular aspects of the mystery surrounding both the original discoveries and the subsequent research which exposed them as frauds.

The drama, for such it is, involves a number of people, and I will at this stage introduce the principal characters and the parts which they play.

The main excavators at Piltdown were:

Charles Dawson, a solicitor, living at Uckfield, and an amateur archaeologist and historian (Fig.1)

Sir Arthur Smith Woodward, F.R.S., Keeper of the Geological Department, British Museum, and a friend of Dawson. (Fig.2)

Pierre Teilhard de Chardin, student at the Jesuit College, Ore Place, Hastings from 1908. Ordained there in 1911. (Fig.3)

Other friends of Dawson, who worked at the pit at various times, included:

S. Woodhead, a public analyst,

R. Essex, M.Sc., a science master at Uckfield Grammar School,

A. S. Kennard, an amateur but expert palaeontologist.

Three acquaintances of Dawson who knew of the discoveries, and suspected him of planting some fraudulently stained fossils were:

Major Marriot.

Capt. Guy St. Barbe.

H. Morris, an amateur collector.

3

A notable expert who studied the fossils carefully was,

    Sir Arthur Keith, F.R.S., Hunterian professor of the Royal College of Surgeons.

The finds were made in the drive leading to Barkham Manor, owned by a friend of Dawson, Mr. R. Kenward, who lived there with his daughter.

    Miss Mabel Kenward, who died in 1978.

The fraud was exposed in 1953, and reports on the subject were written by:

    Professor K. P. Oakley, of the British Museum (Natural History).

    Sir Wilfrid Le Gros Clark, Professor of Anatomy, Oxford.

    Dr. J. S. Weiner, M.A., M.Sc., Ph.D., M.R.C.S., Reader in Physical Anthropology, Oxford.

Dr. Weiner wrote a book about the hoax entitled *The Piltdown Forgery*, in which he claimed that Dawson was the most likely culprit. He interviewed all those connected with the original discovery who were still alive, namely, Teilhard de Chardin, Sir Arthur Keith, R. Essex, and Miss Kenward. Weiner's accusation of Dawson was refuted by Miss Kenward, and her friend,

    Francis Vere, an author and historian living at Piltdown, who wrote and broadcast in Dawson's defence.

Having met the main characters, we will now examine the tangled web of evidence and suspects involved in what must surely rank as the most notorious scientific fraud of all time.

THE DISCOVERIES

Charles Dawson was an enthusiastic amateur archaeologist, who had made a number of unusual historical finds in the Kent and Sussex areas. Seeing workmen digging in a trench in about 1906–8, he asked them to keep an eye open for anything of archaeological interest. In 1908, one of the workmen struck and shattered what he thought was a coconut, but later realized was part of a fossilized skull. A piece of it was handed to Dawson, who continued excavating in the trench with various friends for several years. In 1911 he found another skull piece which fitted the first piece he had been given, and in 1912 he took them to his friend, Sir Arthur Smith Woodward, F.R.S., Keeper of the Geological Department of the British Museum. According to letters which Dawson wrote to Woodward, he had also found some other fossils, including a tooth of a hippopotamus. Woodward, in his book [38], said that Dawson had found five skull pieces, flint tools and teeth of hippopotamus and elephant before he visited Woodward.

On Saturday, 2nd June 1912, Smith Woodward and Dawson began excavating in the trench. Assisting them was Teilhard de Chardin, who is well known today for his philosophical writings, which

Fig.1.
Charles Dawson

Fig.2.
Sir Arthur Smith Woodward

Fig.3.
Teilhard de Chardin

attempt to reconcile and combine the theory of evolution with the Christian Faith. During the first day of the excavation, another piece of the skull was found by Dawson and a piece of an elephant's molar by Teilhard. On a later occasion, whilst Woodward was watching Dawson digging, a half jaw 'flew out' [40] from the excavation close to the spot where a flint tool had been found. Eventually, a total of nine cranium pieces were collected, which, when fitted together, were very much like a modern human skull, but much thicker than average. The jaw, however, closely resembled that of an ape, but the teeth in it were flat topped, which is a human characteristic. That both cranium and jaw belonged to the same individual was assumed, and this was thought to indicate that man's brain had developed in advance of the rest of the skeleton. The skull bones discovered are illustrated in Fig.4 whilst Fig.5 gives the names of the main human skull bones and teeth for general information.

During this season's dig (the trench was flooded during the winter months), they found another piece of the Pleistocene elephant's tooth (later considered to be *Elephas planifrons*), and teeth of hippopotamus, mastodon and beaver, as well as several flint tools, one of the tools being found by Teilhard.

In December 1912, the findings were presented to a packed meeting of the Geological Society in London. A number of experts, however, were not convinced, as the brain case was too human, compared with the very ape-like characteristics of the jaw. Unfortunately, the jaw was broken and the canine tooth was missing. Had this tooth been found, it would have clearly indicated whether the jaw was human or ape-like. In apes the canines are pointed, whereas human canines are flatter. Woodward was convinced that this tooth could be found, and even made a model of the tooth to show how it would look.

In honour of its discoverer, the skull was named *Eoanthropus dawsoni* (Dawson's Dawn man).

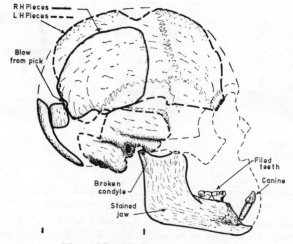

Fig.4. The Piltdown I skull pieces

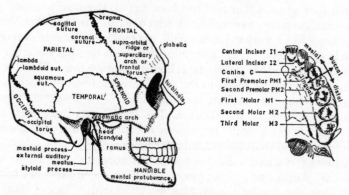

Fig.5. Main features of the human skull and teeth

The canine tooth

On 29th August 1913, Teilhard de Chardin stayed overnight with
Dawson and went with him and Woodward to the Piltdown pit the
following day. Woodward wrote the following eyewitness account
of the finding of the missing canine tooth:

> For some time, we had been making an intensive search for the missing
> teeth of the lower jaw round the spot where the half of the jaw was
> found. We had worked and sieved much of the gravel, and had spread
> it for examination after washing by rain. We were then excavating a
> rather deep and hot trench in which Father Teilhard, in black clothing,
> was especially energetic and, as we thought, a little exhausted; we sug-
> gested that he should leave us to do the hard labour for a time while he
> had comparative rest in searching the rain-washed gravel. Very soon

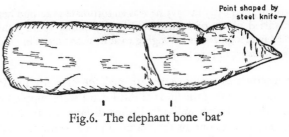

Point shaped by
steel knife

Fig.6. The elephant bone 'bat'

Fig.7. The Piltdown II fossils

he exclaimed that he had picked up the missing canine tooth, but we were incredulous and told him we had already seen several bits of iron-stone which looked like teeth, on the spot where he stood. He insisted, however, that he was not deceived, so we both left our digging to go and verify his discovery. There could be no doubt about it, and we all spent the rest of the day until dusk crawling over the ground in the vain quest for more.[38p11]

The discovery was reported at a meeting in December 1913, which mentioned the finding of a third piece of 'Stegodon' (*Elephas*) tooth, a beaver's incisor, a fragment of a rhinoceros tooth, and the turbinal nose bones of the skull.

The finding of the tooth, which was partially flattened as in humans, convinced many scientists that the jaw and cranium were from the same individual. It did much to strengthen the importance of the finds. Further excavations, in 1914, resulted in the discovery of some teeth of rhinoceros and mastodon, and more important, part of an elephant's thigh bone, which looked rather like a 'bat' or club (Fig.6), apparently shaped as some form of tool. [42]

The Piltdown II site
In addition, in a field two miles away, usually referred to as the Piltdown II site, two pieces of thick cranium and a molar tooth were found by Dawson (Fig.7). In his 1917 report, Woodward said:

One large field, about 2 miles from the Piltdown Pit, specially attracted Dawson's attention, and he and I examined it several times without success during the spring and autumn of 1914. When, however, in the course of farming, the stones had been raked off the ground and brought together in heaps, Mr. Dawson was able to search the material more satisfactorily; and early in 1915 he was so fortunate as to find here two well-fossilized pieces of human skull and a molar tooth, which he immediately recognised as belonging to at least one more individual of *Eoanthropus dawsoni*. [43p144]

These discoveries further strengthened the case for the Piltdown man, as it indicated that the finds at Piltdown I were supplemented by the discovery of another individual some distance away. However, it is almost certain that one of the cranium pieces came from the same skull that was being discovered at Piltdown I site. In addition, there is no record of when the discoveries were made and even the field in which they were found cannot be identified with any certainty. The whole of the circumstances surrounding the finds at Piltdown II is veiled in the mists of obscurity.

EXPOSURE OF THE HOAX

In 1950, the fluorine test was applied to the skull and jaw to check if they were of the same age, and to what stratum they should be attributed. The tests confirmed that they could both be attributed to the middle or probably upper Pleistocene Age [44]. These tests, however, were completely contradicted by a second fluorine test three years later.

The human skull and ape-like jaw of Piltdown were the opposite form of development to that indicated by the Pekin man finds and others, which were being excavated prior to the Second World War. These possessed an ape-like brain but were said to have human characteristics in the jaw and teeth. These two lines of man's evolution appeared to contradict each other, and eventually the possibility of fraud was considered. Further fluorine and other tests on the Piltdown jaw and skull pieces in 1953 showed this time that they were of completely different ages, the skull being upper Pleistocene, as originally believed, but the jaw was found to be quite modern although it had been stained to appear old and the teeth had been filed [45]. Investigation of the other fossils also found, showed that many of them were faked and imported from other sites [46]. The elephant bone 'bat' was apparently shaped with a steel tool, probably a knife, in modern times.

Publication of the discovery of the fraud caused considerable embarrassment in scientific circles, for the experts of the day, who had made such sweeping statements based on these bones, had been completely fooled by the hoaxer. Such was the concern that a motion was tabled in the House of Commons, 'That the House has no confidence in the Trustees of the British Museum . . . because of the tardiness of their discovery that the skull of the Piltdown man is a partial fake.'

The British Museum mounted a special exhibition of the methods by which the fraud was exposed, which was presented as a 'triumph of science', but the odium that the fraud had lain undetected in their possession for forty years remained.

Investigations began to discover the culprit. Attention focussed on Dawson, the enthusiastic amateur, and in 1955 Dr. Weiner, published *The Piltdown Forgery*. In this he felt that the weight of evidence suggested that Dawson perpetrated the fraud. He did allow however the slight possibility that he may have been the innocent victim of a hoaxer with the character of Mephistopheles. Some people living locally, however, were convinced that Dawson was not guilty, among them Miss Mabel Kenward, who lived at Barkham Manor where the finds had been made, and her friend, Mr. Francis Vere, a historian, who examined the evidence. Vere subsequently published *The Piltdown Fantasy* and *Lessons of Piltdown*, which are a thoroughly researched and convincing proof that Dawson was not the culprit. The reader is referred to these publications for the detailed refutation of the evidence which implicates Dawson.

Sir Arthur Keith, a professor at the Royal College of Surgeons, and a President of the Royal Anthropological Institute, who worked extensively on the Piltdown fossils, was also impressed by Dawson's personality. In his book, *The Antiquity of Man*, he said in a footnote,

> Mr. Dawson died on 10th August 1916, aged fifty two, deeply regretted by all who knew him, not only on account of his great discoveries *but also because of his sterling ability and unselfish personality*. [p486]

If Dawson was not the hoaxer, the question arises, 'Who was?'

A suspect

One of those who assisted in the excavations is invariably exonerated, in view of his absence from the country when several faked items were discovered. In the course of reading about this intriguing mystery, I noticed three comments made by different writers, which dramatically altered the sequence of events as they are usually given, even in official publications. This new evidence made it possible for all the faked material to have been placed by the person I now suspected.

I refer to Teilhard de Chardin.

UNRAVELLING THE EVIDENCE

In order to simplify the unravelling of complex situations and evidence, I set out briefly, under the subject headings I will use, my approach to the problem and my reasons for suspecting that Teilhard de Chardin was the hoaxer.

1. Chronology of events

It is essential to establish the correct sequence of events concerning dates of discovery, arrivals and departures, as they are important aspects of this whole problem. It will be shown that the published accounts are incorrect on several important features as follows:

A. EARLY DISCOVERIES OF GENUINE SKULL PIECES

Woodward and Teilhard are usually exonerated because the first cranium piece, which Dawson found and which is considered to be a fake, was discovered in 1908, one year before Teilhard met Dawson and four years before Woodward visited the site. Evidence will be produced to show that this cranium was not a fake but a genuine fossil, and therefore Teilhard could have planted the other fakes before the systematic excavation began in 1912.

B. LATER FINDS

Teilhard is further exonerated, as he left England in October 1913, whilst the fraudulent elephant bone 'bat' was found in 1914 and the discoveries made at Piltdown II site not until 1915. We will show that according to Teilhard, the Piltdown II finds were in fact made in 1913 before he left England. He could, therefore, also have planted these fossils. Furthermore, we will see that Teilhard was in England *after* the elephant's 'bat' had been discovered in 1914.

Having shown that Teilhard *could* have been the perpetrator of the hoax, we will briefly consider Woodward's position and then examine the following evidence, showing how it exonerates Dawson and implicates Teilhard.

2. Evidence

A. ICHKEUL FOSSIL
B. ELEPHANT BONE 'BAT'
C. ANTHROPOLOGICAL EXPERTISE
D. STAINING OF BONES

3. Additional evidence

A. EARLY FINDS
B. CANINE DISCOVERY
C. MORRIS' NOTE
D. KNOWLEDGE OF HOAX

Fig.8 is a table of the accepted sequence of events at Piltdown, and the events as I consider they actually occurred.

Having set out the major headings, we will now examine the evidence in detail.

YEAR	ACCEPTED SEQUENCE OF EVENTS	REVISED SEQUENCE OF EVENTS
1908	Dawson finds skull piece	Skull piece handed to Dawson
1909	Dawson meets Teilhard	Dawson meets Teilhard
1910		
1911	Dawson finds further skull pieces fossils and artefacts	Dawson finds further skull piece(s?)
1912	Dawson finds Hippo tooth EXCAVATION BEGINS (Dawson, Woodward and Teilhard) More skull pieces, jaw, fossils and artefacts found Geological Society meeting	(Dawson finds Hippo tooth ?) EXCAVATION BEGINS Skull pieces, jaw, fossils and artefacts found. Geological Society meeting
1913	(Piltdown II fossils found ?) Canine tooth found Teilhard's final departure from England Geological Society meeting	Teilhard shown Piltdown II site Canine tooth found Teilhard leaves England Geological Society meeting
1914	Elephant 'Bat' found Geological Society meeting.	Elephant 'Bat' found Teilhard returns to England. 'Bat' discussed, Teilhard present (Appendix I) Teilhard's final departure from England Geological Society meeting
1915	Piltdown II fossils found ?	Piltdown II fossils found
1916	Dawson died	Dawson died
1917	Woodward publishes Piltdown II finds	Woodward publishes Piltdown II finds

(Fake items are underlined)

Fig.8. The sequence of events at Piltdown

1. Chronology of events

A. EARLY DISCOVERIES OF GENUINE SKULL PIECES

In various publications, evidence is produced to show that, like the jaw, the cranium fragments were faked and planted in the excavation, probably by Dawson. It is my contention, and that of Vere and Miss Kenward, that they are genuine fossil skull pieces which were found embedded in the gravel by the workmen, and I set out the following evidence in support.

(i) When the 'evidence' of the faking of the skull pieces was published, Miss Kenward wrote to the papers. On the 23rd February 1955 the *Telegraph* published her letter in which she said:

One day when they were digging in unmoved gravel, one of the workmen saw what he called a coconut. He broke it with his pick, kept one piece and threw the rest away.

From this, it is clear that the skull was found in *undisturbed* gravel. The bones were stained with iron for their full thickness, as would be expected in the iron rich water of Piltdown.

(ii) Vere gives [32p7] an account of the circumstances of the initial discovery of the skull which he had obviously obtained from Miss Kenward.

More recently, the first discovery of the skull pieces was most graphically described to me by Miss Mabel Kenward herself. She remembers seeing from her window her father, Mr. Robert Kenward, standing by the pit looking at the workmen, while they were digging in the gravel. One of them said there was something just like a coconut in the pit, and her father said that they should take care how they got it out, but before he could stop them, a blow from the pick shattered the skull and pieces flew in all directions. He picked up as many pieces as he could find and came into the house, whereupon Miss Kenward exclaimed, 'What on earth have you loaded up your pockets with all those old stones for?' He laid them out on the table and looked at them, but later returned them to the workmen, telling them to give them to Mr. Dawson next time he came. She could not say, of course, whether all the pieces were given to Dawson by the workmen. Presumably, as recounted by Miss Kenward and Woodward, the workman kept one piece which he later handed to Dawson, and threw the rest away.

Although there are noticeable differences in the various accounts, it is quite clear that the skull was embedded in undisturbed gravel and had to be broken out with a pick.

(iii) Major Marriot, who was living at the time of the excavations, considered that Dawson was 'salting the mine', and told his daughter that the jaw and tooth were faked [36p164]. He thus appeared to accept that the *skull pieces at least* were not fraudulently stained. As he almost certainly knew of the circumstances surrounding the discovery of them by the workmen, he probably accepted them as genuine, but considered Dawson guilty of adding the faked jaw and tooth.

(iv) Knowing that the workmen had found one piece and thrown the rest away, Dawson would have been very foolish at that stage to have tried to switch skulls, as it is suggested he might have done. It would have required the finding of only one piece of the original skull to have cast doubts on any of the finds which he planted.

(v) The official report of the discovery [40] says that one of the skull fragments found had been hit with a pick, thus substantiating the finding of the 'coconut' by the workmen.

The tests for gypsum
Chemical tests, carried out within the British Museum (Natural History) Department of Minerals, revealed the presence of gypsum ($CaSO_4$) in a piece of the Piltdown cranium, which was considered to be unusual [46p268]. Tests of the ground water indicated that it could not have been deposited by natural means, and further somewhat sophisticated experiments were carried out on sub fossilized bones (i.e. partially fossilized) from other sites unconnected with Piltdown. These tests showed that if these sub fossil bones were soaked in certain iron sulphate compounds (which the forger would use to darken the colour of his planted bones), then under certain conditions, gypsum would be deposited in the bone matrix. From this it was inferred that the presence of gypsum in any of the Piltdown fossils was evidence of forgery. Gypsum was found in many of the fossils, and as they included the early pieces of skull discovered by Dawson, this was taken as further evidence of his guilt. These tests are important, as they are the only *technical* evidence to show that the skull pieces were planted in the same way as the other fossils.

The report, however, is unsatisfactory on three major counts, and several minor ones. The technicalities of the report obscure the arguments, but my basic objections are very simple.

Firstly, and most convincingly, the skull pieces are considered to have been artificially stained in view of the presence of gypsum, yet the unfossilized jaw, which had obviously been doctored with iron and chromium compounds that produced a surface stain, *contained no gypsum whatsoever*. How Dawson could be accused of forgery by the presence of gypsum in the skull pieces, when none was found in the admittedly fake jawbone defies common sense.

Secondly, all the skull pieces were stained with iron *for their full thickness*, and had clearly been lying in the iron rich water of Piltdown for a considerable period. (The fake jaw was only superficially stained.) *There was therefore no need whatsoever for the hoaxer to stain these pieces*, the whole purpose of his staining technique being to colour match his imported items with the dark skull pieces which he knew were naturally embedded in the gravel.

Thirdly, to obtain the deposition of gypsum, *partially* fossilized bone had to be used. But every skull piece found was *fully* fossilized, there being no organic matter present, both when tested in 1912 by Woodhead and by electron microscopy in 1953. These tests on sub-fossilized bones may, therefore, have little bearing upon the *fully*-fossilized skull pieces.

It was said that partially fossilized bone was used by the forger as the loss of some of the organic content made the bone pervious for his chemical staining technique [49]. The skull bones would be in a partially fossilized state for a long period of the time when they lay in the gravel, prior to their discovery in 1908. By this time they would be fully fossilized and much *less* pervious than fresh bone, which incidentally *is* pervious to chemicals in solution. [64p42]

(The amount of Nitrogen left in the bones indicates the degree of fossilization, and there appears to be a discrepancy regarding the quantity of Nitrogen originally in the skull bones when discovered. There is 4 per cent Nitrogen in fresh bone, whilst the skull bones showed 0·2 to 1·4 per cent. It was suggested that this Nitrogen content may have been due to absorption of a gelatine preservative. This possibility was rejected, as it was pointed out that the porous skull bones should have absorbed *more* Nitrogen than the compact dentine material of the teeth, but the reverse was the case [45p144]. But surely if the jaw and teeth were fairly fresh, they would have considerable *organic* Nitrogen in any case, the fossilized skull bones obtaining their smaller amount of Nitrogen from the gelatine preservative. No tests to check on this possibility are mentioned in the report, but electron microscopy tests *were* carried out to investigate this aspect, and the collagen, which contains the organic Nitrogen, was found to be *entirely absent* in the skull pieces [36p39]. It would, therefore, appear that their measured Nitrogen content was due to the preservative treatment carried out by the British Museum authorities themselves!)

Other points, upon which the report could be criticized, are as follows:

(i) Dawson was said to have found five pieces of skull before taking them to Woodward. All of these five pieces contained chromium (from Dawson's efforts to 'harden' them), but none was found in the later pieces discovered by Woodward and others. As we shall see, the presence of chromium in a fossil was taken as in indication that it was fraudulent, as the forger appears to have used a chromium compound as an oxidizer in his staining techniques.

Five pieces were tested for gypsum, and all the tests were positive. Two of them, however, were pieces found by Woodward (right parietal and a small fragment of the occipital) [46p269 and 38p10]. These pieces, therefore, do *not* have the 'tell-tale' chromium, but *do* have gypsum. This is further evidence that the presence of gypsum in the pieces was due to their lying in the ground, and not due to the staining technique.

(ii) Due to the low sulphate content of the soil, it was considered that the gypsum could not have been introduced by natural means. But a test made recently does not rule out the possibility that the water may have been much richer in sulphates during the long period when the skull lay in the gravel.

In addition, sulphates *were* present in the Piltdown water (obtained from a well a quarter of a mile away). Their concentration of 63 parts per million of SO_3 was not negligible. By way of example, at concentrations only five times more than this, special considerations have to be given to the protection of concrete foundations in the ground. Similarly, a small amount of sulphates (3·9 mg. per 100 g.) *was* found in the Piltdown gravel.

Conversion of the calcium phosphate of the bone into calcium sulphate by the sulphates in the ground water over a long period of time is surely the most obvious explanation for the presence of gypsum in the skull bones.

We have considered this question of the presence of gypsum in some detail, in view of the importance attached to it by the reports exposing the fraud. The presence of chromium was also considered as evidence of fraud, however, and gypsum was found in some beavers' teeth but no chromium. The report comments: 'These were presumably stained by another technique, which dispensed with the use of a dichromate solution as oxidizer' [46p252]. Thus it is necessary to assume that, in order to explain the presence of gypsum, the forger used more than one technique. Indeed, from this line of reasoning, we must infer that he used *three* methods, for the jaw contained chromium but no gypsum!

From all this, we would suggest that these tests are not conclusive, and that the presence of gypsum or chromium in the early skull pieces found by Dawson does not prove that they were fraudulently stained.

Visitors to the site

After being handed the first piece of cranium, Dawson took his friend Mr. Woodhead to the site only a few days later to explore it, but they found nothing. Dawson is hardly likely to have taken a colleague to the site so soon after the first discovery, if he had intended later to plant fake bones.

After this initial find, Dawson spoke to a number of friends about his discovery, and some of them helped him in his excavations. Any one of these could have been the hoaxer, and had ample opportunity, for excavations in the early days were only carried out during weekends and holidays. The fact that the trench could be seen from the windows of Barkham Manor meant that only those who were within the circle of Dawson's acquaintances were allowed to work there. One interloper was seen by Miss Kenward and warned off, as she told the writer personally.

Among the many visitors was Sir Grafton Elliot Smith, who carried out extensive investigations of the Piltdown skull. He was accompanied by Dr. Davidson Black who was studying under him, and who later became famous for his Pekin man discoveries. Whilst at the site, Black was fortunate enough to find part of a rhinoceros molar tooth. [42]

It is worth mentioning in passing that the fossil skull found at Piltdown is a perfectly human type, but of unusual thickness. However, skulls of this thickness are possessed by a very small percentage of people who are living today. A similar thickness is noted in the Swanscombe skull and possibly it is this factor which assists in their preservation.

Considering the above evidence, it can be seen that the discovery of the genuine cranium fossil in 1908 does not exonerate Woodward or Teilhard from possibly planting fake bones after their arrival on the scene.

Teilhard's involvement

Teilhard, twenty-seven years old, came to Hastings in 1908 to attend the Jesuit College, where he was ordained in August 1911. He began searching one of the local quarries for fossils, accompanied by a Jesuit friend. This came to the notice of Dawson, who met him in 1909, which was the beginning of their friendship. Although there is no specific mention of his visiting the site before June 1912, when systematic excavation started, he would doubtless have been invited to go there by Dawson. He worked very closely with Dawson in the Hastings quarries, and in a paper by Woodward in March 1911, dealing with the finds there, Dawson paid tribute to the assistance of Teilhard and his friend, Father Pelletier, and he paid a further tribute to them in another paper in November 1913.

When they first met at the quarry, Dawson revealed with great enthusiasm the exciting news of his finds at Piltdown. He may well have told him the precise locality or even taken Teilhard to the site before June 1912. There are only four occasions recorded in the official reports *when Teilhard accompanied Dawson and Woodward to the site.*

Dawson, in his 1912 address said: 'Father P. Teilhard S.J., who accompanied us on one occasion discovered one of the implements *in situ* . . . also a portion of the tooth of a Pliocene elephant . . .' [40]. In his 1913 report on the discovery of the canine tooth, he said: 'It was in the middle of this spread that Father Teilhard de Chardin who worked with us three days last summer, on 30th August 1913, discovered the canine tooth of Eoanthropus' [41]. These four visits with Dawson do not exclude the possibility that Teilhard may have worked at the site alone. Indeed, if we are to accept the evidence of Mr. Essex given later, there was at least one occasion when he did.

Sir Arthur Keith records that Teilhard 'shared in all the toils at Piltdown' [16p664] and Leakey says that many others were aware of this also.

Speaight relates a small incident which indicates how closely Teilhard's name had become linked with the Piltdown discoveries. In 1915 while Teilhard was serving in the war as a medical orderly, he met Max Begouen, who was to become his lifelong friend. When Teilhard introduced himself, Begouen's immediate response was: 'Ah, you're the Piltdown man.' [p59]

I myself asked Miss Kenward, now over eighty years old, how often Teilhard had come to the site. She said that he had been to tea twice, but she could not remember how often he had worked at the excavations.

Recalling those early days when the hoax was later exposed, Teilhard wrote in a letter of 1st March 1954 that he was not often allowed to leave his cell at Ore Place, and knew nothing about anthropology. [12p11] This is not substantiated by Cuénot however, who said he was allowed to go more frequently on scientific excursions, and as we know he was often at the Hastings quarries as well as Piltdown. He doubtless had *some* knowledge of anthropology, for he had collected rock specimens and fossils from his childhood. Furthermore in 1912 he accepted an invitation to work with Professor Boule, the professor of Palaeontology at the Paris Museum and an expert in fossil man.

Other early finds

It would only require one or two visits to the site for the hoaxer to realize its potential, and Dawson's enthusiasm, with his honest but naive approach, made him an easy victim. Fake teeth of hippopotamus and elephant were said to be found by Dawson before the June excavations (but we examine this evidence in Appendix II). Leaving these fossils in the pit is the work of a moment, and they would give an early date to the stratum, which would certainly arouse the interest of the British Museum authorities. When Woodward appears on the scene, the fake flint tool, *Planifrons* tooth and ape's jaw are quickly 'discovered', the first two by Teilhard himself. Teilhard, meeting Dawson in 1909, would thus have had ample opportunity to prepare for the hoax.

It is interesting that when Smith Woodward began the excavations in 1912, he particularly required some secrecy in carrying them out, possibly because he wanted to make sure the finds were authentic, or alternatively, and more likely in view of his subsequent conduct, because he was jealous of sharing with any other professional colleague the prestige of being the discoverer of an important humanoid fossil. Present at that first dig were Woodward, Dawson, a workman and Teilhard, who, Dawson had assured Woodward, was 'quite safe'.

B. LATER FINDS

As we have already mentioned, Teilhard is further exonerated because it is said he left England in October 1913, whilst
 (i) the shaped elephant's bone was found in 1914, and
(ii) the finds at Piltdown II were not made until 1915.

(i) THE ELEPHANT BONE 'BAT'

The announcement of the discovery of the shaped elephant's bone was a joint paper by Woodward and Dawson, read at a meeting of the Geological Society on 2nd December 1914 [42], which says that it was discovered 'during the season's dig'—no precise date being given. This elephant 'bat' was a large piece of bone from an elephant's femur, which had been found when a hedge had been removed to allow the digging to extend further. It had been shaped (with a knife in modern times) and covered with yellow clay to make it look as if it had been found at the bottom of the pit and thrown on to the field by the workmen. Its discovery some months after Teilhard's departure from England obviously in no way exonerates him, for there was nothing to prevent him from burying the bone, to await its discovery by others long after he had left.

The date for Teilhard's final departure in October 1913 however is wrong, for he returned in 1914. On p.54 of his biography, Speaight says that on the 24th September 1914 Teilhard began his tertianship at *Canterbury.* This return of Teilhard in 1914, *after* the 'bat' had been found confirms the evidence of a Mr. Robert Essex.

Mr. Essex's suspicion

We will now consider the evidence provided by a Mr. Robert Essex, who was the science master at Uckfield Grammar School at the time when the discoveries were made, and knew all those involved in the excavations. When the fraud was discovered, he remembered several incidents which occurred at the time of the excavations and considered that he knew the identity of the hoaxer. He communicated his evidence and the name of his suspect to the British Museum authorities and to Vere. No mention of this evidence whatsoever appears in Weiner's book, but R. Essex is mentioned in the acknowledgements as one of many 'who gave information and answered specific queries'. Vere gives this evidence in both his books, but using X in place of the name of the man Essex suspected. Essex also wrote an article in the *Kent and Sussex Journal* in July 1955, which is of such interest that I give it in Appendix I.

Essex's evidence is particularly valuable, as, apart from Teilhard and Miss Kenward, he was the only person with an interest in the original excavation who was still alive when the fraud was finally uncovered. I made every effort to trace the correspondence files of both Essex and Vere, to ascertain the identity of 'X', but to no avail. Vere, who knew the identity of 'X', was clearly very suspicious of Teilhard in his second book. [33]

My attention, however, was later drawn to a letter in the *New Scientist* of the 14th January 1971 [48], written by a Mr. J. Head. He recounts that ten years ago he had met Essex, who had told him that he considered that Teilhard may have been the hoaxer. *Thus the identity of Essex's and Vere's Mr. 'X' is given in this letter as Teilhard.*

I would now refer my readers to the article by Essex, which I give in the Appendix I. In this, on a date unfortunately not given by either Essex or Vere, the 'bat' was being discussed whilst the person Essex suspected was close by. As we have seen from Mr. Head's letter, Essex suspected Teilhard, and we can therefore deduce that *Teilhard was at Uckfield after the 'bat' had been found,* presumably during his return to Canterbury in 1914.

In this article by Essex, he mentions that he saw half of a fossil human jaw in a bag owned by 'X', which was quite unlike the fake jaw discovered later. Clearly, one (or both?) halves of the genuine jaw to the skull piece had been found, and 'X' could now substitute the fake half jaw without fear of the real jaw being later discovered and thus ruining the hoax.

(ii) THE PILTDOWN II FOSSILS

Both Vere and Weiner date these discoveries in the year 1915, obviously basing their datings on Woodward's account in his 1917 paper, which we have quoted on p.7.

Teilhard however claimed that Dawson showed him the field in 1913 after *he had made the discoveries.* He could therefore have planted these fossils.

This information was contained in a lecture given by Professor Oakley to the Geological Society in 1972, which was later printed in *Antiquity* in March 1976. In this he says:

> The only manuscript record of this second site is a postcard from Dawson to Woodward dated 30 July 1915. In a letter to me written on 28 November 1953, Father Teilhard had this to say about Dawson's second site. '*He just brought me to the site of locality 2 and explained to me that he had found the isolated molar and small pieces of skull in the heaps of rubble and pebbles raked at the surface of the field.*' That must have been in 1914, because Father Teilhard returned to France before the end of that year and did not return to Britain until after the 1914–18 war. Why should Dawson have concealed such an important find from Smith Woodward for nearly two years? [49p10].

Speaight's biography of Teilhard gives a similar account as follows:
'In answer to a letter from Kenneth Oakley announcing the exposure
he replied. . . .' Speaight then quotes a lengthy extract from Teilhard's
letter which a footnote dates as 28th November 1953. He then continues:

> In a further letter Teilhard confirmed that, on his second visit to the
> second Piltdown locality in late July 1913, the pieces of skull and a tooth
> had already been found. He remembered Dawson pointing out the little
> heaps of raked pebbles as the place of the discovery. [p318]

Before we proceed to examine this statement of Teilhard in detail,
I must emphasize that whether the fossils were found in 1913 or 1915,
there was nothing to prevent Teilhard from placing them in the field
which he knew in 1913 was being searched, for discovery by Dawson
long after Teilhard had left for France. This is the same point I have
made regarding the elephant 'bat', and he cannot be exonerated on
this account.

I will first of all consider the problems which arise if Teilhard's
statement is correct, and then look at the possibility that he fabricated
this story of the 1913 date for the Piltdown II discoveries.

Teilhard's letters
There are several problems regarding Teilhard's correspondence
when the hoax was discovered.

(i) Speaight, having quoted an extract from a letter Teilhard wrote
    to Oakley, then says that, 'In a *further* letter Teilhard *con-
    firmed* . . .' the date as late July 1913 for his second visit to
    Piltdown II [p318]. The immediate impression is that this
    second letter was also to Oakley, but from the latter's article in
    Antiquity, this is not so, as he presumed it was in 1914. To
    whom was this second (and more informative) letter addressed?

(ii) Oakley's presumption of 1914 as the date for Teilhard's Pilt-
    down II visit is corrected by the 'further letter' as being late
    July 1913. This agrees well with Speaight's account, for he
    gives details of Teilhard's visit to England in late July, his
    discovery of the canine tooth in August, and departure several
    weeks later.

(iii) Weiner mentions [p111] that Teilhard was conducted to the
    place by Dawson in 1913 (August on p.142). His footnote
    refers to a 'personal communication', presumably to Weiner
    himself. This may be the letter referred to by Vere [32p31]
    dated 2nd March 1954, in which Teilhard said, 'Dawson
    showed me the field where the second skull (fragments) were
    found. But, as I wrote to Oakley, I cannot remember whether
    it was before or after the find.'

If this assumption is correct, such seeming vagueness on Teilhard's part conflicts with his very clear statement to Oakley, in the letter he wrote only four months *previously*, that when he was taken to the site by Dawson, the fossils had already been found.

Teilhard's accounts have every appearance of giving two different stories. Furthermore, even the admission that he could not 're-member whether Dawson showed him the site after or before the find', is strange. He must have known that he left England in 1914 and that the finds were supposed to have been made in 1915, and there should therefore have been no possibility of their being discovered *before* he left. Indeed it was this statement which prompted me to examine the evidence more closely. Cuénot in fact confirms that Teilhard saw these fossils after the war, for he says: 'In August of 1920 we find him in England, excited at being shown the new frag-ment of cranium and the new fossil tooth "found" at Piltdown in 1915' [p31]. Thus Teilhard is 'excited' on seeing these fossils in 1920, although he knew they had been discovered in 1913, at which time he may well have been shown them by Dawson or Woodward. When he saw them in 1920, should he not have told the experts that they were actually found in 1913 in order to correct the scientific record— or would this have caused too many questions to be asked?

It may be objected that possibly Teilhard's memory was faulty, and he simply got the wrong date forty years after the events took place, but it must be emphasized that he gives a very accurate description of his visit, specifically remembering Dawson pointing out the heaps where the finds had been made. Furthermore, his statement that it was late July 1913 agrees precisely with Speaight's account of his arrival in England. Although he wrote these letters when he was seventy-three years old, and was suffering from a weak heart, he did not appear to have any diminution of his mental powers.

Weiner states that in October 1913 (two years before the Piltdown II discoveries) Teilhard left England for many years [p92]. One can only presume that he was unaware of Teilhard's admission to Oakley that the Piltdown II fossils had been discovered before that date, and that Teilhard actually returned to England in September 1914.

A fabricated account?

So far we have assumed that Teilhard's statement was correct, and have seen the difficulties which this raises. Teilhard may, however, have fabricated the story that Dawson showed him the field where he had found the fossils as early as 1913. Teilhard's account of seeing the 'heaps of rubble and pebbles raked at the surface of the field' could have simply been obtained from Woodward's 1917 report, in which he mentions that 'the stones had been raked off the ground and brought together in heaps'.

Professor Oakley asked the pertinent question: 'Why should Dawson have concealed such an important find from Smith Woodward for nearly two years?' Indeed, why should he? Dawson wrote two cards to Woodward, one dated January 1915, announcing the discovery of two cranium pieces, the second dated 15th July 1915, which is on public display at the British Museum (N.H.), mentions the molar he had found. If Dawson *did* find them in 1913, why should he wait for two years for no apparent reason before telling Woodward? Furthermore, in Woodward's 1917 paper, he said that he searched the field with Dawson several times in 1914 without success. Are we to believe that Dawson was prepared to spend his own and his friend's valuable time searching this field for fossils, knowing all the time that he had found three fossils the previous year, but which he would not reveal to Woodward until next year? I would suggest that this is extremely unlikely. I believe that Dawson *did* find the pieces at Piltdown II in 1915 and duly reported them to Woodward. By now, however, they were both highly suspicious of the whole affair, and decided to keep quiet for the time being, Woodward only publicizing the fossils after Dawson's death.

An indication that Woodward was suspicious of the authenticity of the Piltdown II fossils is provided by his book, *The Earliest Englishman*, which was published in 1948, four years after his death. In this, he gives no details whatsoever of the discovery of the fossils at Piltdown II. His *only* reference to them in the whole of his book is a passing comment, when he says:

> We are confirmed in this belief by Mr. Dawson's discovery of a similar grinding tooth, together with two fragments of a second Piltdown skull, in a patch of gravel about two miles away from the original spot. [p65]

Vere [33p15], whilst admitting that he has no evidence, conjectures that someone may have done a little editing between Woodward's death and the publication of his book. As we will see, this could also apply to Woodward's statement about Dawson's early finds. If his book was altered, it would involve one or more persons other than the three upon whom the main suspicion falls.

Teilhard's accounts of Dawson showing him the field in 1913 after the fossils had been discovered have several contradictions, and I contend that the possibility that it was a complete fabrication, in an effort to discredit Dawson, must be considered. If this view is correct, it would give further weight to my contention that he was the instigator of the hoax.

One further strange fact is that Dawson was *not* the only person to discover fossils at Piltdown II. In his 1917 report, Woodward says:

> Shortly afterwards, in the same gravel, a friend met with part of the lower molar of an indeterminate species of rhinoceros, as highly mineralised as the specimens previously found at Piltdown itself.

One would expect that any person making an important discovery would be acknowledged in the report, yet Woodward fails to give the name of this 'friend'. Did this mysterious 'friend' discover a rhinoceros tooth fragment, which was deliberately planted to establish a link with Piltdown I, where Davidson Black had similarly found a part of a rhinoceros tooth which was just as highly mineralized?

Woodward's loss of interest in this site *after* the discoveries is strange. Why did he never give the precise location of this field, and why did he never revisit the site after his vain search with Dawson in 1914? These are questions which have never been satisfactorily answered, but his strange handling of the evidence suggests that he suspected that the fossils found at this site may have been 'planted' for Dawson and others to find in due course.

Summarizing the main arguments given above, I trust that it has been adequately established that neither the date of Teilhard's arrival nor of his departure prevent him from having planted the fake jaw, teeth and flints at Piltdown I or the fossils at Piltdown II .

SMITH WOODWARD

It is not beyond the bounds of possibility that Woodward was the culprit, or was in league with the real hoaxer. His inexplicable delay in publishing the Piltdown II finds in 1917, which were found in 1915 is rather strange. Nevertheless, it is unlikely that he was the real instigator of the hoax, for the following reasons:

(a) He was known to be particularly clumsy with his hands, which makes it very unlikely that he would have the technical skill required to file the teeth, break the jaw at certain precise points and carefully pack the pulp cavity of the canine tooth with grains of sand.

(b) After he retired, he lived at Haywards Heath and even as late as 1935 carried out additional excavations at his own expense, in the hope of further finds. This is hardly the action of a man who knew that most of the discoveries at the site had been forged by himself.

These are not particularly strong reasons for exonerating Woodward, but on the other hand, in all my research I have found no evidence to suggest that he was either the initiator of the fraud, or even a willing accomplice. The most likely explanation of his actions is that he suspected that some of the fossils had been planted and became evasive in his statements, so that firm proof of this fact would be more difficult to establish.

One of the most serious charges against Woodward is his almost obsessive guarding of the original fossils. Even very eminent scientists, among them Sir Arthur Keith, were only granted comparatively infrequent and brief periods of inspections. As they could only work upon plaster casts, there was no possibility of the jaw being detected as a fake. His secrecy could be interpreted as an awareness of the existence of the hoax, although it may simply be an extension of his early desire to keep the excavations secret, or professional jealousy.

In his book, Woodward gives accounts of Dawson's first meeting with Teilhard at the Hastings quarries, and the latter's discovery of the canine, but makes virtually no other reference to Teilhard's part in the excavations. Speaight mentions that, only a few weeks after the June excavations, Woodward visited Teilhard at his Hastings College to rifle his fossil collection for the British Museum, but I can trace no suggestion of collusion between them.

2. Evidence

I will now examine certain items of evidence and see how they affect Dawson and Teilhard.

A. ICHKEUL FOSSIL

When Dawson, Woodward and Teilhard began excavating on 2nd June 1912, Teilhard unearthed in the pit a flint tool and a stegodon tooth (*Elephas planifrons*), both of which were fakes. When the hoax was discovered the tooth was found to have a particularly high level of radioactivity. This is unusual for fossils found in Western Europe, but it was found that fossils from Ichkeul, near Bizerta, North Tunisia, had a very similar level of radioactivity, and *Elephas planifrons* is abundant there. It is almost certain that the Piltdown fossil tooth came from this location. An important factor is that *this site was not publicly identified until after 1918*.

The likelihood of Dawson obtaining such a fossil from so remote a site is extremely improbable, particularly when its existence was not made public until after the First World War. There is no mention that he ever travelled much outside England.

Teilhard had been a lecturer at Cairo University from 1906–8. Being with the scientific élite and having an interest in palaeontology, he is almost certain to have heard of any interesting sites in North Africa, and would have had ample opportunity to visit Ichkeul. *Indeed Ronald Millar states* [24p232] *that he had actually stayed near this site! I must say that I consider this fossil one of the most important pieces of evidence which casts suspicion on Teilhard.*

Planifron fossils are plentiful at Ichkeul, and if Teilhard picked up a tooth during his visit there, which he later used at Piltdown, he would little realize that its radioactivity would pinpoint its source and thus provide very incriminating evidence.

B. ELEPHANT BONE 'BAT'

In Essex's article (see Appendix I), Montgomery told Dawson that he had seen a fossil just like the elephant 'bat' in the Dordogne area. Teilhard was born not more than 100 miles from the area, and even as a small child was an avid collector of stones and similar artefacts.

In the Geological Society Report of 1915 [42], a description of the bone specifically mentions that 'the decay has widened the cracks into small superficial grooves resembling those in a sub-fossil femur of *Elephas* from a lake deposit in Egypt, now in the British Museum'.

It is possible (but unlikely) that Dawson may have possessed such a fossil, and one could not therefore exonerate him on this evidence alone for he *may* have obtained such a bone in pursuing his palaeontological interests.

Teilhard, however, had ample opportunity to collect such an item, for whether it came from the Dordogne or Egypt, his close association with both of these sites is of interest when considering the evidence against him.

C. ANTHROPOLOGICAL EXPERTISE

The hoaxer must have been an expert anthropologist to have fooled the professional scientists, who would be inspecting the fossils very closely. Breaking of the upper condyle of the jaw prevented them discovering how the jaw articulated with the skull and thus how far the jaw was developed towards the human type. Had the jaw not been broken at this point, the shape of the upper condyle would have made it obvious that it was only an ape's jaw.

Similarly, the omission of the canine tooth prevented the experts from determining if the jaw was human or ape-like.

The filing and staining of the canine tooth, the discovery of which has already been described, was also the work of an expert. The tooth had been filed with care, packed with grains of sand and given an appearance of fossilization.

A considerable list of items could be catalogued to indicate the very high level of skill and expertise possessed by the forger. Suffice it to say that when the fraud was exposed, his skill was acknowledged by Weiner, Oakley and Le Gros Clark, who, in their presentation of their findings in 1953 said:

... from the evidence which we have obtained, it is now clear that the distinguished palaeontologists and archaeologists, who took part in the excavations at Piltdown, were the victims of a most elaborate and carefully prepared hoax ... the faking of mandible and canine is so extraordinarily skilful and the perpetration of the hoax appears to have been so entirely unscrupulous and inexplicable as to find no parallel in the history of palaeontological discovery. [45]

Dawson was a complete amateur in these matters. Indeed, he had to ask his own dentist to show him how to fit a tooth into a jaw. His original interests were in local history and ancient tools and artefacts. He did not have the technical skill or expertise displayed by the fabricator.

Teilhard, on the other hand, was a keen student of palaeontology, even before he came to England, and went on to obtain international recognition as an expert, writing numerous papers and assisting at the excavation of the Pekin man, as we shall recount later. He would have had more than sufficient knowledge to know which animal fossils should be implanted in the gravel, to give it the correct age for dating the finds.

In addition, he would be aware that the atmosphere in scientific circles was ripe for the finding of an ape man link. The Java man finds had been publicized in 1895 with considerable arguments regarding their interpretation, and further links between man and animals were expected to be found at any time, in order to confirm the theory of evolution and man's descent from apes.

D. STAINING OF BONES

When Dawson found the first (five?) fragments of the cranium, before he called in Smith Woodward, he dipped them in bichromate of potash, mistakenly thinking that this would harden them. This chemical does not harden bones, and it is an indication of Dawson's ignorance of chemistry to have thought that it would do so.

Dawson sent these pieces to the local public analyst for a report. Had he deliberately stained them with intent to defraud, he is hardly likely to have wanted them to be analysed. In addition, the staining had been done in conjunction with a friend and many knew of it, including the experts. That Dawson 'stained' the early finds of the cranium is invariably considered to incriminate him in the staining of the jaw with iron compounds, but this is a much more complex procedure and quite a separate matter.

The remaining (four?) pieces of the cranium found after Smith Woodward had been called in were *not* stained in bichromate of potash. Here again, had Dawson intended to fool the experts with a planted cranium, he would surely have stained *all* the fragments before placing them in the pit for the excavators to find.

Dawson's staining

The allegation that Dawson was experimenting with the staining of bones was made by a Captain St. Barbe. In 1913 he entered Dawson's rear office unannounced and found him 'surrounded by porcelain pots containing brownish liquids, in which bones were soaking'. Dawson said he was experimenting with bone staining to discover how it went on in nature. A few weeks later, he referred to the staining again, saying that he was experimenting with flints as well as bones. Again this would seriously incriminate Dawson as the fraudulent stainer of the jaw, but:

(a) This incident occurred some time in 1913, long after the jaw had been discovered. He would surely have completed his experiments *before* the 1912 excavations, had he been the hoaxer.

(b) Had he intended to defraud the experts, his office is hardly the most secretive place in which to carry out his staining experiments.

(c) He is unlikely to have volunteered the fact that he was also carrying out experiments on flints, some weeks after St. Barbe entered his office.

In fact, even whilst the excavations were being carried out in 1912 and 1913, it was suspected by some of Dawson's local acquaintances that the finds were fraudulent. Indeed, his reaction to the word 'Dordogne' during the discussion recorded by Essex indicates that he was aware that he had been the innocent dupe of a hoax and that he had suspicions who the guilty person was. His experiments with staining of bones were probably to see if staining had been used as a basis for the fraud. In addition, Vere suggests he may have been induced to 'harden' his skull pieces in bichromate by the hoaxer, to cover up the latter's use of a chromium compound for staining, and to further incriminate Dawson. Alternatively, knowing Dawson had 'hardened' the skull pieces in bichromate of potash, *could not the forger have deliberately used a chromium compound to throw suspicion upon the skull pieces which he knew were genuine?*

Mr. H. Morris, one of Dawson's rivals, furnishes further evidence that the fraudulent nature of the finds was common knowledge. When Dr. Weiner was investigating the fraud, he traced a cabinet full of eoliths or flint stones, which Morris had collected. In one of the drawers several notes were found, in which Morris accuses Dawson of staining flints, etc. He appears to have been jealous of Dawson's fame, but somewhat eccentric in writing these accusing notes and then shutting them in his drawer. One of the interesting notes he made, however, will be referred to later.

Chemical expertise

All the skull pieces found were stained with iron salts for their full thickness. Piltdown soil is particularly rich in iron compounds. When the hoaxer fabricated the orang-utan's jaw, he had to stain it with iron to make it look like the cranium fragments. To do this required a knowledge of chemistry of a high order. Ferric ammonium sulphate was probably used, together with chromium compounds, which are oxidizing agents, presumably to obtain iron oxide. Ferric ammonium sulphate has an unusual reaction on the calcium of bones. The chemical expertise required for such a process can be seen, whilst the presence of chromium in many of the fossils was considered to be evidence of fraud.

Teilhard's knowledge of chemistry was considerable, *for he had been a lecturer in this very subject whilst at Cairo University.* He would know the oxidizing effect which chromium compounds have upon ferric ammonium sulphate. Strangely enough he was also interested in the staining of bones. When the hoax was exposed, he wrote the letter to Professor Oakley, dated 28th November 1953 (which we have mentioned before—p.20), which Speaight quotes. In it he says:

> . . . water in the wealden clay can stain at a remarkable speed. In *1912*, in a fresh stream near Hastings, I was unpleasantly surprised to see a fresh-sawed bone (from the butchers) stained almost as deep brown as the human remains from Piltdown. [29p318]

Now, butchers do not usually discard their bones in nearby streams, and his statement gives every indication that it was *he* who deliberately placed a fresh-sawn bone in the stream, and observed it over a period of time, during which he noted that it was quickly stained *as deeply as the Piltdown fossils.* If this is correct, could he not have been carrying out a simple test to check how rapidly, and to what colour, fresh (ape's jaw?) bones would be stained in the waters of the weald, as part of his careful preparation for the hoax?

3. Further evidence

I feel that the evidence outlined above strongly indicates that Teilhard de Chardin could have been the perpetrator of the Piltdown hoax. If this is considered as a possibility, it would explain some other incidents.

A. EARLY FINDS
Teilhard was the actual discoverer of several of the fake items.

(i) On the very first day of the June 1913 excavation, he 'laid hands on' the fragment of the 'Stegodon' tooth, which came from Ichkeul.

(ii) Later, he found the fake flint tool actually in the pit, all the others having been found in the spoil heaps.

(iii) Later still, *near the same spot*, the stained jaw 'flew out' of the excavation when struck by Dawson's pick.

B. CANINE DISCOVERY

In Woodward's account of Teilhard's finding of the canine (see p.6) certain phrases become particularly significant. When Teilhard found the tooth, they were 'incredulous', as they had already seen several bits of ironstone . . . on the spot where he stood. He insisted, however, that he was not deceived, so we both left our digging. . . .' Thus it is evident that Teilhard 'found' the tooth where Dawson and Woodward had already searched with sufficient thoroughness that at first they did not believe he had found anything, and he had to insist he had, before they would investigate his discovery.

Furthermore, in his letter to Oakley of 28th November 1953 [29p318] he remembers his discovery of the canine, and says, '. . . when I found the canine, it was so inconspicuous among the gravels . . . that it seemed to me quite unlikely that the tooth would have been planted. I can even remember Sir Arthur congratulating me on the sharpness of my eyesight.' Having carefully filed and painted the tooth and packed it with sand granules, the hoaxer would indeed be foolish to so place it that it could easily be overlooked. All would be explained, however, if it was Teilhard who had brought it to the site.

C. MORRIS'S NOTE

One of the notes, scrawled by Morris and found in the cabinet, as mentioned on p.27 was the following: 'Judging from an overheard conversation, there is every reason to suppose that the "canine tooth", found at Piltdown was imported from France,' followed by: 'Watch C. Dawson. Kind regards.' Had Morris heard that it was *Dawson* (whom he disliked intensely), who had imported the tooth from France, he would surely have said so. The connection of another fossil with France should be noted and surely, if the canine came from France, the jaw could have come from there also.

It is not suggested that an account of an overheard conversation, written by an eccentric collector, should be seriously considered as satisfactory evidence. However, if nothing else, it does show that many local amateur collectors were aware of the fraudulent nature of Piltdown, even at the time when the excavations were being carried out. This we will now consider.

D. KNOWLEDGE OF A HOAX

Weiner relates how the possibility that the Piltdown specimens had been deliberated fabricated occurred to him, when he considered that the many conflicting aspects of their nature could be explained by such a 'hypothesis'. That Piltdown was a hoax is presented as a new discovery in the scientific world, yet in Chapter 12, which he entitled 'The Eye Wink', it is quite clear that the fraudulent nature of the finds was common knowledge among many of Dawson's local associates, even at the time when the finds were made.

We have already mentioned Morris and Captain St. Barbe; others were Major Marriot, Mr. Pollard and A. S. Kennard, who all mixed socially.

Weiner gives some interesting information regarding Kennard's views. He was an experienced amateur palaeontologist, whose ability was sufficiently recognized to warrant the offering of a post as an assistant in a professional capacity at the Geological Survey at South Kensington, when he retired from his business. Kennard appears to have had reservations regarding the elephant 'bat' for this is implied by his comment, recorded in the discussion on the paper [42] in December 1914, when Woodward and Dawson presented the find. He said:

> . . . he wished to congratulate the authors on the discovery of a new problem from Piltdown. From the differences between the cut portion of the bone and the natural surface, he considered it possible that the bone *was not in a fresh state when cut* . . .

Did he imply that it had been cut in its fossilized state, i.e. in modern times?

Even more arresting is the comment made by R. Smith of the Department of Antiquities of the British Museum during the same discussion on the paper. He said 'the possibility of the bone having been found and whittled *in recent times* must be considered'. Such a comment is surely more than Weiner's description 'ironic', being a thinly veiled accusation that the fossil had possibly been deliberately shaped to look like an ancient tool. One would expect a sense of shock to go through the meeting, but official accounts are hardly suitable for recording the atmosphere at such a gathering. Suffice it to say that in the replies, Woodward considered that the bone was fresh when it was cut, but they had not made any experiments in cutting bone with flint.

Weiner records that Kennard 'let it be known on several occasions (in the 1940's) that he believed Piltdown Man to be a hoax' and, '. . . intimated to Mr. Hinton (in the Natural History Museum) *he did not consider Dawson the forger*. He died in 1948 and his knowledge of the forger's identity went with him.'

We have here a respected palaeontologist, who was a member of a closely associated scientific body, making serious accusations regarding the authenticity of the Piltdown fossils. The fossils, which the Natural History Museum authorities guarded so carefully under lock and key, and which numerous highly qualified scientists had spent many hours analysing and discussing, he considered to be nothing more than frauds. Surely even a hint that *any* of the numerous exhibits in the Museum were frauds should result in an immediate investigation. No such action, however, appears to have been taken. Kennard is said never to have intimated who he considered the hoaxer to be.

The sudden realization that Piltdown might be a fraud was obviously not as original as the British Museum experts appeared to think. One of them was suspicious as early as 1949 however. When, during the first series of Fluorine tests [44], Oakley saw the low F-content of the fossils of Piltdown man compared with some of the other animal bones, his 'instinctive reaction was to regard *Eoanthropus* as bogus' [49]. Furthermore, the white drillings from the teeth during the test were similar to those obtainable from modern teeth, which should have aroused suspicions in any case.

What is also rather surprising is that Essex said he went to the British Museum authorities and laid before them all his information, but apart from Weiner's inclusion of his name among many others in his preface 'who gave information and answered specific queries', no other mention is made of his important evidence by any member of that body.

4. Two strange accounts

(a) *Teilhard's word*
In trying to unravel a mystery such as we have at Piltdown, one naturally considers the significance of all clues, no matter how small. It would be quite wrong, however, to place too much weight upon the significance of one word in any accounts of the events. With this warning in mind, I will mention in passing a comment by Teilhard.

When the June excavations began, the only people who knew of the existence of the skull pieces were Woodward, Teilhard and some of Dawson's local friends. Although the skull was *later* to become known worldwide, the knowledge of its existence by such a small group of people hardly merited his description—'. . . the *famous* human skull . . .' [29p44], in his letter of *3rd June 1912*. This was written only one day after excavations had started, and the jaw had not yet been found. Did he know it would become famous?

(b) *Teilhard as witness*
Finally, I would refer once more to the letter quoted by Speaight,

which Teilhard wrote to Dr. Oakley on the 28th November 1953, one
extract already having been quoted above. In this same letter Teilhard
says:

> No one would think of suspecting Smith-Woodward. I knew pretty
> well Dawson—a methodical and enthusiastic character. When we were
> in the field I never noticed anything suspicious in his behaviour. The
> only thing which puzzled me, one day, was when I saw him picking up
> two large fragments of skull out of a sort of rubble in a corner of the
> pit (these fragments had probably been rejected by the workmen the
> year before). [29p317]

If we imagine this incident taking place, we are asked to believe
that Dawson, who was always enthusiastic about his finds, found two
large pieces of skull, quietly pocketed them and said nothing to the
others, *and that he did all this while Teilhard, who was sufficiently close to see
they were* **skull** *fragments, was looking on.* Furthermore, if Teilhard
actually saw this take place, then surely as an ordained priest and as a
scientist concerned for the integrity of his profession, he had a duty to
report this immediately to Woodward, who would then have cross-
questioned Dawson. In my opinion, his account of this event does not
ring true and I question whether it ever took place.

I have already examined Teilhard's account of Dawson showing
him the Piltdown II site in 1913 *after* the discovery of the fossils there,
and suggested that this also was fabricated to incriminate Dawson.
Did Teilhard hope that it would be inferred that Dawson pocketed
two skull pieces at Piltdown I which he would later 'find' at Piltdown
II?

If Teilhard did fabricate these two accounts, and the evidence tends
to support this, it would provide further confirmation that he was
indeed the perpetrator of the hoax.

5. Comments

That Teilhard may have been the instigator of the Piltdown hoax is
considered as unthinkable by most people in view of his international
reputation and integrity as a Roman Catholic Jesuit priest. Some,
however, have suggested that nevertheless this may be correct, and
I give the comments of some of those who have suspected Teilhard.

Leakey's views
Dr. L. S. B. Leakey says in his book *Unveiling Man's Origin* [p90] that
Teilhard had been in Egypt, whilst on p.144 he says:

> The story of the uncovering of this hoax has been the subject of several
> books, but it seems likely that the last word on the subject has not yet
> been written. There can be no doubt at all that at least one of the persons

involved in making the forgeries must have had considerable knowledge of chemistry as well as some training in geology and human anatomy. The perpetrators also must have had access to fossil bones from outside Great Britain, since some of the animal fossils 'planted' with the skull and jaw, at the site, came from places like Malta and North Africa."

This description clearly fits Teilhard very closely. His insinuation prompted a telephone call from the *Sunday Times* to his home in Nairobi, which he fended off by saying: 'I don't say so in so many words, do I?'

In his autobiography *By the Evidence* he recalls a visit he made to the British Museum (N.H.) in 1933 to inspect the original fossils. He says:

> I was not allowed to handle the original in any way, but merely to look at them and satisfy myself that the casts were really good replicas. Then, abruptly, the originals were removed and locked up again, and I was left for the rest of the morning with only the casts to study.

In her biography of Leakey, Cole says he was just finishing a whole book on Teilhard's connection with the hoax. After his death, his wife prevented its publication as Leakey had no new evidence, and she felt it would damage her husband's reputation more than Teilhard's [p399]. Cole relates that *Teilhard actually told Leakey that Dawson was not responsible, but he refused to elaborate.* Leakey pointed out that Teilhard never mentioned Piltdown, and considered that he had not attended the meeting of the Geological Society when the discoveries were announced, as he may have been questioned. Leakey considered that as an ordained priest, Teilhard would have been bound to confess to the fraudulence of the fossils. Leakey appears to maintain that Dawson was involved in the plot, even though Teilhard had said he was not responsible.

Other views

Leakey considered that the Piltdown hoax may have been the work of Teilhard as a practical joke 'in his early and somewhat irresponsible days'. This was also Essex's view (who considered it was aimed at Dawson), and it is Vere's contention in his first book. It would be very difficult to give a precise motive at this distance in time, but if it *was* the work of a practical joker, who can say if he was intent on fooling one man, a group of locals, or a body of experts? It is noticeable that Vere, in his second book, is much more critical, for he makes no mention of practical jokes, and briefly considers Teilhard's role in the Pekin man discoveries.

Millar, who considers Sir Grafton Elliot Smith may have been the culprit but has little positive evidence to support this contention, admits that the case against Teilhard is very black, particularly in view of the Ichkeul tooth. He says that it was 'just possible that he might have added the *Elephas planifrons* molar to gain some kudos'. If this were so, do we assume that there were *two* hoaxers at Piltdown, either working independently or in league together? The first would be too coincidental, and the second would still implicate Teilhard.

Millar mentions [p232] that Sir Wilfred Le Gros Clark and Professor Oakley suspected Teilhard because of the Ichkeul fossil, but felt that his lack of anatomical knowledge and the whole nature of the man exonerated him. Clark also considered Dawson must have had a professional accomplice.

An article in *New Scientist* [47] quotes Sir Solly Zuckerman as saying that the hoaxer knew more about primate anatomy than the experts whom he deluded several times. The columnist considers that Teilhard's knowledge of palaeontology, geology, anatomy and biochemistry suggests that he cannot be excluded despite the horror expressed by some distinguished people.

Teilhard's philosophy

It is with considerable hesitation that I state the case against a man who has achieved such worldwide fame and is venerated by many. Indeed, when people have considered the case against Teilhard, it is often dismissed 'in view of the whole personality and nature of the man'.

Teilhard has written several philosophical books, in which he attempts to harmonize evolution and Christianity, and the response they evoke is sharply divided. To his admirers, he is a mystical philosopher at the limits of human thought, who had to create new words to express his concepts, and who was able to visualize a wonderful future, culminating in the full development of man's potential. One of his many admirers, Madame Barthélemy-Madaule is quoted by Speaight [p119]. She says that the philosophy of Teilhard was

> ... preparing to emerge by way of phenomenological reflection, just as we shall be able to read in the total development of phenomena at the end of time their ontological meaning. And it is only in the degree to which phenomenology is incomplete and philosophy provisional that the two approaches are justified. . . . Phenomenology is the image of creation in time. . . . The moment had come to achieve this transfigured science of which Bergson had an occasional presentiment. For Teilhard phenomenology is the living spirit of science on the march, and constitutes the prolegomena to a philosophy.

Teilhard's philosophical nature is doubtless inherited, for his mother was a great-niece of Voltaire.

Teilhard is much revered by his admirers, but does have many critics. One of them is C. S. Lewis who wrote to a friend saying:

Have you read this book by the Jesuit de Chardin (The Phenomenon of Man) which is being praised to the skies? This is evolution run mad. He saves 'continuity' by saying that before there was life there was in matter what he calls 'pre-life'. Can you see any possible use in such language? Before you switched on the lights in the cellar there was (if you like to call it so) 'pre-light'; but the English for that is 'darkness'. Then he goes on to the future, and seems to me to be repeating Bergson (without the eloquence) and Shaw (without the wit). It ends up of course in something uncomfortably like Pantheism; His own Jesuits were quite right in forbidding him to publish any more books on the subject. This prohibition probably explains the 'succès fou' he is having among our scientists . . .

CONCLUSION

I would contend that, based upon the evidence given above, an adequate case has been established that Dawson was innocent of any complicity in the hoax, and that the person responsible for placing the faked fossils in the pit at Piltdown was Teilhard de Chardin S.J.

Further evidence

When writing the first edition of this book, I felt certain that Teilhard was not the only person involved, but I had very little evidence to confirm my suspicions. Further information, however, was subsequently brought to light due to an incident which we will now consider.

PROFESSOR DOUGLAS' ACCUSATION

There was a renewed surge of interest in the Piltdown Hoax following the tape recorded accusations of Professor J. M. Douglas, which he made a few months before his death in February 1978. At the time of the Piltdown discoveries Douglas was a junior assistant to Professor Sollas of the Department of Geology at Oxford, a position which he held from 1937–50. Douglas accused Sollas of providing Dawson with the technical expertise to carry out the hoax. He suggested that Sollas' motive was his 'bitter dislike' for Smith Woodward and he refers to a few incidents which illustrate this. One such was the 'Sherborne bone' incident, in which two boys from Sherborne school found a partially fossilized bone with a horse's head scratched on it. It was forwarded to Woodward in 1912 who considered it genuine. In 1924 Sollas claimed it had been a forgery by the boys, thus trying to discredit Woodward.

Douglas considered that when Sollas saw how many experts accepted the Piltdown fossils as genuine, he decided not to expose the fraud. The situation was left like this until it was exposed in 1953.

I have examined Dr. Halstead's report of Douglas' tape recording in Nature (2nd November 1978 v.276p11), various newspaper reports and their correspondence columns. I am convinced that the claim that the hoax was carried out by Sollas simply because of his 'bitter dislike' of Woodward is quite unacceptable.

The most obvious objection is that Sollas would have been very foolish indeed to have fabricated the hoax *with the later intention of exposing it*, for the search to find the culprit would have begun. The trial would have inevitably pointed to Sollas and resulted in his disgrace. Furthermore, when the Piltdown fossils were found he appears to have accepted them as uncritically as most of the other 'experts'. He is hardly likely to have done this if he intended later to expose them as fraudulent.

There are many other objections to Professor Douglas' contentions. The plot was spread over several years and involved an elaborate technique of a high order, as acknowledged in the 1953 British Museum report. Moreover, as we shall see, *several* experts were involved. When Woodward gave his first paper in December 1912, he had already collected enough fake items for him to be ridiculed. Yet many more items continued to be found as late as 1915. To claim that Sollas did not expose the fraud because of its enthusiastic reception by many experts is *not* supported by the facts, as surely the planting of fakes would have ceased.

As soon as the whole point of Professor Douglas' view of Sollas' motives is negated, several other glaring inaccuracies become apparent.

(a) Dawson's friendship
Douglas *must* have known that Woodward had been a *personal* friend of Dawson for thirty years, and had helped him to reach an honoured place. To claim that Dawson could be induced to help in ridiculing his friend is not only unacceptable but positively misleading.

(b) Dawson exculpated
After Dawson's discoveries in June 1912, a few local personalities thought Dawson might have added a few fossils to the (genuine) skull he had discovered. It was not until 1955 that Dr. Weiner—in his book 'The Piltdown Forgery'—made the first claim that Dawson had faked some of his archaeological discoveries. Thus there was not the slightest hint of Dawson being a faker *before* 1912. Yet Douglas

blandly suggests:

> He (Dawson) of course, was a man who was known to have committed many fakes . . .,

and even:

> . . . it may have been put to Dawson that to make a fool of a man of the standing of Sir Arthur Smith Woodward would be very, very difficult and if successful would be, so to speak, the highlight of his many fakeries.

Douglas obviously intended to incriminate Dawson on grounds which are clearly refuted by the evidence.

(c) Sollas' enmity

Sollas is said to have had a 'bitter dislike' of Woodward and it is claimed that they were 'bitter enemies'. Yet Douglas admits that he was not sure if Woodward also disliked Sollas, or whether Dawson was aware of the enmity between them! Actually, Woodward approached Sollas for the loan of an assistant and wrote an obituary on Sollas for the Royal Society. Furthermore, some years after the discoveries Sollas complimented Woodward on his reconstruction of the skull 'which he accomplished with great success'. All this hardly supports Professor Douglas' claim that their enmity was the mainspring of the Piltdown plot.

With regard to the Sherborne fossil, Sollas is said to have known that this was a fake in 1912, but did not expose it until 1924. R. A. H. Farrar in a letter in the *Daily Telegraph* on 7th November 1978, however, gives evidence which indicates the genuineness of the fossil. Having read the correspondence, I am inclined to consider the fossil as genuine. One strange aspect is that Bayzand, Sollas' assistant, claimed it was known by many of the boys at the school to be a fake. Yet years later, one of the two discoverers still maintained he had made a genuine find. This would certainly reflect upon Bayzand's reliability, if not his integrity. There is a mystery even in this strange little incident. I think it is possible that Sollas, who was probably one of the hoaxers, claimed that the Sherborne bone was a fake for a double purpose. Firstly, it got rid of this 'awkward' fossil, for a semifossilized bone engraved with a horse's head appears to show that man was cultured at a much earlier age than most experts were prepared to accept. Secondly, it discredited Woodward, so that if ever the Piltdown hoax was exposed, this could be referred to, in order to deflect attention away from the real culprits.

From all this I would contend that Professor Douglas' account is very inaccurate and quite misleading. This may be due to a faulty memory in old age. But perhaps there could be some other reason, for he—

(a) Unwarrantably incriminates Dawson,

(b) Claims Sollas was the only expert in the hoax, and

(c) Provides a motive for the hoax which has all the marks of being concocted from very minor incidents.

I would suggest that Professor Douglas' explanations only cloud the issue and deflect attention from the vital questions as to the identity and motives of the perpetrators of the hoax.

FURTHER CONSIDERATIONS

Dawson's 'faked' Roman bricks

It became apparent to me during the research for this book that various efforts had been made to besmirch Dawson's integrity and clear Teilhard from any hint of suspicion. A classic example of this is the thermoluminescence age tests carried out in 1973 on some Roman tiles from Pevensey, as one of them had been found by Dawson in 1902. These tests were reported by Dr. Peacock in 'Antiquity' (June 1973).

The thermoluminescence test is a sophisticated method of trying to determine the age of a piece of fired clay or pottery by raising its temperature and measuring the light-energy released.

These Roman bricks bore inscriptions which dated them about 400 B.C., and only two pieces (out of possibly four) were located, one held by the British Museum and the other by the Lewes Museum.

The test of the British Museum brick was carried out at Oxford University and gave a first result of not more than 360 years old. However, a second 'special' test reduced this figure to a date of firing between 1900–1940 A.D. Similar tests carried out by the British Museum themselves gave ages of 70 and 85 years respectively for the two tests. The report mentions that the Lewes brick 'also proved to be modern', yet no figures are given. The author of the report, Dr. Peacock, claims that the bricks are forgeries. He says,'In my opinion the time is now ripe for a full investigation of Dawson's numerous and often bizarre discoveries'.

Are these tests reliable? It would appear not. In describing the method, the Encyclopaedia Britannica makes the very damaging comment that 'Hope, rather than accomplishment mainly characterises the status of thermoluminescent dating at the present time' (1980) and that the method 'gives somewhat varied results'.

In the tests on the bricks, the report admits that heat would be needed to set the wood glue used to join the pieces of the Lewes specimen, but doubts if the temperature reached 350°C, which would destroy its thermoluminescence. Could not these specimens have been heated either in the tests or accidentally during their life? Such heating would certainly make them appear very recent. In reading this report, I had the same sense of its inadequacy as I had when reading the tests for Gypsum carried out on the Piltdown fossils (p13). In both cases, the tests were instigated by the British Museum. In each case 'special' sophisticated tests were carried out. There was the same feeling that, in both cases, the evidence was being strained to fit a pre-judged result.

Doubt on the validity of these tests was voiced by Mr. K. Painter who, as Assistant Keeper of the British Museum's department of Prehistoric and Romano British Antiquities, should be well qualified to judge the reliability of the tests. In an article in the Guardian on 5th June 1973, he said that the tests cast doubt on the brick. But he added,

> I do not feel that this particular test alone is conclusive. It won't prove anything one way or another. One must await further tests.

> Whatever else he did, Dawson was an avid collector. He could not have faked all that he found . . .

He concludes:

> One does not wish to be uncharitable, but if Dr. Peacock feels that all Dawson's finds should be re-examined then it is up to him to sit down and do it.

This same article gives the comment of a woman 'official' from the British Museum Anthropological department, whose name for some reason is not disclosed. In her condemnation of Dawson's integrity, she mentioned, 'We have known *for some time* that the Roman bricks found by Dawson were no older than the turn of the century.'!

Here is a strange affair indeed. The Anthropological department had known for some time that the bricks were fakes (before the tests were made?), whilst the Romano British department still considers that they may be genuine. It would seem that the Anthropological department were keen to prove Dawson guilty even in areas other than their own.

Just imagine what Dawson would have to have done if he *were* guilty. The faking of these bricks would have involved collecting clay of the same type as the class from which the Pevensey bricks were made, making an embossed stamp with authentic looking Roman lettering, secretly firing the bricks in a kiln, breaking them up, and planting them at a time and in a position which would not arouse suspicion amongst the excavators. He is supposed to have done all this without raising the slightest suspicion or leaving any evidence of his equipment. Thus we are expected to believe that Dawson was a superb forger, able to fool the experts not only in anthropology but in the field of Roman artefacts also! Such a proposition is surely incredible. I would maintain that there is no adequate evidence that Dawson faked these tiles or was involved in any way in the fabrication of the Piltdown hoax. Indeed, I would consider that these tests are a blatant effort by the Museum authorities to discredit Dawson by every possible means, in order to distract attention from their tattered reputation following the Piltdown debacle. That such unsatisfactory tests should have been resorted to simply discredits their reputation even further.

Often, when the experts are being defended, Teilhard's name is linked with them. This linking occurs again in the report of the brick tests. This report, somewhat unnecessarily, mentions that:

> It has been suggested that Teilhard de Chardin was the author of the Piltdown hoax, but since he did not meet Dawson until 1908 he could have had no part in the Pevensey forgery, which weighs against this to some extent.

Teilhard's 'innocence'

I am certain that Teilhard de Chardin was the main hoaxer and the link with the Piltdown pit. He may have fabricated the evidence himself, for as we know, he was experimenting with the rapid staining of bones in the iron rich waters of the Weald (p28) I am sure there was collusion between Teilhard and others. As we have seen, Teilhard knew of Dawson's skull find at Piltdown as early as 1909.

Professor Oakley tries to clear Teilhard's name (letter, *The Times*, 7th November 1978), for he suggests that he may have given the Ichkeul planifrons tooth to Dawson. However, Dawson would not have been so foolish as to have dropped it into the pit. Teilhard would then surely have recognized it, and the game would have been up. Furthermore, Professor Oakley appears to have forgotten that it was Teilhard *himself* who 'found' the tooth on the first day of the dig! (p5) .

Stephen Jay Gould of Harvard University has also written two articles about Teilhard's involvement. The first was in *New Scientist* (5th April 1979 v82 n.1149). In this article, which contains many inaccuracies, he puts forward the usual idea that it was all a practical joke by Dawson and Teilhard to fool the experts—a joke which went too far. Teilhard is said to have been 'dismissed as a young and unwitting dupe', but Gould portrays him as a 'fun loving student'. This description hardly fits a man of twenty seven years of age, who had been trained in a strict Jesuit seminary and had spent much time overseas, including holding a teaching post in Cairo University!

The second article appeared in *Natural History Magazine* (August 1980). Gould here says Teilhard's two evasive letters to Oakley (see p20) when the hoax was discovered, clearly implicate him with Dawson. Yet once again the whole affair is dismissed as a joke going too far. Gould imagines that Teilhard 'cried inwardly as he watched Smith Woodward and even Boule himself make fools of themselves—the very men who had befriended him and taught him'. Gould's colleagues however considered Teilhard hid '. . . passion, mystery and good humour behind a grab of piety'. Much could be written in criticism of the article, but one item is his handling of Teilhard's work in China, where he said he pursued 'distinguished research in geology and palaeontology'. No mention is made of Teilhard's part in the 'discovery' of Pekin man. Did Gould not want Teilhard's name too closely linked with this fossil, which Gould in his first article described as 'legitimate'? Surprisingly, however, there is a large picture of Teilhard examining the Pekin man fossil skull!

Several similar instances of the way in which Teilhard is exonerated could be cited, but one further example must suffice. In the Editorial of *Antiquity* for December 1972 (p263), a letter written by Teilhard on 6th August 1913 is quoted, in which he refers to a forty eight hour visit to Dawson. The Editorial also notes that the collators of the collection of letters,* from which this quotation had been taken, in a footnote say: 'At that time Teilhard had no part in Dawson's discoveries, whom he trusted'! Inspection of the full footnote in the original publication, however, shows that this quotation is preceded by the words, 'See above, letters 94 and 97'. If we turn to these, we find that the first, written on 26th April 1912, mentions a visit he received from his geological friend, Dawson, whilst the second, written on 3rd June 1912, describes his visit to Piltdown *when he carried out several hours of excavations with Dawson and Woodward.* Knowing this, how could the compilers claim that Teilhard 'had *no part* in Dawson's discoveries' and give it as a footnote to a letter as late as the 6th August 1913,

---

*Lettres de Hastings et de Paris 1908-14. Edition Montaigne Aubier, Impasse de Quai de Conti, Paris IV. Annotated by Auguste Demoment and Henri de Lubac.

over a year after he had begun digging at the site? Furthermore, why did the editor of *Antiquity* not trouble to turn to the other letters referred to, before quoting the remainder of their footnote? Had he done so, he would have realized their comment was quite unjustified, as was his warm approval of their views.

I give this as just one small example of how the readers of even prestigious journals would be quite unaware of how their views had been affected, simply by the way the evidence has been presented.

With regard to all these examples, I must say that the many strenuous efforts by a number of eminent people to protect Teilhard de Chardin's name from any serious accusation of malicious forgery constitute one of the most notable aspects of the whole of the Piltdown plot and exposure.

Some other 'helpers'?

Although Teilhard was clearly the main hoaxer who deposited the fake fossils at the site, it is certain that he received advice and assistance from some highly qualified experts of the day. Sollas himself was probably amongst them. On p16 I mention that Grafton Elliot Smith and Davidson Black, his pupil, visited the site in 1914, on which occasion Black found part of a rhinoceros molar tooth. In 1915 at Piltdown II site, an unnamed 'friend' found another part of a rhinoceros tooth *'as highly mineralised as the specimens found at Piltdown itself'* (p23). I would suggest that these were parts of the same tooth or collection of teeth, and there is the possibility that Black was the unnamed 'friend' who planted the fragment at Piltdown II to give this site a link with Piltdown I. Indeed, he may have had some part in the planting of all the fossils at Piltdown II.

GRAFTON ELLIOT SMITH

One of the most intriguing characters in the whole drama is that of Elliot Smith. He had very close connections with all the principal characters, but who, as far as I have been able to trace, never seems to have been *directly* involved in the actual work of Piltdown or Pekin. Millar [p234] considers he was the prime culprit at Piltdown, but admits that he has no evidence to support this contention. Although, like Millar, I have no evidence of his direct involvement, there are some facts which would suggest he did have some connection with the various 'discoveries'. These are:

(a) He was working in Cairo *during the precise period of Teilhard's stay*. I have no evidence that they met, but as they were both in the field of science, education and research, and both were greatly involved in geological discoveries, it is almost certain that they met at some time to share their common interest. Incidentally, Millar excuses Smith, for he says he was in a 'backwater appointment in Cairo' at the time of the Piltdown 'plants'. This, however, is incorrect, for it was during this period that Dawson was searching for the *genuine* skull pieces. The fake material appeared after he met Teilhard in 1909. Teilhard in fact visited Ichkeul, where he picked up the Planifrons tooth, on his way to England.

(b) In the 2nd October 1913 issue of *Nature*, Smith boasted that he predicted in his address to the British Association in September 1912 that a human brain with ape-like features was a stage in man's development, and that he did not know of the existence of Piltdown until 'some months' later. The interesting thing is that the main discoveries were made in June 1912 and were not announced until December 1912. Yet as early as November, Smith wrote to a colleague that he wished to compare the brain cast of the Piltdown skull with that of La Quina. Clearly he was aware of the Piltdown finds long before they were announced in December, probably being kept fully informed by Teilhard.

(c) He visited Piltdown at least once, accompanied by his pupil, Davidson Black, the latter being fortunate in finding the fake rhinoceros tooth.

This evidence is admittedly by far from adequate. Nevertheless it would seem that, at the very least, Smith was well aware of the hoax being carried out at Piltdown, and indeed may well have been the instigator. His motives for so doing will be considered later.

Smith had a number of pupils who were to rise to eminence in the field of palaeoanthropology. As we shall see, Black went to China and there discovered the famous 'Pekin man'. Smith visited this site and later wrote a glowing account of the work. Two other pupils were Dart, who found two Australopithecines in South Africa and Oakley, who developed the fluorine test which was used to prove that various Homo sapiens fossils were not authentic.

In his day Smith was considered to be one of the foremost experts on human evolution. Yet we must ask how good a scientist was he? Even at the Symposium of the Zoological society held in his memory in 1973, it was admitted that many of his views on man's evolution were found later to be wrong.

The net of suspicion widens

When the Piltdown fossils were exposed as a hoax in 1953, attention was inevitably centred on the three men who made the original discoveries in 1912—Dawson, Woodward and Teilhard. Although it was thought that Dawson may have had some expert assistance, no specific personalities were ever named. When interest in Piltdown was rekindled in November 1978 by Professor Douglas' accusation, however, further revelations occurred which well and truly 'let the cat out of the bag'!

The British Museum's involvement in the hoax

Professor Douglas' efforts to incriminate Dawson and Sollas were based on extremely weak evidence. Publication of his accusation, however, stirred up a great deal of controversy and as a result some surprising information floated to the surface. By far the most astounding statement was that contained in a letter from Dr. L. B. Halstead, to *The Times* on 25th November 1978. Dr. Halstead possesses Douglas' tape recording and knows many of the present day members of the Natural History Museum well. In his letter he said:

> There is evidence that the medieval orang utan lower jaw which made up the Piltdown jaw came from the Natural History Museum itself and was provided by Dr. M. A. C. Hinton (a former Keeper of Zoology). *Indeed, according to Hinton himself the Piltdown man hoax was initially planned and executed within the Museum.*
> *The current scenario would seem to be one of an extensive conspiracy involving Hinton, a few other colleagues in the Museum, with Teilhard de Chardin contributing a Tunisian elephant tooth and the 'missing' canine.* The expertise involved in the wide extent of the Piltdown hoaxes still assuredly points to Sollas.

Dr. Halstead confirmed this accusation in a letter published in *Nature* on 22nd February 1979, in which he says:

> My letter also mentioned that Dr. M. A. C. Hinton had stated that the hoax was initially planned and executed within the Natural History Museum . . . From the people that knew Hinton well, it is accepted that *he must have been involved in the promulgation of the hoax, and it is even claimed that he 'virtually confessed' to this prior to his death.*

[It is interesting that Halstead also mentions in this letter that 'unfortunately the short paragraph referring to Hinton's possible involvement was edited out' of his original article in *Nature* on Douglas' tape recording. Why was this revealing statement edited out? Was it an attempt to suppress the evidence of the British Museum's involvement in the plot? Are we not entitled to all the facts?]

Here then we have members of the British Natural History

Museum named as the instigators of the hoax! Furthermore, in an External Service broadcast on the BBC on 14th November 1978, Dr. Halstead said:

> There are other people connected besides Sollas and they are members of the Natural History Museum staff and they're very difficult to pin down, but it's well-known amongst the British Museum people that a group of young men in the Museum, young scientists, about the 1910–11 period also intensely disliked Smith Woodward. They knew that his ambition in life was to find the missing link, and the missing link was found.

and:

> . . . the suspicion points very strongly to Dawson, Charles Dawson, the local solicitor, who was known to be responsible for hoaxes in Sussex. And the suspicions always pointed to him. Everybody said 'ah, that's the man'. Now that's very convenient, because it diverts attention away from Oxford on the one hand and the Natural History Museum on the other, and now 25 years later we now have some, I think, very, very good evidence pointing very strongly that Professor Sollas was probably the instigator, but certainly very deeply involved. We know there is evidence around that the people in the Natural History Museum were also involved: this is very difficult to winkle out, but we know it's there.

He also said the jaw 'quite evidently' came from the Museum, quite likely from certain people in the Zoology Department, where there was a box of unregistered orang-utan material.

Whilst such revelations may come as a shock to many, I have always felt that the Museum experts may have been at least 'accessories after the fact'. This is witnessed by the way in which the *original* bones were quickly removed from L. S. B. Leakey's inspection (p33). Indeed, Halstead himself said in his broadcast:

> And in the British Museum this was sort of hidden away. There was a lot of secrecy surrounding it; people weren't actually allowed to look at it, so there was obviously something very funny . . .

From this it would appear that the fact that Piltdown was a fraud *was known at very high level, even from the beginning*! That the Museum experts, or some of them, were actually accomplices in the fraud simply widens the web of intrigue a little further. Probably some members of the Museum staff could reveal a great deal more, but are prevented by their signing of the Official Secrets Act.

Hinton's statement that the hoax was 'planned and executed within the Museum' makes Weiner's account in his book very strange reading. Weiner (like Sollas, a Professor at Oxford) appears never to have heard at any stage the rumours that the Piltdown fossils were fraudulent. However, he says that quite independently, he realized 'with astonishment' that this was a possibility. In order to prove whether this was so, he approached the Natural History Museum, the very place where it was originally fabricated!

In his talk, Halstead pointed out a very interesting connection, for he commented on the '. . . link between Oxford and the British Museum in the hoax and in the exposure of the hoax.'

The motive

We will now consider the very important question of the motive of those who perpetrated the hoax. As will be apparent, I have always been suspicious of the part played by the Museum authorities, and Hinton's statement simply confirms this. I would consider that various experts were involved in differing degrees in carrying out the hoax.

What could have been their motive?

This is generally dismissed as simply an attempt, by one or two people who disliked Sir Arthur Smith Woodward, to make a fool of him. Such an explanation, however, cannot be seriously entertained. As we have already pointed out, very skilfully-made fake material continued to be placed over several years. This was much more than was necessary to make a fool of Woodward, who certainly did not suffer during his lifetime because of the hoax. The most obvious objection, however, is the supposed aim of eventually revealing the fact that it was all fraudulent. We are expected to accept the idea that one or more persons, (whether highly placed with reputations to safeguard, or young students with careers to consider) would assist with, or have knowledge of, a fraud *which it was later intended to reveal at the most appropriate moment.*

It is quite obvious that, if the hoax were traced to its source, it would do far more damage to the reputations of the plotters than it would to that of the intended victim. I am therefore convinced that it was *not* intended to expose the hoax at any time.

What other possible motive could there then be?

To discover the answer we must consider the situation in the field of anthropology about 1910. Darwin had predicted a link between man and apes in his *Origin of Species* over fifty years before. The only fossils to support this theory were Dubois' hotly-contested discovery some thirty years later of Java man, which was composed of a giant gibbon's skull-cap and a human leg-bone. Nothing had been found for *twenty years* before the Piltdown 'discoveries'.

This lack of convincing evidence would obviously be exasperating to those who fanatically supported Darwin's theory. Indeed many writers admit that Piltdown man was enthusiastically accepted because, as Elliot Smith and Sollas claimed, '. . . it was a combination which had long been previously anticipated.' Weiner in his book muses whether 'there could have been a mad desire to assist the doctrine of human evolution by furnishing the "requisite missing link".' [36p118]

I would suggest that this would provide sufficient motivation for one or more persons to give a 'nudge' to the evidence which was so reluctantly forthcoming. Furthermore, I would suggest that this is the only motive which adequately fits the facts. Confirmation of this can be seen in the activities of Teilhard, Black and Elliot Smith in the later 'production' of Pekin 'man' and in Teilhard's involvement in the later Java finds.

I am not necessarily saying that any of the other 'missing links' have been deliberately fabricated in the way in which the Piltdown fossils were. But at the very least, it would seem that the experts deceive themselves regarding their interpretation of their discoveries. Where such self deception crosses the hair-line border into deliberate deception of the public I cannot say, but simply leave it to my readers to reach their own judgement as they weigh the evidence presented in this book.

APPENDIX I

THE PILTDOWN PLOT
A Hoax That Grew

By R. Essex, M.Sc.
(An article appearing in the *Kent and Sussex Journal*,
July–September 1955, vol.2, no.4, p.94–5,
reproduced by kind permission of Whitethorn Press Ltd.)

A defence of Charles Dawson, the Uckfield solicitor and geologist. The first-hand account of some happenings of the years 1912 to 1915. Mr. Essex is the only scientist left who was in Uckfield and in day-to-day contact with Charles Dawson during the important years 1912 to 1915. He saw and remembers many things that recent investigators of the Piltdown mystery seem to have missed.

Two books have already appeared on the Piltdown Problem. The first is by J. S. Weiner *The Piltdown Forgery* (Oxford University Press), and it begins by tracing the steps that enabled a group of scientists to show that the Piltdown jaw was that of a modern ape, then it deals with the steps which led to the statement that *all* the Piltdown finds were planted and thirdly it gives the results of Dr. Weiner's conversations with a number of people living in the neighbourhood of Piltdown. As a result of all this, suspicion is pointed in Charles Dawson's direction.

The second book is by Francis Vere of Piltdown, *The Piltdown Fantasy* (Cassell) in which the author critically examines all the evidence, including some which Dr. Weiner did not consider. He comes to the conclusions, first that the hoax would have been short-lived had Smith Woodward not been quite so possessive and if he had, instead, allowed other scientists to examine the jaw itself instead of merely handling a plaster model of it: second that all the Piltdown finds were not planted, because the first finds, the skull parts, were discovered embedded in the gravel and had to be got out with a pick-axe. Thirdly, that if all the finds had been planted, the fluorine test could be ignored since it only applies in the case of specimens which come from the same deposit, and fourthly he comes to the conclusion that Dr. Weiner's travels in Sussex resulted in the collection of a lot of gossip about Charles Dawson which will not bear critical examination.

Being practically in daily contact with Charles Dawson during the important years 1912–15, the present author saw many things which those who have recently been investigating the hoax have ignored.

First. Another jaw not mentioned by Dr. Weiner came from Piltdown much more human than the ape's jaw and, therefore much more likely to belong to the Piltdown skull parts which are admittedly human. I saw and handled that jaw and know in whose bag it came to Dawson's office. The jaw was also seen by Mr. H. H. Wakefield, then an articled clerk of Dawson's, and he has given written evidence of seeing it. Dawson never saw it, and the owner probably never knew until 1953 that anybody but himself had seen it. It happened in this way. I was science master at Uckfield Grammar School, Charles Dawson was Clerk to the Governors and his office was quite near to the school, so near that in getting to Uckfield High Street one had to pass his office windows. One day when I was passing I was beckoned in by one of the clerks whom I knew well. He had called me in to show me a fossil half-jaw much more human than an ape's and with three molars firmly fixed in it. When I asked where this object came from, the answer was 'Piltdown'. According to the clerk it had been brought down by one of the 'diggers' who, when he called and asked for Mr. Dawson, was carrying a bag such as might be used for carrying tools. When he was told that Mr. Dawson was busy in court he said he would leave the bag and come back. When he had gone, the clerk opened the bag and saw this jaw. Seeing me passing he had called me in. I told him he had better put it back and that Mr. Dawson would be cross if he knew. I found afterwards that when the 'digger' returned, Mr. Dawson was still busy in court, so he picked up his bag and left.

From that time until December 1953, I was under the impression that I had had a preview of the jaw from Piltdown seen and examined by the experts. But when, a year and a half ago, I saw a photograph of the Museum jaw from the inner side, I realized that it and mine were not the same. I travelled down from York and put all my information on the matter before the experts at the British Museum. One big difference regarding the jaws was that whereas mine had three molars firmly fixed, the long accepted jaw had two and a cavity or empty socket. An interesting point arises here. The *Encyclopaedia Britannica* says the jaw had two molars and an empty socket. *Chamber's Encyclopaedia* published in 1950 says it had three molars in position.

Some time after my visit to Dawson's offices, related above, I was near Piltdown with one of my colleagues when we met Robert Kenward, son of the owner of the farm on which the Piltdown gravel pit lay. He asked us if we had seen X (naming the owner of the bag). X apparently was distractedly searching for something he had lost and would not tell Robert what it was.

The third link is this. I was standing outside Dawson's office talking to him and to John Montgomery, the Headmaster of Uckfield Grammar School and himself a member of the local Archaeological Society, and a little apart were two or three others talking. When Charles

Dawson said he had never seen anything like the 'sixteen-inch bat' found at Piltdown, Montgomery told him he had seen one in the Dordogne. Montgomery told me afterwards exactly how he saw it, but the point is that as soon as Montgomery said 'Dordogne', Dawson's eyes glanced across to the nearby group of people, one of whom was the owner of the bag. Then he turned abruptly indoors. That information I gave in much more detail, to the experts months before their report was issued.

I am certain Dawson suspected something, although at the time I had no idea what he suspected. He was not the man to broadcast suspicion. In support of this, there is a fact not generally known. It is on record that Dr. S. Allison Woodhead, then Head of the Agricultural College at Uckfield and afterwards County analyst did *one* analysis for Dawson. As a matter of fact he did several. I knew Dr. Woodhead very well, and I am certain that even to him Dawson never mentioned this suspect or his suspicions in general.

Dr. Weiner mentioned Dawson's experiment with bones and seems to think that Dawson was trying to fake. He was trying to see if they could be faked, which is not the same thing. Further the tale of the boiling of bones in Dawson's office is a complete fairy tale. Dawson did not know enough chemistry to do any real work on such matters; he might have made a few simple tests suggested by Dr. Woodhead. Unfortunately, Dawson died before he could finish.

It might be asked why suspicion has turned on to Dawson. Amongst the people who know the facts there is not one who suspects him.

I have given all the above facts to the scientific team in charge of the matter. I have named X and I have identified him. It is not my business to pillory him publicly. He conceived a joke. It worked far better than he could have hoped in one way and in another it failed; but that was not his fault. It was in a measure the fault of the scientists who did not subject the 'jaw' itself to critical examination and partly it was due to the fact that the people concerned became scattered. Dawson died, Smith Woodward retired; and X ? If Dawson had lived I am certain he would have found out the whole affair, and I should have loved to have been there to listen to the dressing-down to which X would have had to listen. Then he would have had to collaborate in cleaning up the mess.

Incidentally the hoax was not conceived as a whole. It grew. When the first bait was swallowed and the hoaxer did not get the satisfaction of seeing the face of his victim when he realized he had been galled, he tried again and again and in the end all the hoaxer had was the knowledge that in the British Museum was his hybrid offspring which he could not publicly claim, together with a few teeth and a bat.

APPENDIX II

THE PROBLEM OF DAWSON'S EARLY DISCOVERIES

A careful consideration of various statements by the three investigators concerning what exactly Dawson *did* discover before they began excavating in July 1912, showed that there were important discrepancies between the accounts, which cast some doubt on the authenticity of certain statements. I will first set out the main points of the various accounts of Dawson's early discoveries, which were made by the three men.

(a) DAWSON'S REPORTS

Dawson, in his first report in December 1912 [40], makes it clear that he discovered *only two skull pieces* before they began excavations, for he said that the first piece of skull was handed to him 'some years ago', then in 1911 he found another piece which fitted the first one, and he took these to Woodward who was impressed. He then continues, '*We* started digging . . . *we* recovered from the spoil heaps as many fragments as possible. . . . Besides the human remains *we* found two small broken pieces of a molar tooth of a Pliocene elephant. . . .' (He then lists all the other fossils discovered at that time.) He later says, 'Among the flints *we* found . . .' and in a footnote attributes the discovery of one of the flints and the portion of elephant's tooth to Teilhard, 'who accompanied us on one occasion', as we have noted.

Thus in the official records, Dawson said he found only *two* skull pieces, *and everything else was discovered after Teilhard and Woodward went to the site.*

(b) TEILHARD'S LETTER

Speaight gives a letter, written by Teilhard, dated 3rd June 1912 (Sunday) which appears to be an account of the first day's excavation —the previous day (Saturday). He says, 'Dawson unearthed another fragment of the famous human skull—he had already found three other pieces—and I myself laid hands on the fragment of an elephant's molar.' [p44]

Weiner says that Teilhard's figure of three is supported by Dawson's obituaries, although this does not appear in the one written by Woodward in the *Geological Magazine* in 1916.

Teilhard makes no mention of the flint tool (later discovered to be faked), which Dawson said Teilhard found. Did he perhaps find the tool during a visit to the pit when Dawson and Woodward were *not* present?

(c) DAWSON'S LETTERS

On the files of the British Museum, there are several letters which
Dawson wrote to Woodward, and Weiner gives some extracts as
follows:

14 February 1912	He had 'come across a very old Pleistocene bed ... which I think is going to be very interesting' —'with part of a thick human skull in it'—'part of a human skull which will rival *Homo heidelburgensis*'.
26th March	Hippopotamus tooth enclosed with a note saying 'will you kindly identify enclosed for me? I think the larger one is hippo'. (Woodward confirmed that it was.)
28th March	'I will of course take care that no one sees the *piece* of skull who has any knowledge and leave it to you.' (Vere says this letter specifically mentions the hippo tooth he had sent on the 26th.)
23rd May	'Some time tomorrow (Friday), ... I will bring the *piece* of skull and a few odds and ends found with it, or near it, in the gravel bed.'

(d) SMITH WOODWARD'S BOOK

Shortly before he died, Sir Arthur Smith Woodward dictated (he
was then blind) his book *The Earliest Englishman* in which he gives his
account of the discoveries. He says that Dawson found three pieces
of skull which fitted together, and a further two separate pieces which
he brought to Woodward in the spring of 1912 for his opinion. He
continues, 'We also hoped to find other fossils because Mr. Dawson
had already picked up flint tools and teeth of hippopotamus and elephant in the same deposit.' [p8]

When the excavation began, he says, 'We found three pieces ... and
I found in another heap an important fragment.'

He later says, 'On different days we also picked up three undoubted
flint implements, besides several "eoliths" and fragments of a tooth
of an elephant. . . .' [p11]

(Eoliths are stones which have simple breakage patterns. There was
great controversy about this time whether they were fashioned by
early man or due to natural causes.)

Finally on p.32 he says, '. . . two teeth of hippopotamus which have
already been mentioned as having been found by Mr. Dawson during
his earlier examination of the gravel pit.'

COMMENTS

From all these accounts it is important to ascertain whether the faked flints and animal fossils were found before or after 2nd June. If these fossils *were* all found after 2nd June, suspicion would clearly fall on Woodward, whilst Teilhard would be even further implicated, for it would be unnecessary to assume that he had visited the site before the excavations began. As we have seen, Dawson said in his paper that the flints and animal teeth were found after the June excavations. Teilhard makes no mention of them and, moreover, Dawson does not appear to have shown these important fossils to any of his friends who saw the skull pieces before that date.

Considering first Dawson's letters, it would appear from these that he had found a hippo tooth, skull pieces and 'a few odds and ends'. Regarding the hippo pre-molar, it was from a different source to the molar, was stained dark brown *throughout*, and contained some gypsum and the 'incriminating' chromium [36p68]. As the *molar* appears to have come from Maltese caves, there is no real evidence that the pre-molar was a forgery, for the chromium may well be due to Dawson's 'hardening' of it in a chromium compound. Thus, there does not seem to be any direct evidence that this particular fossil was fraudulently stained, and it was probably a genuine fossil found *in situ* at Piltdown, for hippo teeth have been found in England.

The skull pieces, as I have shown, were genuine fossils, and we have, therefore, only Dawson's extremely vague reference to 'odds and ends' as evidence from him that possibly fake fossils were found before June. Could it not simply be that they were merely examples of the very controversial 'eoliths' or else shaped pieces of ironstone looking like small fragments of fossilized bones, all subsequently to be dismissed by Woodward when Dawson brought them for his inspection? Ironstone fragments can look very similar to some fossils, and Woodward, in his description of the discovery of the canine, mentioned that 'they had already seen bits of ironstone that looked like teeth'. Similarly, when Dawson wrote to Woodward on the 26th March, he had included another fragment, which Woodward identified as being simply a piece of ironstone. [24p120]

If this explanation is accepted, Woodward's book is the only evidence which states specifically that any fossils, later found faked, were discovered before June 1912, and we will examine this in detail. Before leaving Dawson's letters, however, I must point out that the only records which Dawson would certainly have read and approved before his death were those in the Geological Society for the years up to 1915. *All other correspondence and writings were publicized after his death, when he could no longer comment on their accuracy.* Were he alive today, he might well be able to give a satisfactory explanation for the contents of his letters at present on the files of the British Museum.

Woodward's book

Woodward's book contradicts the report presented to the Geological Society in December 1912, in which Dawson gives all the fossils which were discovered during that first season's dig. Woodward clearly says that Dawson had already picked up flint tools [p8] and later on p.11 he says that *'we'* picked up *three* further tools. Thus one would presume that some *five* or more tools had been found. *But Dawson's 1912 report lists only* **three** *tools being found at that time,* and in fact he said: 'Among the flints *we* found. . . .' There is clearly a discrepancy, and one is left wondering if Woodward was right on p.8 in saying that Dawson had found flints before June 1912.

Doubt regarding this same passage is further strengthened by the reference to the fragments of elephant's *(Elephas)* teeth. Woodward says that Dawson had already picked up teeth of hippopotamus and elephant, and then later says *'we'* picked up fragment*s* of tooth of an elephant, indicating that at least three fragments had been found. Again Dawson reported: *'we* found *two* small broken pieces' of elephant teeth. This is confirmed by Teilhard's letter, for it is clear that Teilhard was the *first* to discover the tooth of an elephant, the second piece presumably being found some time later.

Woodward may have used the term 'we' to include Dawson's early finds, but it is clear from the context of the passage that this is not so, and as a trained scientist he should have been accurate with his statements. He makes no mention of some other flint tools and a further piece of elephant tooth found in 1913 in his account of that season's results.

Thus, of the three items he mentions as being picked up by Dawson alone, the flint tools and elephant tooth are in some doubt, and the hippo (pre-molar) tooth is the only item Dawson refers to in his correspondence, which was probably a genuine fossil.

Was Woodward's book altered?

Woodward's failure to mention the flint tools and elephant teeth found during the 1913 dig, and to attribute Dawson with the discovery of such items before June 1912, in contradiction to the Geological Society's report, could infer that he wished to protect his name, should the fraud be discovered at any time. Alternatively, there is the possibility that Woodward's manuscript was altered between his death and the publication of his book four years later. As I have already pointed out, Vere suggested this possibility in view of the fact that Woodward makes no mention of the controversial Piltdown II discoveries, except for one passing comment.

Removal of Woodward's reference to Dawson's finds does not affect the sense of the passages and could be said to enhance them. Ignoring Dawson's vague reference to 'bits and pieces', it is possibly significant that Woodward's statements, that Dawson had found tools and elephant's teeth before June 1912, are the *only* evidence which clearly exonerates Woodward and Teilhard from complicity in the early stages of the hoax.

SECTION II

APE-MEN 'EVIDENCE'
—its presentation

Ever since the publication in 1859 of Darwin's *The Origin of Species*, man has been trying to discover the possible links between himself and the animal world. Immense sums of money have been expended both directly in expeditions and excavations and indirectly in research on the resulting fossils, in an effort to establish this vital link.

Yet despite all this effort, there exists only a very small collection of bones to support the various 'missing links', whose credentials, I hope to show, do not bear a close examination. Museum visitors throughout the world are confidently presented with full-size 're-constructions'. Students gaze at artists' impressions of the various ape-men, but few people are aware that these visualizations are based upon a mere handful of bones.

Before investigating the specific ape-men who are cited as the vital links, we will consider seven important aspects of this field of research:

1. Reconstructions.
2. Artist's impressions.
3. Brain capacity.
4. Geological periods.
5. Absolute dating.
6. Correlation of dating.
7. Teeth.

1. Reconstructions

That the very life-like models of ape-men exhibited in museums rely entirely upon just a few fossil bones may come as a surprise to many. I will show by the following examples that such reconstructions depend largely upon the imagination of the modeller.

(a) *Java man*
The bones found by Dubois are illustrated in Fig. 30 (p141). Fig. 9a shows Dubois' model. Numerous drawings were made of Java man (later classified as Homo erectus), and Fig. 9b gives one of the latest—by Richard Leakey.

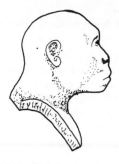

(a) Dubois's   (b) Richard Leakey's

Fig.9. Java man reconstruction

(b) *Neanderthal man*

Constable in *The Neanderthals*, maintains that Neanderthal man was the precursor of *Homo sapiens* (modern man) and not an aberrant offshoot of man's ancestors. He shows on p.25 how early reconstructions of faces, modelled upon the skull from La Chapelle-aux-Saints, were given an ape-like appearance, whereas they could equally well be made to look like a person living today. He clearly shows that such reconstructions depend entirely upon the appearance which the modeller *wants* to give the face.

(c) *Pekin man*

The reconstruction was modelled on various bones from different parts of the site and the result is given in Fig.24. We will be considering this skull in greater detail in the section of Pekin man.

(d) *Germany*

Broderick [5p145] gives an account of how misleading reconstructions can be. In a glass case in Vienna is a cast of a man's head, who had the thick neck and protuberant nape which many Germans possess, known as Steilkopf. One would have expected the skull of the original owner to be thick and short with heavy features. The actual skull of the individual was exhibited alongside however, and was delicate in appearance and quite narrow.

2. Artists' impressions

The comments on reconstructions apply also to drawings. When an artist is required to depict the feature of a member of the missing link family tree, he exercises a similar degree of imagination.

(a) *Nutcracker man* ('*Zinjanthropus boisei*')
The skull, which was incomplete, was reconstructed from 100 pieces
and is shown in the frontispiece. With so many pieces to fit together,
the difficulty of ensuring that the shape has been accurately reconstructed is obvious. This frontispiece shows four different drawings
based on the same skull. The different interpretations make it clear
that they depend entirely upon the artist's imagination and are not
based upon any scientific evidence whatsoever.

(b) *Nebraska man* ('*Hesperopithecus*')
This is a classic case of excessive imagination. In 1922 W. J. Bryan,
a politician of Nebraska, was campaigning in the courts against
children being taught in schools that they were descended from apes.
H. F. Osborn, head of the American Museum of Natural History,
received a tooth from a Mr. Cook who had found it in Pliocene deposits in Nebraska. Osborn considered that it had characteristics that
were a mixture of human, chimpanzee and Pithecanthropus, and
upon this evidence declared it was a further missing link, which he
called Hesperopithecus. He declared:

> . . . the Earth spoke to Bryan from his own State of Nebraska. The
> Hesperopithecus tooth is like the still, small voice. Its sound is by no
> means easy to hear . . . This little tooth speaks volumes of truth, in that
> it affords evidence of man's descent from the ape.

In England Sir Grafton Elliot Smith, F.R.S., Professor of Anatomy
at Manchester, fully supported Osborn. The *Illustrated London News*
published a reconstruction of Hesperopithecus and his wife, which is
shown in Fig. 10. Later investigation, however, proved that the tooth
was not of a man but of an extinct form of pig! Little publicity was
given to the discovered error.

In this section I have given just a few of the many drawings which
have been made, and very many more could have been provided.
Other examples are illustrated later in this book when we deal with
'1470' man (Fig.56 p200) and Ramapithecus (Fig.59 p211)

The acceptance by the public of such reconstructions (illustrated
above) is understandable in view of the general ignorance of the basis
upon which they are made. Writing about Java man (*Pithecanthropus
erectus*) G. K. Chesterton once said:

> . . . people talked of Pithecanthropus as of Pitt or Fox or Napoleon.
> Popular histories published portraits of him like the portraits of Charles
> I or George IV. A detailed drawing was reproduced carefully shaded

Fig.10. 'Hesperopithecus'

to show the very hairs of his head were all numbered. No uninformed person, looking at its carefully lined face, would imagine for a moment that this was the portrait of a thigh bone, of a few teeth and a fragment of a cranium.

3. Brain capacity

In order to assess how close any particular fossil skull may be to that of modern man, it is usual to compare their brain capacities. The average brain capacity of the human skull is 1,350 cc. for a woman and 1,500 cc. for a man, whilst for modern apes the figure is approximately 500 cc. Thus any intermediate type can be positioned between these figures.

To make the brain capacity the main basis of comparison, however, is unsatisfactory for the following reasons:

(a) Although the average brain capacity for modern man is about 1,400 cc., the actual range is very wide. Australian aborigines can have brain capacities as low as 830 cc. [5p84], whilst the two largest brain capacities ever known, 2,800 cc. belonged to an idiot and a U.S. Senator.

Fig. 11 illustrates diagrammatically this very wide range of human brain capacities, and their comparison with those of chimpanzees and gorillas.

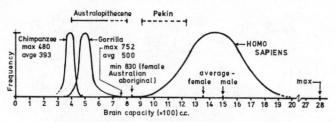

Fig.11. Diagram of ranges of brain capacities

(b) Man does not possess the largest brain in the animal world, those of the whale, dolphin and elephant being larger. Although having larger brains, they do not display the higher mental capacity which is possessed by man.

Furthermore, Neanderthal man actually had a slightly larger average brain capacity than modern man. He might therefore be expected to be more intelligent than man, and thus better able to survive. However, Neanderthal man disappears from history for no obvious reason. In discussing this paradox, scientific authorities usually explain it by saying that a larger brain does not necessarily betoken a higher intelligence. Yet the assumption that capacity *is* a measure of intelligence is the basic factor used in positioning a fossil on the scale between the apes and man. We are thus asked to believe that the correlation between size and intelligence applies to brains smaller than man's, but not to larger brains. Assumptions are clearly changed in order to fit a theory!

(c) Attempts have been made to investigate the brain to discover which particular part of its structure enables man to be so much more advanced than animals in his mental capacity. Research on the size, convolutions, nerve cell structures and electro-chemical reactions show that they are all somewhat similar to those of animals. Such findings fail to account for man's self-awareness, abstract thinking, use of symbols and speech, and appreciation of beauty and order.

Skull reconstructions

An important factor in determining the brain capacity of skulls which are broken or incomplete, is the accuracy with which the pieces are fitted together. Even very small errors of positioning the pieces or estimating the shape can lead to very large differences in the measurement of the volume of the brain. It is well known that doubling the dimensions of a regular shape, say a sphere or a cube, increases the *volume* by 2 × 2 × 2 = 8 times. Similarly, if the dimensions are increased by, say, only 10 per cent, the volume increases by 1·1 × 1·1 ×

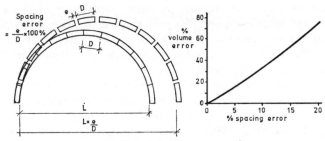

Fig.12. Diagram of effect of skull reconstruction errors upon volume of brain capacity

1·1 = 1·33, i.e. 33 per cent. This indicates the rapid change in volume due to a slight change in the dimensions.

Let us consider a skull approximately the shape of a half sphere, broken into pieces approximately 25 mm. (1 inch) square. If these pieces were incorrectly positioned with a gap of only 1 mm. between each piece, the volume would be 12 per cent too great. If the gap were 2 mm., the volume would be 26 per cent too large. This is illustrated in Fig. 12.

This aspect of reconstructing skulls is important, for very often only small, broken parts of a skull are found. These parts can be assembled, but for areas of the skull where no fossils are available, the shape has to be assumed. As we have shown, any inaccuracy in such assumptions will have a considerable effect upon the brain capacity of the skull, making it either much larger or smaller than it should be.

Taking together both aspects of the brain capacity, which we have been considering—the wide range of size (which is not related to ability) of human brains, and the difficulty of estimating the volume of fossil skulls—precise allocation of any particular fossil link on the scale between man and the apes becomes quite arbitrary. Referring to Fig.11, a fossil whose brain capacity is said to be 1,000 cc. could either be claimed to be a half-way stage between the 500 cc. of apes and the 1,500 cc. of man, or alternatively classed as a small human skull. Even today a few perfectly normal people possess capacities as low as this.

Subconscious motivation

An investigator can spend a considerable number of years in very arduous conditions in the hope of finding an important fossil link. On discovering, say, a few pieces of a very ape-like skull, one can well imagine—and indeed sympathize with—his desire to emphasize even the smallest human characteristic which it may possess. Under such circumstances, the subconscious compulsion to exaggerate the cranial capacity would be very powerful, particularly when assumptions have to be made regarding the shape of the complete skull. A scientist cannot claim to be any more free of professional ambition than other man. The desire for the prestige of finding a fossil link could cloud his judgement.

Similarly, if a human-like skull is discovered, any ape-like features may be given undue prominence. The premise may then be made that, as it has some primitive features, the brain capacity would probably be small, following which any reconstruction the skull may require would subconsciously be shaped accordingly.

In many reports of fossils, considerable importance is attached to the measured brain capacity, but as we have indicated, the unreliability of such a yardstick, from various aspects, should always be borne in mind when the subject is discussed in this work or any other.

4. Geological periods

When a fossil is discovered, it is important to determine where it should be placed in the sequence of existing known fossils. There are several ways of doing this.

(a) *Faunal*
If the fossil is found in a stratum which has fossil remains of ancient animals, these can be used to correlate it with other discoveries. There are a number of animals which are related to specific periods, and the remains of fossil men, which accompany them, can be allocated accordingly.

(b) *Artefacts*
Frequently, along with the remains of ancient man are found stone choppers, blades, axes, etc., which have been made by breaking up or shaping large stones, and using the resulting sharp edges and splinters as tools. This stone industry shows such a wide range of skills that classifying names can be attached to various periods and techniques. From the simple hand-held stone chopper (Abbevillian, Chellean, Acheulian) through the Levalloisian and Mousterian types to the skilled artefacts of the Aurignacian, Magdalenian and Neolithic cultures, all these tools help to determine how advanced the craftsman was compared with other sites.

Boule and Vallois who deal with the subject in considerable depth in *Fossil Men*, nevertheless admit that 'it would be fruitless to link this that or the other industry to a definite phase of human evolution'. [p150]

(c) *Glaciation*

Many geologists believe that the northern part of Europe was covered by glaciers at four different times in the Pleistocene period. These main glacial periods occurred in the order—Gunz, Mindel, Riss and Würm, and there were varying periods, known as Interglacial periods between them. In addition, some of the glacial periods had brief warm phases within them, called Interstadials.

Whilst these glacial periods do not actually date any fossils directly, they are of assistance in allocating them to a particular period, when used in conjunction with fossil animals, for the latter can often be ascribed to a warm interglacial or a cold glacial period.

(d) *Stratigraphy*

Correlation between one fossil and another found some distance away can sometimes be made referring to the order of the strata above and below each of them. For example, a well defined layer of sand may lie between a bed of gravel below and clay above, and this sequence of strata may be recognizable over a considerable area. A fossil found in the sand could be presumed to be older than another found in the clay, even though the latter is at a lower level due to the undulations of the strata.

All these methods are known as Relative dating, as they enable fossils to be placed in a sequence. However, they are unable to determine how many years ago they lived, for which we need to know the Absolute date.

5. Absolute dating

A number of methods have been used in an effort to determine precisely how long ago various strata were laid down or culture existed. The main methods are Varves, Tree Rings and Radiometric dating. It is not proposed to investigate these in any detail in this work, but we will briefly describe each method and point out some of the basic problems which are involved in their use.

A. VARVES

As glaciers partially melt in the summer, the melt water carries the fine material which settles out as a thin band of clay in the lake which often forms at the foot. Each thin layer of clay is known as a 'varve', and if one is laid down each year, then the age of the glacier can be obtained by counting the varves. By noting the pattern or sequence of very thick or thin varves at one site, a similar pattern at another site enables the time scale to be correlated between them, and thus dates going back several thousand years can be obtained.

Zeuner [39] gives a considerable amount of information on this method, but the difficulty of obtaining correlations between one set of varves and another, and the conflicting results, is apparent. What is surprising is the admission that one varve does not necessarily represent one year. He notes [p36] that several workers in this field have shown that there was considerable doubt whether one season only produced one varve, and quotes an example of Schneider who described one section, 4·6 cm. thick with four varves, all laid in the classical Swedish area *in one season*. Zeuner comments:

> In this he may be going too far, but his critical attitude illustrates the urgency of further research on the formation of varved sediments. It appears that we have in the past been too confident in the belief that all varves are annual.

One worker claimed that a particular series of varves in one area had covered a period of only 129 years [50p423], which was drastically less than the 2,500 years claimed for this sequence by De Geer who was the originator of this method of dating. Despite much admitted criticism of annual varve counting, which we consider undermines the whole basis of the method, the technique is nevertheless still considered acceptable by Zeuner and others. [26p80]

In any event, scientists admit that varve counting is only useful for dating up to twenty thousand years at the most. It is therefore of little value in determining the very early ancestry of man, which is usually given as being some two million years ago.

B. TREE RINGS

This method is very similar to counting varves, the annual growth rings on trees being used instead. It has similar difficulties, however, i.e. the need to assume that each year only produces one ring, and the problems of correlation between different trees and other areas. It also has a very short time scale, only going back to 6000 B.C.

C. RADIOMETRIC DATING

Many rocks contain a small amount of radioactive elements, which decay into stable elements at a known rate. When molten rock erupts to the surface of the earth, it is assumed that the radioactive element is 'fresh' and none of the stable decay products are present. Over a period of time, the 'pure' radioactive element gradually decays into its stable elements and, knowing the rate of decay, by measuring the proportion of original radioactive element to the decay element, the elapsed time since the molten rock erupted can be determined.

Two radioactive elements which are measured are:

(i) Uranium 238 which eventually decays into lead, and

(ii) Potassium 40 which decays mostly into calcium, which is difficult to measure, and a small percentage decays into Argon 40 gas.

A measure of how rapidly this decay takes place is given by the *half life*, i.e. the time taken for half of the original element to decay. For U238 this half life is 4,510 million years and for Potassium 40 it is 1,310 million years. Obviously, to try and measure the amount of decay which has taken place in 2 or 3 million years will be very difficult, as only a minute amount of the stable product will be present. As these elements are themselves only a very small proportion of any rock sample, extremely careful laboratory techniques and sensitive equipment are necessary to measure the incredibly small quantities involved.

All these methods however are based upon a number of presumptions, some of which cannot be verified. It is assumed that:

(a) There were no products of decay already present when the rock was first formed. Thus, if, originally there was Argon in a rock as well as Potassium, it would appear very old even at the start.

(b) None of the original radioactive material has been leached out at any period. Both Uranium and Potassium can be leached out of rock. Even in granite this leaching can occur in significant quantities. In one instance an iron meteorite lost 80 per cent of its Potassium by having distilled water run over it for $4\frac{1}{2}$ hours.

(c) None of the products of decay were lost or gained during the course of time. There is evidence to show that Argon will diffuse from areas of high pressure to those of lower pressure. Argon will migrate from the lower rocks to the higher ones, giving the latter an appearance of great age.

Thus, there are several factors which could account for the apparent great age of the rock strata. Furthermore, there are inconsistencies in many of the estimated ages, of which the following are a few examples:

(a) Lava flows in the sea at Hawaii occurred in A.D. 1800 and were tested by the Potassium–Argon method [52]. As we have seen above, it is a basic assumption that the rock, when newly formed, is 'fresh' and contains only radioactive Potassium. *The tests, however, gave dates for the rock varying from 160 million years to 2,960 million years.*

The authors admit that, 'It is possible that some of the abnormally high potassium–argon ages reported *by other investigators* for ultrabasic rocks may be caused by the presence of excess argon contained in fluid and gaseous inclusions.'

These results alone are surely sufficient to cast great doubt upon the validity of such methods.

(b) Dr. Melvin Cook in *Prehistory and Earth Models* (London, Max Parrish, 1960, pp.53–62), investigated two important Uranium ores and showed that the Lead 208 could not have come from the decay of the Uranium, but must have come from Lead 207, which had captured a free neutron in the mineral. Correction for this factor effectively reduces the apparent ages of the rocks to zero! This explanation could well account for the seeming great ages for strata which this method provides.

(c) In July 1969 Richard Leakey sent samples of volcanic tuff to London for dating the '1470' skull which he had just discovered. Using the Potassium–Argon method of dating, *they gave a date of 220 million years,* which was an impossibly high figure for the emergence of man's ancestors. On receipt of a further sample of tuff, crystals which appeared fresh were selected and gave an age of 2·6 million years, which is the figure now used for this fossil.

This last example was quoted in an article (*Sunday Telegraph*, 3rd November 1974, p.15) by Professor E. T. Hall, who is the Director of the Research Laboratory for Archaeology and the History of Art at Oxford. In this he gives an objective view of radiometric dating and the caution with which these dates should be received. He is highly critical both of his professional colleagues who attach dates to rocks and artefacts with such certainty, and of the archaeologists and anthropologists who believe them so implicitly.

He comments:

What have the scientists here told the archaeologist? They have said that they have made a series of minute measurements on pieces of volcanic ash which were buried near the fossilised bones of some early primates. That is all the scientists have said. They have told the archaeologist the results of their measurements. All further inferences are speculative. Of course most archaeology is speculative. [*Sunday Telegraph*, November 3rd 1974 p15.]

Any reputable scientist these days puts forward his views with commendable modesty. In contrast, the pronouncements of science, backed up by incomprehensible tables of data, tend to acquire a spurious infallibility for the layman or for quasi-scientists like archaeologists. They believe because they want to believe. [Ibid.]

It must be a great temptation to an archaeologist when a unique process comes up with a date which changes his work from the merely interesting to the sensational. The public has a great appetite for sensation. But the greatest temptation is the one which leads an archaeologist selectively to believe evidence which seems to confirm the theories on which he thinks his professional reputation rests. When the evidence comes from complex scientific techniques which are error prone and involve principles not wholly understood even by the scientists themselves, the dangers are great indeed. [Ibid.]

These comments by Professor Hall are quite damning of the whole method of trying to date the age of formations simply by measuring the quantities of minute amounts of radioactive elements and stable elements they contain. Whilst throughout this work I quote various published datings, I must emphasize that I do not in any way accept the 'millions of years' which geologists and anthropologists so frequently and confidently quote. There are a number of fundamental objections to the method, whilst on the other hand, there are some simple facts, which the scientists have never explained, which indicate that this earth has not existed for the vast periods of time claimed for it. It is not the purpose of this work to cover both these aspects in detail, but I will be considering them in a later work.

Carbon 14

A different technique of radiometric dating is the measurement of radioactive Carbon 14. Powerful cosmic rays bombard the atoms in the air, the resulting neutrons reacting with nitrogen to produce radioactive C14. This is absorbed by living animals and plants as a normal part of the carbon cycle of life. When the animal or plant dies, no further C14 is absorbed, and the C14 slowly decays, having a half life of 5,730 years. As before, comparing the existing C14 activity with the presumed original level gives the time elapsed since death.

The C14 method of dating was hailed as the long awaited means of reliably measuring the age of archaeological discoveries up to 20,000 or even 40,000 years old. Such has not however proved to be so, for there are a growing number of test results which conflict with each other and with known dates, and these throw considerable doubt upon the reliability of the method. To give just two examples, C. A. Reed quotes a few of these discrepancies [51] and expresses his disenchantment with the method, whilst D. Collins says, 'It is not generally appreciated that up to a third of all dates have to be rejected as impossible....' [10p51]. One famous laboratory in fact refuses to give a date to any sample giving an age greater than 3,000 years, as it is considered that they cannot date it accurately.

I will be dealing with the unsuitability of the C14 technique for dating fossil bones in the section dealing with the Galley Hill skeleton, but will here raise one large anomaly in the assumptions used in the method. The present level of the C14 decay rate is 1·63 disintegrations/sec./sq. cm., but calculations from the known rate of neutron bombardment on nitrogen in the air show that the expected level should be much higher at 2·5 disintegrations/sec./sq. cm. In 1955, Willard

Libby, the discoverer and developer of the method, acknowledged that a discrepancy of 20 per cent existed, but dismissed it at that time as being within 'experimental error'. I consider that an error now known to be 53 per cent must be accounted for if the method is to be acceptable.

One suggestion has been put forward which would explain this difference. It is possible that the C14 activity has *not* been constant at 1·63 as is assumed, *but is still rising slowly to the equilibrium of 2·5* disintegrations/sec./sq. cm. This would mean that the C14 decay rate was much lower than the present level of 1·63, giving a much reduced age for the specimen. By way of illustration, if a piece of ancient wood shows a present-day activity of say 0·3 the *assumption* that it started with a level of activity of 1·63 will give it a grossly overestimated age. If, however, it actually started with a level of activity of only 0·7 (due to the lower level of C14 existing at that time), then its true and more recent age could be calculated. I have illustrated this diagrammatically in Fig.13.

The radiometric dating gap

One important aspect of radiometric dating methods is the gap between the periods covered by the Potassium–Argon technique and the radio-carbon method. Dr. Stuart Fleming, who is in the same research laboratory as Professor Hall, says that the latest date which he considers meaningful for Potassium–Argon is ·43 million years. At this figure, Argon contents are as low as 1 part in a thousand million. Radio-carbon, however, is only suitable for dates later than 25,000 years. [57]

This gap covers the precise period during which *Homo sapiens* is said to appear on the scene of history, and dates during this period can only be estimated from artefacts, etc. Furthermore, with such minute traces of Argon being relied upon for obtaining a date, clearly even a very small increase would give a large increase in the apparent age. Is it not possible that some Argon has migrated to the surface rocks from much deeper rocks due to the pressure, as we have said, or because of the higher temperature? Some loss of Argon to the atmosphere by those strata nearest to the surface would then give an appearance of age increasing with depth, but all dates obtained would still be far too high.

Summary

In radiometric dating, not only is the rate of decay of the radioactive material assumed to be constant but it is also assumed that many other factors remain constant throughout the whole age of the material dated. As we have seen, these assumptions are, at best, highly questionable. Whilst some of these factors would reduce their age,

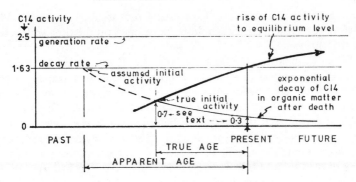

Fig.13. Diagram of possible C14 dating errors

most of them would considerably increase the apparent age of rocks which were subjected to the tests.

There are clearly many problems surrounding the radiometric dating methods, which rarely appear in general literature dealing with the subject. I would suggest that much further research is necessary before the ages applied by these techniques to the rocks can be accepted with any degree of confidence.

6. Correlation of datings

During the course of reading for this work, I naturally compared the period ascribed to a particular fossil by one author with the period given by another writer. It is understandable that there will be some discrepancies, but these were so significant that I investigated this aspect further.

The chronological sequence of events and cultures as given by a number of authors was set out in tabular form and correlated, the results being compared in Fig.14.

There was slight difficulty in deciding which particular feature should be used as a basis to compare the different authorities. The basis could be fossil men, stonework cultural periods, time scale or glacial periods. It was decided that the last of these should be used, as glacial periods are most frequently referred to by writers in giving relative datings to various fossil men. The main glacial periods are accordingly set out on the left-hand side and all other information given by the writers is correlated to them. The information was obtained from the time charts published by each author. Certain fossils, however, particularly Swanscombe, Fontéchevade and Vertesszölles, which cannot easily be fitted into the normally accepted sequence of fossils leading up to modern man, did not always appear in these charts. If mentioned within the text, they may be ascribed to a glacial period, and could therefore be plotted direct, or if given a date B.P. (Before the Present), they would be positioned on the time scale used by that author.

When comparing the divisions of the Pleistocene era (Lower, Middle and Upper), it should be borne in mind that certain of the writers may have been working to a different definition of these periods from others. At the International Geological Congress in 1948, it was agreed that what had been known as the Villefranchian period, in the late Pliocene, should now be included in the early Pleistocene, and the Middle Pleistocene would extend from the beginning of the Gunz-Mindel Interglacial to the end of the Riss glaciation. It has not been uniformly adopted however, and there still appears to be some confusion. Thus, what has formerly been dated as late Pliocene would now appear as early Pleistocene.

A similar problem arises with the absolute dates used. Due to recent results of radiometric tests of fossils and rocks, the beginning of the Pleistocene has extended from 1 million years to 2 million years. This extension of the time scale should not of course affect those fossils which are relatively dated by referring them to a specific glacial period, for we are comparing different authors on the basis of where they place fossil men in relation to the four main glacial periods, not in relation to the absolute time scale.

The publications have been put in date order, to see if there is a more general agreement between them in recent years, but this would appear not to be so, the later works showing as much variation as those earlier. These wide discrepancies are obvious, particularly with regard to Pekin and Java man, which we have emphasized on the chart. One can only conclude that a large degree of speculation must be involved in the compilation of each expert's dating chart.

7. Teeth

Teeth are a particularly dense part of the anatomy and are therefore more likely to survive the passage of time. Any tooth discovered which might possibly be ascribed to an ancestor of man, is subjected to the most minute examination and measurement of every possible aspect of its size and shape, and particularly of the patterns of the fissures in the crown of the larger teeth. Based upon such meagre evidence, far reaching assumptions and pronouncements are made concerning the original owner of the tooth. More often than not, such predictions are eventually found to be quite incorrect—Hesperopithecus being only one of several we recount (see Section 2 (d)).

Eckhardt [56] investigated the range of size in the teeth of three types of very early fossil apes, known as Dryopithecus sivalensis, Dryopithecus indicus and Ramapithecus punjabicus. These teeth and

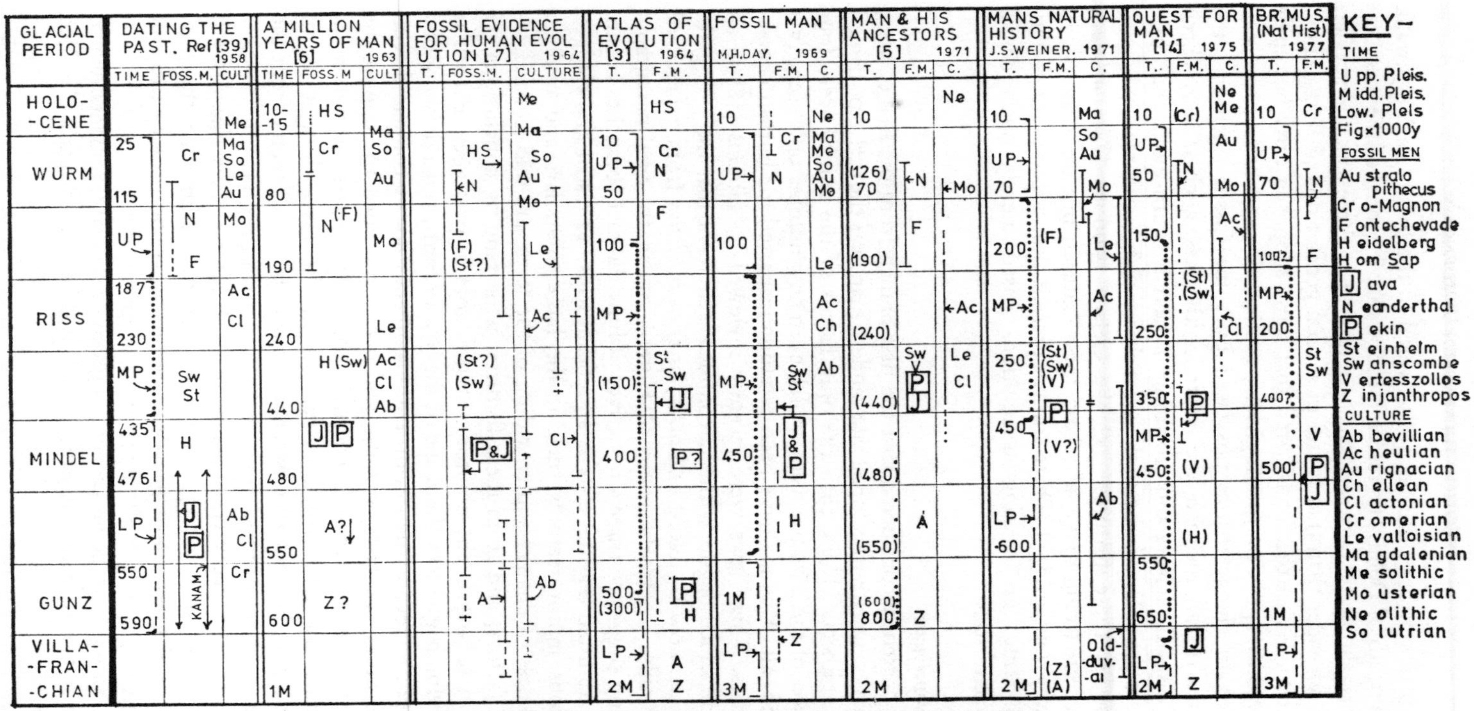

Fig. 14. Comparison of datings by various authorities

fragments of jaws had been discovered in the fossil bearing Siwalik hills north of Delhi. His research found that for most of the measurements, the range between what are classed as three separate species, was no wider than that found in several generations of living chimpanzees. He further considered that these supposed early hominids were only apes—morphologically, ecologically and behaviourally.

Certain characteristics possessed by some fossils (including the South African ape-men, the Australopithecines) such as large cheek teeth, small incisors and crowding of heavily worn molars and premolars are said to indicate their development towards man, who also possesses these features. Yet the Gelada baboons (*Theropithecus*), which are living today, also have these features, but are obviously in no way 'human' [55]. These animals present clear proof of the futility of making far reaching assumptions based merely upon dental characteristics.

Ramapithecus

It is currently considered that the first branch from the line of apes, which eventually developed into modern man, was the early ape named Ramapithecus. Until 1970 the only fossils of the animal were four *portions* of the jaws and teeth, which even now number only some two dozen, all of which have been carefully inspected for human characteristics. These jaws were recently reviewed by Simons [58] in an article which begins with the confident statement that the '. . . pathway can now be traced *with little fear of contradiction* from generalized hominids . . . to the genus of Homo', but in the final paragraph, having suggested three alternatives of how the early branches began, it is admitted that there were 'significant gaps in present knowledge'. Various minor features such as the large premolars and canines, thickness of enamel and crowding of the teeth, are said to be significant factors, and from these features, wide ranging conclusions are drawn regarding the environmental factors in past ages. Particular attention is given to the shape of the row of teeth, and a drawing of a composite reconstruction of a Ramapithecus jaw is compared with three other ape jaws, but no evidence is provided to support the accuracy of this reconstruction. Eckhardt [56] has shown how inaccurate jaw reconstructions can be, and he gives illustrations of completely different reconstructions made by two experts from the same fragment of fossil jaw, which we show in Fig.15.

(Even more recently, an article by M. Pickford—*New Scientist*, 8th September 1977, vol.75, n.1,068, pp.578–80—claims that the total number of *Ramapithecus punjabicus* specimens was now forty-three, but all seemingly consist of only jaws and teeth).

In Simon's article an account is given of several fragments, which were re-named Ramapithecus, which had been incorrectly classified

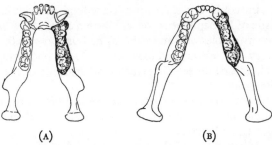

(A)   (B)

Fig.15. Sivapithecus indicus—two reconstructions of jaw from the same fragment (A) by G. Pilgrim, (B) by W. K. Gregory—Reference [56p98]

by their original discoverers. Two interesting letters in *Nature* in 1970, however, show how one effort to classify a jaw fragment as Ramapithecus was disproved, and furthermore, they cast considerable doubt on the whole subject. D. Pilbeam, a colleague of Simons, claimed to have recognized a 'new' mandible of *Ramapithecus punjabicus* in the collection of the British Museum (Natural History) [53]. He considered that this fragment of a lower jaw, with badly broken teeth, had affinities with Australopithecus. In his article he said:

(a) The fragment had been unrecognized and 'unidentified until now', and could be assigned with some confidence to *Ramapithecus punjabicus*, forming the most complete mandible known of this species.

(b) It came almost certainly from the Nagri beds, which provide a date of 12–9 million years.

(c) Its dentition foreshadows Australopithecus, one factor being the 'crowding' of the teeth which is common in *R. punjabicus*, Australopithecus and Homo.

(d) The tip of the root of the canine could be seen on an X-ray, and it indicated that it was very reduced.

(e) The depth of the jaw below two of the teeth was measured as 26·6 and 31 mm.

Presumably because of the reference to Australopithecus, Professor L. S. B. Leakey examined the original and wrote a most devastating reply in a later issue of *Nature* [54]. In this he points out:

(a) Pilbeam's memory must be very short for he (Pilbeam) had previously identified this fossil in 1965 as *Dryopithecus laietanus*, and had stated 'that it could not possibly pertain to Ramapithecus'.

(b) Had the fossil come from the Nagri beds, the discoverer, an experienced geologist, would have said so. Leakey considered Pilbeam misleading in assuming that it was 'almost certainly of Nagri age'.

(c) Pilbeam could not claim that 'crowding' of teeth is a characteristic of Ramapithecus for, in his own article, he admitted that
other mandibles of Ramapithecus had only *two* teeth.

(d) Leakey and others examined several X-ray photographs of the
fossil, and could see no evidence whatsoever of the tip of the
canine root.

(e) Re-measurement of the depth of the jaw below the teeth gave
'entirely different, and significantly smaller readings than those
which he had recorded'.

We have given a few of the details of this dispute at some length,
in order to emphasize that bold statements can be made on evidence
which is not just simply inconclusive but factually wrong.

THE NATURAL HISTORY MUSEUM'S EXHIBITION

We have so far examined the general evidence and the way in which
this is presented. On this subject, the British Natural History
Museum's exhibition 'Man's Place in Evolution' uses much of the
inadequate evidence presented above. I have deferred criticism of
this important exhibition to Appendix VIII near the end of the
book, when the reader will have a better understanding of the
inadequacy of the various fossils in the display.

SECTION III

EARLY HOMO SAPIENS
—their unwarranted rejection

In virtually all textbooks dealing with early man, the main fossils put forward as displaying the development from apes to men are:

(a) The African ape-men (*Australopithecine and Homo habilis*).
(b) 'Nut cracker' man (*Zinjanthropus boisei*).
(c) Java man (*Pithecanthropus erectus*).
(d) Pekin man (*Sinathropus pekinensis*).

and a discussion of the many examples of:

(e) Neanderthal man.

Java man, Pekin man and similar skulls have more recently been 'lumped' together and given almost human status by classifying them as *Homo erectus* (Upright man).

Since the discovery of '1470' man by Richard Leakey at Lake Rudolf, and other finds, the proposed line of man's ancestry has changed, and we show in Fig.16 a current view, although not accepted by all experts. The three human 'type' fossil skulls—Vertesszöllos; Swanscombe and Fontéchevade—I would contend are of modern form, and we will be considering these when dealing with Neanderthal man.

In all the published charts, *Homo sapiens* is only shown as appearing in the late Pleistocene period. However, a number of human fossils have been found in strata very much earlier than those of the accepted ancestors of man, as shown also in Fig.16. Clearly, these early fossils completely contradict the present theory of man's development, and for this reason they are rejected as frauds or intrusive burials, i.e. buried in a stratum earlier than those in which they lived, whether by man or by natural causes. Sometimes such fossils are subjected to various tests, and a discrepancy in any one result is considered to be sufficient to reject the fossil as being an intrusive burial. Thus the eyewitness accounts of the original discoverers are completely ignored. I will give some of the evidence, which will show that such rejection of these 'non-conforming men' is unwarranted.

A considerable amount of information regarding these early men is given in Keith's *The Antiquity of Man* 1925 edition [16], which I have summarised below. Keith was one of the very few experts prepared to consider these fossils, but his reluctance to accept them as positive evidence is apparent when reading his book. He gives many

PERIOD	ANCESTORS OF HOMO SAPIENS	'EXTINCT LINES'	UNACCEPTED EARLY H. SAP.
HOLOCENE (Recent) ——10 000 y ——	↑ ⌐HOMO SAPIENS		
UPPER PLEISTOCENE ——100 000y ——	FONTECHEVADE	Neandertal	
MIDDLE PLEISTOCENE ——500 000 y ——	SWANSCOMBE VERTESSZOLLOS Pekin Java		OLMO CLICHY GALLEY HILL
LOWER PLEISTOCENE ——2-3 My ——	'1470' Man	⌐Australopithecune Zinjanthropus Homo Habilis	NATCHEZ ABBEVILLE
PLIOCENE ——7-12 My ——	Ramapithecus		FOXHALL CASTENEDOLO CALAVERAS

Fig.16. Dating chart of early fossils

illustrations, but these are not always clear, and there is some difficulty in correlating his geological datings with those used today, for when he wrote this work, he gave the Pleistocene as beginning during the Gunz-Mindel Interglacial period. He also divides the examples of early stone artefacts into Chellean and Pre-Chellean, which would probably be labelled as Oldowan and Abbevillian cultures in the classifications used today.

Here then are some of the fossils of *Homo sapiens* found in very early strata, the details of their discovery, and the evidence, in my view very inadequate, upon which they were dismissed.

The Calaveras skull

In 1866, a local blacksmith spent his time digging a tunnel in gold-bearing strata under Bald Hill, California, when, 130 ft. below the surface, he found what at first he thought was a tree root, thickly encased in cemented gravel. Recognizing in it a part of a lower jaw, he brought it all to the surface and later showed it to a Mr. Scrivner and Dr. Jones. Subsequently, Professor Whitney, the State Geologist of California, examined both the skull (Fig.17) and the site, and after making very careful enquiries, he was convinced that the find was genuine. Together with Dr. Wynam, he subjected it to a very close examination, to see if it corroborated the story of the discoverer, which it did, to such a degree that its genuineness was proved beyond all possible doubt. It was in a Pliocene deposit, in which expert geologists had found many artefacts of human work, such as stone pestles and mortars, hammer stones, spear heads, etc. [16p472]

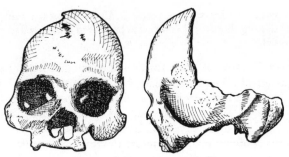

Fig.17. The Calaveras skull

Professor Hrdlicka investigated the fossil and found that it had a calcerous surface coating, similar to some other skulls which had been found in caves, and this was considered sufficient to cast doubt on its origin. This fossil and several others in North America were also dismissed by Professor Hrdlicka, for he said that the skulls closely resembled modern Indians. This surely is an unacceptable argument, for one might just as well say that it should be rejected as it too closely resembles a human skull! That it was not the skull of a modern Indian is proved by the fact that it was almost completely fossilized, and must therefore have been buried for a considerable time. Sir Arthur Keith, who quotes Hrdlicka's rejection of the skull, admits, 'It does not prove however that the original specimen is not really ancient.' [p472]

Professor Whitney gave an extensive account not only of his investigations of the discovery of the skull, but of many other human fossils found in different areas, and numerous artefacts [59]. The evidence was criticized by Holmes in 1899 [60] who made out a case for the very modern looking pestles and mortars falling into the collapsed mine workings from adjacent Indian encampments, or being left in the mines by Indian workers. To explain why so many artefacts were found under such widely differing circumstances, he suggested that, '. . . the notion that finds of human relics in the gravels tended to excite heated discussion, would spread quickly from camp to camp until the whole region would be affected.' His account of the discovery and history of the skull really confirms that it was genuine, and his efforts to show that it was a practical joke are far from convincing.

The Calaveras skull was not the only modern fossil found in early strata in this area. All these discoveries were reviewed in 1924 by John C. Merriam of the Carnegie Institute of Washington. The very brief report of his talk to the National Academy of Sciences in Washington says:

> There are many evidences . . . indicating the occurrence of man on the Pacific Coast for a period which must in all probability be measured

in terms of many thousands of years. . . . Up to the present time, all the human remains discovered are of what have been recognised as modern types. [62]

The report dismisses all these fossils and concludes that none of them can be assigned a Pleistocene date *with certainty*. From this it would appear that there was *some* evidence that these fossils were of Pleistocene age, but in Merriam's view, it was not convincing. No details, however, of the discovery at Calaveras or elsewhere are given to support his contention, and therefore the reader is unable to judge if his conclusion is valid.

The fossil is still rejected as a 'practical joke' of the miners (or a 'cowboy' [66p3]), but in accepting this explanation we have to believe that:

(a) The hoaxer obtained a fossil skull from a cave.
(b) It was then cemented into a solid mass with material from the mine, with sufficient skill to avoid detection.
(c) A story of finding the skull in the tunnel was fabricated, which the investigations of Professor Whitney failed to expose.
(d) All this was done simply as a 'practical joke' to fool the experts, by ordinary miners, who gained neither money nor prestige from the hoax, and who never later publicized the hoax in order to ridicule the 'experts'.

Surely the genuineness of the skull is a far more acceptable proposition than the reasons for its rejection.

The Castenedolo skull

In 1860 Professor Ragazzoni was searching for Pliocene fossil shells in a pit at Castenedolo, Italy, when he uncovered, on the face of the pit, parts of a human skull. Realizing their significance, he carefully inspected the strata above the fossils and could find no disturbance of the junction between them, which would indicate an intrusive burial. He searched further and found some other pieces of skull, but when he showed them to his colleagues, few of them believed him. Nothing more was found until 1880, when a friend of Ragazzoni's excavated in the pit about 18 m. (60 ft.) away from the original discoveries and found at the same level the scattered fossil remains of two children. He left them in position for Ragazzoni to inspect, and the strata above were again found to be intact. Later a woman's skeleton was discovered, the skull having the same capacity as women have today.

Professor Sergi later visited Professor Ragazzoni, and after investigating the whole matter was convinced that the finds were genuine. Ragazzoni passed custody of the fossils to Sergi who did not do much more with them, until 1912 when Sir Arthur Keith commented upon the discovery of a modern skeleton at Ipswich in Pliocene Strata. The two scientists corresponded and both were convinced that modern men existed in Pliocene times. Sergi wrote a paper (*Rivista di Anthropologia*, Vo.XVII, Fasc.I–II, Rome) in 1921, in which he confirms his own earlier conclusions and brings the account up to date.

Despite all this evidence, few scientists mention these two fossils, and others considered later, in their books. Indeed, by an interesting turn of logic, the fact that 'most authorities' ignore them is quoted as being a valid argument for continuing to refute their claim to be valid fossils!

Of the few who do mention them, Sir Arthur Keith said of Castenodolo:

> The unfossilised condition of the remains and other circumstances make us certain we are here dealing with intruded burials. [16p340]

With regard to the dating of the fossil, he did however say:

> About the age of the coral stratum there is no dispute . . . it belongs to the older Pliocene formation. The overlying blue clay . . . is not much later in date than the coralline stratum. [p335]

The bones are generally rejected in view of their lack of fossilization, and furthermore Professor Issel is said to have shown that the human bones were not impregnated with salt as he had found in some other bones [26p188]. The degree of fossilization, however, is no guide to the antiquity of a bone. In one of the papers exposing the Piltdown fraud, the example is given of a bone still containing most of its Nitrogen being found *below* a bone which had lost almost all its Nitrogen. The lower bone in this London pit was found in unoxidized clay whereas the upper bone was embedded in sand [46p254]. As the Castenodolo bones were found in a clay stratum, could this not be the reason for their preservation in an unfossilized state?

The explanation of an intrusive burial is preferred against the first-hand eyewitness accounts of reputable scientists that:

(a) The strata above the fossils were completely intact.

(b) They were found embedded in a matrix of the same material as the stratum in which they were found.

In the face of this evidence, *and the fact that the bones were scattered over a wide area*, how it can seriously be maintained that they were intrusive burials defies simple logic.

The Olmo skull

This was found in 1883 at Olmo, Italy, at a depth of 15 m. (50 ft.) below the surface in a railway embankment cutting. Charred wood and extinct Pleistocene fossils were found at the same level which was investigated by Signor Cocchi, the Curator of the Museum of Geology of Florence. The cavity of this human skull was still filled with the mass of blue clay (in 1925) just as it was found.

Doubt is cast on its value, due to various reasons such as:

(a) It is contemporary with the deposit in which it was found, but it is no older than the Swanscombe skull.

(b) The uncertainty of its geological age (Boule and Vallois in *Fossil Men*, who give it only three lines).

(c) It may have been brought from the surface by a landslide.

There is a general vagueness of evidence supporting the reasons for rejection, compared with the investigations on the spot.

The Foxhall jaw

In 1863, the Foxhall jaw was found in the 'Red Crag' layer of a sandpit near Ipswich. The original jaw has disappeared, but it was admitted to be completely human, and the contemporary drawings show this.

Its disappearance is held to invalidate its claim for serious consideration. This principle, however, is not applied to the Pekin man fossils which have also vanished and are similarly not available for close examination.

Although the jaw has been lost, Reid Moir found numerous stone tools in a layer *below* that which contained the Foxhall jaw, a number of them being a special 'beak' shape of stone known as 'Rostro-Carinates'. Such was the incredulity with which this was received, that a special commission of experts visited the spot and agreed that Moir's claim was fully justified [16p309]. Today, however, some regard these artefacts to be of natural origin. [26p267]

Keith dates these layers as considerably before the Gunz glaciation, and as early Pliocene, although this would probably be redefined as late Pliocene today.

The Galley Hill skeleton

This skeleton was found by a workman in the side of a gravel pit near Dartford, Kent, 2·5 m. (8 ft.) below the surface. It was seen by Mr. Heys, a schoolmaster, and Mr. Elliot, an amateur archaeologist, before it was removed from its position. They carefully inspected the strata above and testified that they were unbroken. Pre-Chellean Palaeolithic stone tools were frequently found in this layer by both these amateur archaeologists. Keith admits that *pre*-Chellean tools were found in the strata which, on his Fig.264, would place it in the Gunz-Mindel Interglacial. As this dating is too early even for him to accept, he produces reasons for giving a Chellean date (Mindel-Riss

Interglacial on his figure) to the fossil. He begins by saying that as so much of the skeleton had been found 'it is almost certain that the remains have not been entombed by Nature, but by the hand of man' [p258]. Although he agrees on more than one occasion that the overlying strata were intact, he then simply says, with virtually no supporting evidence, that, '. . . we are forced to the conclusion that the Galley Hill skeleton represents a man of the *Chellean* period.'

THE GALLEY HILL REPORT

The 'problem' of the existence of a human skeleton in such a very early stratum, resulted in it being placed in the 'suspense account' to which these non-conforming fossils are despatched. However, the difficulty of reconciling this fossil (and the Swanscombe skull found half a mile away) with the accepted progress of man was such, that in 1948, a grant from the Viking Foundation of America, enabled extensive field studies to be undertaken of the Galley Hill–Swanscombe region and the fossils to be closely examined. [64]

The original skeleton had been repossessed by the owner, but some small pieces of the bones, still in the possession of the British Museum authorities, were subjected to the Fluorine test. In most ground waters, there is a small percentage of fluorine which, over a period of time, becomes chemically locked in the bone material. The amount of fluorine in the bone increases with time, and so determining the fluorine content of two bones from the *same* excavation would show if they have both been buried for the same period.

In an early paper on the Fluorine method of test [63], it is emphasized that a comparison of F content between two fossils is only valid if they have come from the same site or area, for one may be subject to water with a high F value as against the other, thus nullifying the validity of the test.

The fluorine content of the Galley Hill bone fragments was measured and found to be about 0·4 per cent. No other bones had been found at this site and it was therefore compared with the bones from the Swanscombe pit, which were found to average 2 per cent. Mainly because of this discrepancy, the Galley Hill bones were promptly declared to be an intrusive burial. *But the pit at Swanscombe was over half a mile away from the Galley Hill pit.* (See Fig.18.)

The low F content of the Galley Hill skeleton was the main reason given for its rejection, but this result may have been due either to the difference of F content of the ground water between the two sites, or to the fact that the Galley Hill skeleton was in an almost impervious layer, thus greatly reducing the rate of the fluorine exchange.

Dealing first with the ground water, no tests are given in the report to check whether there was any significant difference in the fluorine content between the two locations. The importance of this aspect is mentioned by Tobias [20p180] in a discussion of discrepancies regarding an East African fossil, the Kanam jaw—see Appendix VII. He quotes an unpublished report by Oakley (who developed the Fluorine test), which says:

> . . . the distribution of uranyl ions in ground water, *like that of fluorine ions, is subject to very considerable variations from place to place.*

This factor alone might therefore account for much, if not all, of the difference between the two F contents. Carnot, who discovered the action of fluorine on bone in 1893, found a general increase of fluorine with time, but the results were 'influenced so greatly by local variables as to be of no direct value' [46p266]

The permeability of the loam

An even more important feature is the stratum of clayey loam in which the skeleton was encased. On this, the report is much more informative. The fossil was exposed at the bottom of a 'loamy' stratum at about half depth of a vertical 10 ft. thick face of gravel. It is obvious that this encasement of the bones could affect the flow of water and therefore the rate of fluorine exchange, and this is acknowledged in the report, for it says:

> It might be argued of course that the Galley Hill skeleton was protected from the action of percolating water by an impermeable clay matrix. . . .

It claims, however, that the loam *was permeable*, adding: 'This point does not appear to have been considered by previous investigators.' This aspect of its permeability is emphasized in the report several times.

But it may be asked, just how pervious *was* the loam? Almost all materials are pervious in a greater or lesser amount, the question being one of degree. A box of the clay dug out with the Galley Hill skeleton, and labelled by Elliott in 1894, was in the possession of the Geology Department of the British Museum (N.H.) and was carefully analysed. It was considered to be not a clay, but a 'coarse silty loam' which 'in the dry state is very porous in texture'. Presumably it was porous to air when dry, but as we are only interested in its permeability to water, this comment in the report is surely irrelevant and even misleading.

It would have been a simple matter to have the permeability of the sample measured, which is a standard test in most soil testing laboratories. This, however, does not appear to have been done, the assessment that it *was* permeable relying entirely upon a visual inspection and an analysis of the particle size.

The content of the loam is given as 19 per cent sand, 66 per cent

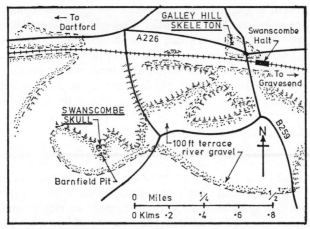

Fig.18. The Galley Hill site

silt and 15 per cent clay. Some of the sand grains exceeded 1 mm. diameter, and from this it was considered that the material was pervious. We would submit, however, that relative to the *gravels* in which the Swanscombe fossils were found, it was comparatively *impervious*. One of the main factors which affects the permeability of a soil is the size of the finer particles, and the presence of 15 per cent clay would considerably reduce the coefficient of permeability to, say, 10^{-6} cm./ sec. for this type of fine soil.

At Swanscombe, no similar analysis was carried out, but the layer in which the skull was found appears to have been a fairly uniform stone (with somewhat less sand content than an adjacent layer). It would appear to be a very pervious layer, between say 10^{-2} and 1 cm./ sec. Thus, the gravel at Swanscombe could be anything from 10,000 to 1,000,000 times as pervious as the clayey silt, which encased the Galley Hill skeleton. This would surely explain the discrepancy between their fluorine content, rendering void the rejection of the skeleton by the report on this basis.

Decalcification

Regarding the decalcification of the Galley Hill site, the report says the soil, '. . . has a pH value of 6·8 (confirming our impression of complete decalcification).'

Decalcification is the chemical dissolution of bones due to the acidity of the ground water. This was considered to be the reason why no other bones were found at this site, indicating that the skeleton discovered was a comparatively recent intrusive burial. But it must be pointed out that a pH value of 6·8 is only *very* slightly acidic compared with the neutral value of 7·0, and that the effect of an acid is not proportional to the pH difference below 7·0 but rises rapidly as the pH value decreases. Thus an 'acidity' difference of ·2 would have little effect upon bones and in any case is within the tolerance of the tests of a neutral material. Clays generally have pH values between 6–6·5, yet bones are often found in clay strata, indicating that no decalcification has taken place. Furthermore, the fact that the skeleton was encased in a virtually impervious layer of clay would preserve it against chemical dissolution.

In addition, the acidity of water at Galley Hill was held to have 'decalcified' the strata, whilst at the Swanscombe pit, the presence of the skull bones showed that at this site the water was *not* acidic. From this, it is obvious that the history of the water conditions at the two sites was *not* the same, but this is nevertheless a basic assumption when the discrepancies in the fluorine contents are emphasized in the report. If the waters had different pH values, could they not also have had differing fluorine contents?

An intrusive burial?
As a result of the Fluorine test, the report considers that the skeleton must have been an intrusive burial and that,

> . . . by the time they saw the remnants of the skeleton sticking out of the face, it is probable that the bulk of any evidence of burial had already been destroyed by the gravel digger.

However, we would consider that it would be extremely unlikely that *all trace* of an 8 ft. deep burial hole had been obliterated when the skeleton itself could still be seen protruding out of the near vertical quarry face. It must be remembered that both the original discoverers looked for a disturbance of the strata and found none [16p251–8]. Had a hole been dug, there should have been *some* evidence visible. The report contends that indications of burials can be lost with the passage of time, and refers to the comments of Hughes as confirmation. Turning to this reference [61], one finds that it is a letter in which he relates his observations of two sites where recent burials in *homogenous* soils were undetectable. Even here, in damp conditions, Hughes notes that the change in porosity of the disturbed soil resulted in it being darker where the excavation had taken place. He notes:

> It is only where there are stratified beds of sand or gravel and the continuity of the layers is interrupted that the infilled grave or pit can be clearly seen in section.

Undisturbed *stratified* layers were mentioned by Elliot in his report, and he indicates that the loam which contained the skeleton was also stratified, for he says:'. . . *beds* of clay or clayey loam.' Elliott specifically stated:

No doubt could possibly arise to the observation of an ordinary intelligent person of their deposition contemporaneously with that of the gravel, for there was a bed of loam, in the base of which these human relics were embedded. The underneath part of the skull, as far as I could see, was resting on a sandy gravel. The stratum of loam was undisturbed. This undisturbed state of the stratum was so palpable to the workman that he said, 'The man or animal was not buried by anybody.'

Thus the skeleton was entombed at the same time as the loam was deposited. It could not therefore have been even an intrusive burial into the loam after it was laid down but before the undisturbed layers of gravel were deposited above, for this would at least have disturbed the layers in the loam.

The report also emphasizes that the skeleton possessed no features which were outside the normal variations of a modern *Homo sapiens*. From this it is inferred that it was too modern for the strata in which it was found, and was an intrusive burial. This argument has an air of circular reasoning, i.e. a modern skeleton is found in early strata, but because it *is* modern, it *must* be intrusive!

Summarizing the report I would submit that the evidence upon which the Galley Hill skeleton was rejected is unsatisfactory.

CARBON 14 DATING REPORT

Finally, in 1961, the skeleton was subjected to the Carbon 14 test and dated as being 3,310 ± 150 years old. This would certainly indicate a recent burial, but is this dating accurate? Little information is given in the report of the test [65p41], but we suggest that there are factors which could cast doubt on this result.

Firstly, only very small pieces of bone were available. We have already mentioned that the Fluorine test had to be carried out on pieces of bone found in the matrix that had been around the skeleton. As the report makes no mention of this factor, it is presumed that sufficient additional bone was discovered for the C14 test.

Secondly, the C14 test is sensitive to many more extraneous factors than is generally realized. F. W. Shotton, in the course of his Presidential Address to the Geological Society mentioned some of the difficulties experienced with dating by the C14 method and said:

> Age estimations of bones can be made on the collagen (which is a small part only of the weight) or on the calcium carbonate content of the bone, or on both together. The carbonate determination seems to be very inaccurate and, as with shells, to lead to serious underestimates. . . . *Obviously bones are suspect material even for relatively recent dates*, and for the 20,000 to 40,000 years range are quite unacceptable. [67]

This surprising statement was made by an expert in the technique in 1967. It would be even more applicable to tests carried out six years earlier, as techniques were then less refined. As the Galley Hill bones were highly fossilized, the small amount of collagen would have virtually disappeared. The report, however, says that the organic fraction (collagen) was used as the source of carbon, and one is left wondering what reliance can be put upon the results of this test.

It would seem that the interpretation of the evidence presented by the Galley Hill skeleton has been strongly coloured by currently held presuppositions. In the light of the above examination of the evidence, and contrary to accepted opinion, I would contend that this skeleton supports the case for the existence of *Homo sapiens* in strata which are given an early date.

The Clichy Skeleton

This was discovered by workmen in a gravel pit in Paris in 1868. A Mr. E. Bertrand, who frequently visited the site for fossils, was shown the fossil, which was still embedded in the soil. According to Sir Arthur Keith, Bertrand gave a talk to the Anthropological Society about his find later the same year. All but one of the French experts accepted the authenticity and antiquity of the skeleton. It was found in a layer which could be correlated to the one in which the Galley Hill skeleton was discovered. Keith again, however, said that as a whole skeleton had been found, it must have been intrusively buried from a Chellean land surface!

In dealing with this particular discovery, Boule and Vallois in *Fossil Men* combine it with another at Grenelle, and then proceed to pour scorn on *both* of them:

> With regard to the skeletons from the alluvial soils of Clichy (1868) and of Grenelle (1870) we merely mention the rashness of the anthropologists who attempted to prove their geological antiquity. Such an attempt, made forty years after the discoveries by individuals who had never seen the deposits, cannot be of much value. The most elementary notions of caution demanded of human palaeontology that it should base its speculations only on evidences of irreproachable origin. This was not the case with regard to the skeletons from the Parisian alluvials. [p151]

As this account of delay in publication differs so considerably from that of Keith's [p276], it can only be presumed that it mainly refers to the Grenelle skeleton. To disparage the Clichy skeleton on the same grounds is to be guilty of the very lack of scientific care, of which they are so critical!

The Abbeville jaw

This was found in a pit in 1863 by the famous Boucher de Perthes, 5 m. (16½ ft.) from the surface, in early Pleistocene deposits. It was included in French lists of early man for some twenty years. Later, however, when it was thought that Neanderthal man was a forerunner of *Homo sapiens*, this human fossil was effectively removed, as it was far too early to be accommodated with the current theory of man's emergence.

The jaw is not even mentioned by Boule and Vallois in *Fossil Men*, but Sir Arthur Keith's views are given later.

The Natchez pelvis

This completely modern type of fossilized pelvis was found at Natchez, North America, mixed with the bones of extinct animals. Keith recounts in his book the details of the investigation, which Sir Charles Lyell carried out on this particular site in 1846, in order to verify the discovery [p465]. Lyell was the lawyer and amateur geologist who wrote in support of the theory of Uniformitarianism in the formation of the geological strata. This theory said that present-day processes of erosion, deposition, etc., were able to explain the existing geological formations given an adequate period of time, say, several million years, for these forces to act. Up to that time, the Catastrophist theory held sway, which provided evidence that the strata had been deposited during one or more large scale catastrophes.

Lyell was searching for evidence of man's ancestry and personally visited the site. He was unwilling to accept that man had existed so early in the geological time scale, but he could find no evidence to the contrary. Keith says, 'Lyell was afraid to use the bone found at Natchez as evidence; it seemed to him suggestive of *too great an antiquity for man*.' Lyell overcame his difficulty by saying that it may have slipped from a recent Indian grave! He admits, 'No doubt, had the pelvic bone belonged to any recent mammifer other than Man, such a theory would never have been resorted to.' [23p159]

Clearly, as early as 1846, Lyell was not prepared to accept the existence of man in such ancient strata, and his dismissal of evidence in this way leaves one questioning whether he was similarly selective in his evidence to support his theory of slow geological changes taking place over immense periods of time. His theory has indeed come under severe criticism by several eminent geologists, among them Professor D. V. Ager, Head of the Department of Geology and Oceanography at Swansea University [1] and S. J. Gould, Professor of Geology at Harvard University. The latter in fact goes so far as to accuse Lyell of deviousness in his arguments, for he says:

Charles Lyell was a lawyer by profession, and his book is one of the most brilliant briefs ever published by an advocate ... Lyell relied upon two bits of cunning to establish his uniformitarian views as the only true geology. First, he set up a straw man to demolish . . In fact, the catastrophists were much more empirically minded than Lyell. The geologic record does seem to require catastrophes: rocks are fractured and contorted; whole faunas are wiped out. To circumvent this literal appearance, Lyell imposed his imagination upon the evidence. The geologic record, he argued, is extremely imperfect and we must interpolate into it what we can reasonably infer but cannot see. The catastrophists were the hard-nosed empiricists of their day, not the blinded theological apologists.

Secondly, Lyell's 'uniformity' is a hodgepodge of claims. One is a methodological statement that must be accepted by any scientist, catastrophist and uniformitarian alike. Other claims are substantive notions that have since been tested and abandoned. Lyell gave them a common name and pulled a consummate fast one: he tried to slip the substantive claim by with an argument that the methodological proposition had to be accepted, lest 'we see the ancient spirit of speculation revived, and a desire manifested to cut, rather than patiently to untie, the Gordian knot.' [68]

With criticisms such as this, which amount almost to a denunciation, it would appear that much of the basis upon which present-day geological theory depends is in urgent need of revision.

Swanscombe, Fontéchevade and Vertesszöllos

Unlike the human skulls we have considered above, these three fossils of early *Homo sapiens* are generally mentioned in the various publications, although often only in passing, and not infrequently they are omitted on any time chart where their closeness to Pekin and Java man would become readily apparent. These three fossil skulls will be considered in the section dealing with Neanderthal man, with whom they are usually associated.

Sir Arthur Keith's views of the early human fossils

We have described these early human fossils at some length, in order to show that except for the last three, most of them are ignored, certainly in all the popular works written for the general public, and by almost all scientists including those of considerable fame and reputation. One outstanding exception to this observation, as we have said, is Sir Arthur Keith, who was prepared to face up to unwelcome facts, even though they did not fit in with preconceived ideas.

In the 1925 edition of his book *The Antiquity of Man*, he gives the histories of several of these fossils of early *Homo sapiens*, although they do not appear in his later works. I can do no better than conclude this section by quoting his comments on certain of the fossils we have already considered.

. . . Can we suppose that the workmen at Galley Hill and Clichy had a supernatural knowledge and implanted these two similar but peculiar varieties of man in the same geological stratum, and in the midst of the same ancient Palaeolithic culture? [p278]

Were our predecessors right in rejecting the Abbeville mandible? I think not. . . . Our predecessors were largely influenced by prejudice. . . . Time will probably show that the pioneer of Abbeville was not only right about the human implements of the terraces, but also about the human remains. [p274]

The story of the Calaveras skull, although grown stale . . . cannot be passed over. It is the 'bogey' which haunts the student of early man— . . . taxing the powers of belief of every expert almost to breaking point. . . . Indeed were such discoveries in accordance with our expectations, if they were in harmony with the theories we have found regarding the date of man's evolution, no one would ever dream of doubting them, much less of rejecting them. [p471 & 473]

As the student of prehistoric man reads and studies the records of the 'Castenodolo' find, a feeling of incredulity rises within him. He cannot reject the discovery as false without doing injury to his sense of truth, and he cannot accept it without shattering his accepted beliefs. It is clear that we cannot pass Castenodolo by in silence: all the modern problems relating to the origin and antiquity of modern man focus themselves round it. [p334]

SECTION IV

PEKIN MAN

To simplify the presentation of the facts relating to Pekin man, we will set them out chronologically, considering in detail certain events and commenting on various publications as they occur.

In dealing with Pekin man, reference must be made to Fr. O'Connell's book *Science of Today and the Problem of Genesis*, which, despite some inaccuracies of varying importance, nevertheless raised a number of interesting aspects, worth further investigation, regarding the discovery of the fossils. Fr. O'Connell was a Roman Catholic priest who was in China from the early days of the discovery to after the Second World War, and although he did not visit Pekin personally, read the accounts of the discovery in both English and Chinese papers, which convinced him that no 'missing links' had been found. He mentions that in a manual of Christian Doctrine, published by Jesuit Fathers in Hong Kong, similar views were expressed.

Fr. O'Connell's book, which is highly critical of Teilhard de Chardin and certain other members of the Roman Catholic clergy, had nevertheless received the official 'Imprimatur' of the Vatican and he reproduces a letter, in which Pope Paul VI's appreciation of his faithful devotion is expressed.

1918. Early discoveries

All the accounts of the discovery of the Pekin man begin with Andersson's investigations at Chikusan, near Choukoutien, in this year. However, O'Connell [p113] says that the Jesuit Fr. Licent, the Director of a geological and botanical museum in China, obtained several grants of 20,000 francs for exploration of the site at Choukoutien as early as 1912. It is understandable that there was considerable interest in 'Choukoutien' as it means 'Dragon Bone Hill', 'Dragon Bones' being the Chinese name given to fossils. The Chinese believe that ground-up fossils have good medicinal properties, and this hill had obviously been known to be a source of fossils for generations.

Earlier still, in 1903, however, Professor Schlosser of Germany, whilst examining a number of fossils which had been purchased *from a druggist's shop* in China, found a tooth which he considered was of an anthropoid, and suggested that early man might be found on this

Continent. Grafton Elliot Smith wrote an article about Pekin man in *Antiquity*, in which he comments:

> Hence he defines the aim of his communication to suggest to later investigators who may enjoy the privilege of carrying out excavations in China the desirability of searching for the remains either of a new fossil anthropoid, a Tertiary man or an early Pleistocene human being. . . . This brilliant forecast was made in 1903, but nothing further was done towards the realization of it until the year 1921, when Professor J. Gunnar Andersson, the Swedish geologist who was acting as the Adviser to the Geological Survey of China, was directed to a deposit of fossil bones at Chou Kou Tien through overhearing the chatter of his native workmen. When he started to examine the rich deposit of fossil bones in the cave at Chou Kou Tien he found amongst these remains a piece of quartz, and at once remarked to his assistants 'This is primitive man', implying by that statement that as quartz did not naturally occur in this spot, some early Pleistocene human agency must have been responsible for its presence among the bones which he was examining. In a way this statement is almost as remarkable as that which Professor Schlosser had made over twenty years previously. [78p29]

It is clear that on very little evidence, early man was expected to be discovered on a continent which at the time was comparatively remote from Europe. Smith's fulsome praise for Professor Schlosser's prediction was completely undeserved, however, for the tooth was later found to be of *Homo sapiens*, which are plentiful in Chinese apothecaries' shops [18p63], and moreover *it has since mysteriously disappeared*. [5p116 and 18p41].

Andersson was apparently employed to carry out a geological survey and, it is said, being interested in palaeontology, was fortunate in discovering the quartz pieces, subsequently handing over further investigations to Dr. Zdansky. Wendt, however, gives a different version, for he says that Schlosser's prediction in 1903 was instrumental in the organization as early as 1914 of the first expedition to the Far East, specifically to find the 'missing link', the team consisting of Andersson, Zdansky, Walter Granger and later Roy Chapman Andrews. [37p183]

In 1921, Zdansky began excavations at Chikusan, but soon transferred to the more productive site at Choukoutien nearby, the work being financed by the 'match-stick' millionaire, financier and swindler, Ivar Kreuger, who shot himself in 1932. Kreuger also founded the publication *Palaeontologia Sinica*, which was to become the main channel for the official publications of the results of the excavations at Choukoutien.

1922. Zdansky's finds

Zdansky returned to Sweden with his collection and, finding in it two teeth, cautiously labelled them 'Homo sp.'. In Pekin, however, they caused great excitement, and 'Pekin man' was talked about for the first time. Publication of the finds, however, were not made until four years later.

1926. Excavation begins

An international congress of scientists was held in Pekin, attended by the Crown Prince of Sweden. At this Congress, Dr. Davidson Black, who was the Professor of Anatomy at the Pekin Union Medical College, made a 'confidential' announcement about the two teeth which had been found at Choukoutien four years before.

Davidson Black, who had been born in Canada in 1884, had received a degree in medicine and in 1914 worked in Manchester with Sir Grafton Elliot Smith on the Piltdown finds (see p.16). He believed that man had originated in the East, and willingly accepted a post in the Pekin Union Medical College, which would allow him to explore this continent. He had investigated sites in China and Siam searching for fossil man without success, but was convinced that the two teeth found by Zdansky at Choukoutien were from the hominid he was keen to discover. Teilhard de Chardin who was cautious at first regarding these discoveries, later became convinced that the teeth were human and gave his views at an official luncheon.

Teilhard, who had lost his position as Professor of Geology in the University of Paris, had been effectively banished to China in 1923 by the Roman Catholic authorities because of his writings and lectures, and was forbidden by them to publish any theological works expressing his philosophical views on Evolution and Christianity. He worked with Fr. Licent in the Geological and Botanical Museum in Tientsin which the latter had founded and they travelled extensively over China, collecting many fossils and geological specimens.

At a reception during the congress, the secretary of the Rockefeller Foundation was present and as a result of the discovery of the two teeth, it was agreed that the Foundation should finance further explorations. The Swede, Dr. Birgher Bohlin, was to be in charge of the excavations at the site, whilst the fossils would be assessed by Dr. Black in Pekin.

Thus, on such meagre evidence, considerable sums of money were to be spent in large-scale excavations in an effort to discover more. Professor Zdansky, however, was concerned by the extravagant claims which were being made by some of his colleagues. In his article in *Antiquity* [78] Elliot Smith quotes Zdansky's paper of 1927, in which he said:

I am indeed convinced that the existing material provides a wholly inadequate foundation for many of the various theories based upon it.

Fig.19. Black's 'Sinanthropus' tooth

> ... I decline absolutely to venture any far-reaching conclusions regarding the extremely meagre material described here, and which, I think, cannot be more closely identified than as Homo sp. ... my purpose here is only to make it clear that my discovery of these teeth should be regarded as decidedly interesting but not of epoch-making importance.

Elliot Smith continues:

> Professor Davidson Black, however, took a different view of the significance of the teeth. To him they were definitely of epoch-making importance. Moreover, he had the courage to act upon his conviction.

Smith mentions that Black, his former student, with whom he had been in correspondence, was convinced that primitive man would be found in China, and had therefore accepted the position offered in Pekin. Black's conviction, that the teeth found by Zdansky were of a primitive man, is in marked contrast to the cautious and objective approach of their discoverer.

1927. The tooth of 'Pekin man'

On the 27th October, just as the season's dig was ending, and little of real value had been discovered, Bohlin found another molar tooth which was immediately rushed to Pekin (Fig.19). Black considered that it had characteristics intermediate between man and ape, and announced the discovery of *Sinanthropus pekinensis* [69]. We would again suggest that to make such a bold pronouncement on the evidence of one tooth indicates a lack of scientific caution, particularly when a similar claim had been made for the false tooth of 'Hesperopithecus' related earlier (p.46).

Dr. Black travelled to America and Europe, with the tooth in a specially made gold receptacle attached to his watch chain for security. The tooth caused a considerable stir in scientific circles, although some scientists felt that it was over-optimistic to make so bold a claim on such slim evidence.

Excavations continued, with huge quantities of bones being discovered, 575 boxes of them being sent to Pekin in the season's dig. Amongst them were some jaws, skull bones and teeth of the 'apemen'. From the pieces of bones, Black later reconstructed his first Sinanthropus skull.

1929. The Cenozoic Laboratory founded

In view of the discoveries to date, the Rockefeller Foundation agreed to finance the setting up of the Cenozoic Laboratory, the title Cenozoic coming from the name covering the Pliocene and Pleistocene eras. Dr. Black was made Director, and dealt with the Sinanthropus fossils, and the Chinese, Pei and Young, were put in charge of the excavation. Teilhard de Chardin was given the position of adviser and collaborator, dealing particularly with the geology and dating of the finds.

The Foundation's grant of $20,000 was a very large sum of money in those days, one dollar alone being sufficient to pay four men for one day's work. At times there were up to 100 men employed on the site, and clearly no expense was spared in the effort to discover more remains of Pekin man.

The Locus E skull

In December, again, just as the season's dig was finishing, W. Pei discovered an almost complete brain case, to be known as the Locus E skull. The news was immediately telegraphed to Black and the 'skull' carefully transported to Pekin for inspection.

Black was naturally jubilant at the discovery of Sinanthropus, whose existence he had earlier announced, based entirely on the discovery of the tooth in 1927.

The skull, which was only the major portion of the brain case and lacked the base, jaw and front of the face, was partly embedded and filled with earth, and Black took many months to free the fossil from this encrustation. He published a press release with a photograph of the side view of the skull, still embedded at the base in the encrustation, and in the report mentioned that no artefacts or trace of fire had been found (see Fig. 27). Boule wrote about the discovery in L'Anthropologie in 1929, saying it was noticeably like the Pithecanthropus skull of Java.

Black worked on the skull in his laboratory at night, making casts, drawings and photographs, and snatched what sleep he could during the day after locking the fossils away in his safe. He said that he worked best and thought most clearly at night. It may have been this routine which contributed to his early death from heart failure in 1934 at the age of fifty.

Black did not issue a full report of the finds until 1931. Teilhard, however, was keen to give an account of the fossil and wrote an article, published in 1930 [76], giving a full description of it. It is here that the real mystery of precisely what was found at Choukoutien begins to deepen.

Before we continue to trace the history of this skull, however, we must digress to consider the even stranger mystery of the meteoric appearance and disappearance of no fewer than ten skeletons.

The ten skeletons

When researching for the first edition of this book, I noticed O'Connell's reference to the discovery of ten skeletons announced in the *Daily Telegraph* on 20th July 1929. As a careful search of the newspaper of that date revealed no mention of skeletons found at Pekin, naturally I did not refer to this incident.

It is now clear that the date was incorrect, and a world wide announcement *was* made of this discovery on 15th-16th December.

In the *Daily Telegraph* of 16th December 1929 appeared a very lengthy article from their Pekin correspondent. This stated that the fossilized bones of ten men, together with a perfect skull (complete with facial bones) had been discovered. An announcement had been made by Davidson Black and other officials of the geological survey of China who were preparing a scientific statement for release to a Convention, which was to be held in Pekin on 23rd December. The skeletons had been found in the cave at the Choukoutien site by the Chinese assistant, Pei. They were found huddled together and this was said to indicate that they led a community life.

Davidson Black had studied the skull and was convinced '. . . that the "Pekin man" was a thinking being, standing erect, dating to the beginning of the Ice Age.' Interviews with Dr. Elliott Smith and Sir Arthur Keith accompanied the article. The interview with Sir Arthur Keith was of more interest, for here was sounded the first note of caution about this particular discovery. The report mentions that he '. . . appeared a little sceptical as to the statement of the "petrified bones of ten men" '. 'Discoveries are not made in this way', he said. As all fossil remains of ape men had been (and still are) very fragmentary, he was clearly suspicious of ten virtually complete skeletons being found, and he would not make any further comment until he had seen the official details of the discoveries.

A very similar report to that in the *Daily Telegraph* appeared in the *New York Times* of 16th December with the added information that nine of the ten skeletons were headless [!] and that the experts were seeking the other skulls, whose absence they could not explain. Two other American experts, however, accepted the discoveries very cautiously, for in the *New York Times* on 17th December Walter Granger said that *if the finds were authentic*, he thought they would have used implements and that they were probably also 'familiar with fire . . .'. In the *New York Times* on 18th December, Dr. Ales Hrdlicka doubted if the bones were as old as the one million years' age claimed for them, in view of the number of skeletons found and their headless condition which indicated modern head hunting practices.

Nature announced the discovery in its issue of 28th December and that Dr. Davidson Black would be making an official statement on the discoveries on 29th December.

Clearly, something very important had been discovered in Pekin. With all this worldwide publicity the stage was set for a detailed report of these skeletons, proving that man was descended from an ape ancestor.

What actually happened?

Nothing whatsoever—absolute silence!

These skeletons are simply not referred to in *any* report, periodical or reference book dealing with Pekin man! It is as if these newspaper headlines had never existed. Indeed, the only fossil later referred to as being discovered in early December is Pei's Locus E skull *cap*. No other bones are ever mentioned.

What could have brought about this disappearing act? It seems to me that the experts, ever keen to publicize their discoveries, appear to have despatched a hurried cable to the world's newspapers. Closer inspection, however, probably showed that the skeletons were far too human for a claim to be made that they were halfway between man and ape. It may therefore have been decided to ignore them completely, and to publicize only the ape skull which Pei is said to have discovered in the lower 'cave'.

As far as I can trace, Black never reported on the fossils on 29th December. But he did telegram Boule (73) on 28th December, saying 'Recovered Chou-Kou-Tien uncrushed adult Sinanthropus skull entire except face. Letter follows.'

Thus in the space of thirteen days the ten skeletons made their brief appearance and mysterious disappearance from the stage of the Pekin Theatre. This was not the only disappearing-act in the play, however. A similar fate awaited the bones showing human workmanship in 1937, and *all* the fossils in 1941.

This strange incident does raise one question. Why has no 'scientist', author or journalist of integrity ever referred to these reports of ten skeletons and questioned what happened to them? For example, why did the editor of *Nature* never query what happened to the important skeletons whose discovery he had announced in his periodical? Is it perhaps an accepted principle in the world of anthropology that the persistent asking of awkward questions is not encouraged—indeed, *positively discouraged*? I would suggest that this is but one further example of the suppression of unwanted evidence being exercised in the publishing world.

Having digressed on this revealing topic, we will now return to the Locus E skull and trace its 'development' over the years.

1930. Two assessments of the skull

Teilhard's article appeared in the *Revue des Questions Scientifiques* in Paris [31p58], and he made the following points in describing the find:

(a) The main site was not a fissure but the filled-up bottom of a cave, the top of which had later been eroded. No trace of fire or any industry had yet been found.

(b) The whole of the brain case of the Locus E was well preserved and not deformed, except for a damaged area around the occiput.

(c) At the time he was writing, the interior of the brain case had not been freed from deposits and therefore the brain capacity could not be measured, but he considered that *it would not be large in view of the relatively small dimensions of the skull and the considerable thickness of the bone walls.*

(d) He reported Black's preliminary comments which pointed out a number of ape-like characteristics, one of them being that,

Looked at from behind, the top of the skull of Sinanthropus is of grossly triangular shape like that of monkeys, rather than oval-shaped, as in man.

Teilhard wrote a further article in *Anthropologie* 1931 [81] which also confirmed the considerable number of ape-like features that the skull possessed.

Surely, with such statements, it is clear that all that had been found was the skull of a large monkey, and the first description of Teilhard's is confirmed by the impressions given by other scientists who visited Pekin during the next few years.

Elliot Smith's view

In October 1930, Grafton Elliot Smith visited the site, and his encouragement of the team working in China was gratefully acknowledged by them in one of their later publications entitled *Fossil Man.* [88p10]

On his return to England, Smith wrote an article in *Antiquity* [78], from which we have already quoted. Referring to the discoveries at Pekin, he made the following comments.

(a) In the diagram he included in his article, which is similar to that in Fig.20, there is no mention that layer 4 is a deep bed of ashes. He also specifically mentions that no trace whatsoever of any tools had been found, despite a careful search of the site, and that Teilhard was particularly looking for archaeological evidence. Pei had, however, found some further pieces of quartz, but the 'vain search for evidence of human craftmanship' had forced those involved to the conclusion that Pekin man was at such an early stage that he had not yet learnt to shape implements'.

(b) Elliot Smith's comment on a photo of the skull found by Pei (the Locus E skull), which he used as an illustration in his article, was that it displayed 'in an even more emphatic way the thickness of the skull *and the diminutive size of the space for the brain*'. He also noted 'the surprisingly small brain capacity'. [p34]

This description of the small size of the skull agrees with that of others who visited Pekin:

Teilhard [31p64] '. . . the cranial capacity (probably poor, given the relatively small dimensions of the skull . . .).'

Breuil [84p15] 'The existence, in such a primitive skull . . . of human characteristics . . . is unexpected.'

von Koenigswald [18p46] 'The cranium was relatively small. . . .'

Thus, all those who actually saw the original skull were struck by the smallness of its brain capacity. The *only* evidence of it having a capacity of almost 1,000 cc. is the volume which Black measured on his *reconstruction* of the skull in 1931 and Weidenreich's remeasurement of the same reconstruction in 1943.

1931. Black's report on the skull

Teilhard published a further article on the fossil skull in *L'Anthropologie* [81p10], in which he says that it 'manifestly resembles the great apes closely'. In fact again the only human characteristic he mentions is its brain capacity, which, he said, Black had measured as being almost 1,000 cc.

Black published his final article on the Locus E skull [80], having issued a preliminary report in 1929 [72] and an interim report in 1930 [77]. As so much hinges on Black's reconstruction of this skull, I have examined his three reports in some detail in Appendix III.

Referring to Black's assessment of the Locus E skull, Boule made the wry comment that,

Black, who had felt justified in forging the term 'Sinanthropus' to designate *one* (emphasis his) tooth, was naturally concerned to legitimise this creation when he had to describe a skull cap. [4p141]

It is quite clear that in his writings, Boule is very sceptical and even antagonistic regarding the extravagant claims made for the Pekin fossils. He expressed his views in his book *Les Hommes Fossiles* which he published before the Second World War. He died during the war and subsequently this book was revised by Vallois, and an English translation was made in 1957. It would appear that Vallois did not fully agree with Boule's strong views on Sinanthropus, for whilst many of the blunt views of the original author have been retained, in a summary entitled, *A New Discussion of the Facts*, the intermediate position which Sinanthropus holds in the line between man and apes is emphasized.

A comparison with Boule's original publication shows many revisions. Where I quote views which are clearly those of Boule, I have attributed them accordingly, but when more general views are given from the English translation, I have simply referred to the title of the book, without ascertaining which of the two authors' views the statement reflects.

Professor Breuil's visit

During this same year (1931), Professor Breuil of the College of France and l'Institut de Palaeontologie Humaine, and a world renowned expert on the Old Stone Age, visited the site at Choukoutien and examined the fossils in the Pekin Laboratory. He spent nineteen days in China, and published the results of his visit the following year.

Before leaving Pekin, Breuil gave a lecture on 3rd November 1931 to the Geological Society of China [84], in which he described the ancient stone and bone industry he had seen at the site and his assessment of them. Much of what he said he repeated in his 1932 paper, and we will consider it later, but the following points are of interest.

(a) Bone workmanship

The standard of workmanship displayed in the cutting and shaping of both the stones and bones which he saw, a subject on which he was a world expert, was sufficiently advanced for him to compare it several times with the Mousterian culture. This would equate it with Neanderthal man, who existed long after Sinanthropus. This late dating of the artefacts was clearly unacceptable to the experts in China, and on the first page of Breuil's article, an interesting footnote by the editor was appended saying:

> Professor Breuil's interpretation of the evidence of artefacts other than those of stone is of particular interest, representing as it does the considered personal opinion of such an eminent authority. The members of the staff of the Cenozoic Research Laboratory are in essential agreement with Professor Breuil's interpretation of the evidence of the use of fire and of the manufacture of stone artefacts by Sinanthropus. It should be noted however that their views with regard to the nature of the bone and horn material and to the advanced stage of the lithic industry, are at the present time of a much more conservative nature. A critical description of the very extensive additional material now available for study will shortly be published in this Journal. ED.

This footnote was to have a sequel, for in 1934 Breuil revisited Pekin to re-examine these bones.

(b) *The skulls*

His explanation for the fact that only the skulls of Sinanthropus had been found was that they had dried out the heads of their dead by hanging them on trees, before bringing them into the cave! This seems rather far-fetched, and one would not then expect to find them mixed up with the remains of other animals.

(c) *Sinanthropus*

His general assessment of Sinanthropus was that it was

> . . . no longer the creature devoid of human ability, *which one could have believed, at first sight, on seeing the head so much like some anthropoids.* It is already man, *despite his animal characteristics,* with a developing intelligence, with the beginnings of superiority over other animals, due to fire and stone working.

Breuil is clearly surprised that such an advanced culture could have come from the skull that he saw, which confirms Teilhard's initial observations that the skull was ape like and of small capacity, and conflicts with Black's later model, which he said had a capacity of 1,000 cc. Breuil may have felt that, as he was the guest of the scientists in China, and a professional colleague, he should be very circumspect in avoiding a direct contradiction of their findings.

1932. Breuil's report

Breuil published the results of his 1931 visit [85] and we give below some brief extracts from his lengthy article, using his chapter headings. In Fig.20 we give a simplified form of the site section which Breuil used, so that the reader can judge for himself the considerable extent of the discovered fire remains. In Appendix IV we give the evidence which indicates that these ashes were discovered two years before Breuil's visit, and that their existence was only reluctantly admitted by the experts in China.

1. THE FIRE AT CHOUKOUTIEN

By far the most significant item Breuil noted during his visit was the great depth of ashes *amounting to 7 m. (24 ft.) in thickness* at the upper level. This was made up of numerous 'ribbon' beds of many different colours, which had been produced by the burning of vegetable matter. At the bottom of the ash heap was a layer of charcoal, indicating that 'the fire once lit was kept burning for long periods of time'. 'Fire was used on a large scale at Choukoutien' and 'the present thickness ob-

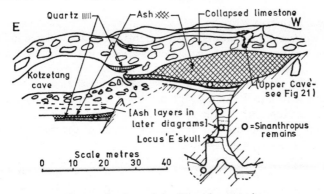

Fig.20. Section of the Sinanthropus site

viously represents a much greater one at the time of the fires'. The heat generated was so intense that phosphates from the bones had formed into nodules and slabs of concretions, and some phosphates of lime had been changed into blue iron phosphates. He found blocks of burnt bones and chipped quartz, all solidified together.

In the lower Kotzetang Cave, which had been recently and artificially formed in the breccia (a naturally cemented mass of stones), he found that a black layer was the base of a furnace with lighter coloured ashes (2–3 m. thick [88p18]), probably mixed with clay, above it. Stones with soot on them and burnt bones were being carried out while he was there.

2. STONE INDUSTRY

In 1931 in the Kotzetang Cave they had found 2,000 pieces of chipped quartz. Breuil saw a bed of them about ·5 m. (18 in.) thick at this spot. He found volcanic rocks splintered into different shapes. 'It is the remains, unfortunately very decomposed, of a great set of volcanic stone tools, broken into large splinters.' Quartz, which was not local to this cave, *but available over a mile away across a small valley,* was of two sorts, whilst some of the pieces were 'larger than a man's head' and carried marks on them indicating that they had been used as anvils. He found that 'most abundant were small splinters, perfectly defined as though due to human hammering with all the characteristics of French Mousterian layers'. Other stones looked similar to those of Upper Paleolithic type, and he saw 'several "bolas" of a rough polyhedron shape'. He said that the stone industry he had seen was unlike any of the stone cultures he knew of in Europe, 'and that it was not unlike a crude Mousterian culture was doubtless accidental'.

3. BONE INDUSTRY

'The worker of Choukoutien had systematically used a large industry of bone tools. . . . The large antlers were too big to be used whole, they had been cut up into pieces and cut with stone tools. . . . First they burnt the bone near the point chosen for the cut, it was then worked with a tool like a gouge making a V-shaped groove, almost to the soft interior . . . the antler was then broken by a blow.' In a footnote he comments that 'the Neolithic men of the flint caves used the same method, e.g. Nointel (Oise)'.

The upper jaws of the deer had certainly been used like a rasp. As with the stone implements, he had difficulty in ascribing the bone industry to a particular period of culture with which he was familiar in Europe.

4. THE REMAINS OF SINANTHROPUS

'There are two brain cases and various pieces of Sinanthropus skulls and a good half dozen jaws, a number of teeth and two small limb bones of the extremities. When the recovered remains of animals are counted in tens of thousands, and, except for the great Pachydermes [Elephants], complete with all parts of their bodies, not one bone of the limbs or trunk of Sinanthropus has been found up to now. This fact, profoundly troubling, if it is not altered during the course of the excavations, demands an explanation, for it tends to show a selection in the bones of Sinanthropus, and of special treatment in the way in which the bodies had been dealt with.'

Breuil concludes that the skulls alone, stripped of their flesh by decay, had been brought back to the place of habitation!

5. WHO IS THE AUTHOR OF THESE TOOLS AND ACTIVITIES?

'Many distinguished experts, independently from each other, have expressed to me the thought that a being, so physically distant from Man, even Neanderthal, was not able to carry out the works which I have just described. In this case, the remains of Sinanthropus could be considered as simple hunting trophies, attributable, as were the traces of fire and industry to a true Man, whose remains have not yet been found. As these originators of the fire and industry are an unknown race who have not left their marks, there is in fact no way of establishing with complete evidence that these experts are wrong.'

Breuil continues by saying that the principles on which Sinanthropus is excluded from human intelligence are *a priori*! He then argues that as Sinanthropus is so close to Java man, then perhaps the latter was more human than we first thought, which is a strange comment in view of the fact that he admitted he could not *prove* that Sinanthropus *was* the author of the works at Choukoutien.

'The existence, in a skull so primitive, so remote from all other known Men, of a human ability to invent tools and instruments for the purpose of making others from them, truly opens up unexpected views of the distant past of our species.'

He clearly accepts that Sinanthropus *is* responsible for the works, but as we have said before, he is surprised by his 'primitive' skull, from which one concludes that he is really referring to the small size of its brain.

6. THE AGE OF SINANTHROPUS

Breuil considers he may have existed during 'the pre-Wurmian paleolithic period, from the older Chellean of Abbeville, with Cromerien fauna, to perhaps as late as the early or middle Levalloisien'. Precise dating from this is not easy, depending upon the authority which one refers to, as can be seen in Fig.14.

It would appear, however, that the periods that Breuil gives are slightly or even considerably later than those to which Sinanthropus is usually attributed, particularly when he likens the work to that of 'the Mousterian Culture'.

An assessment of the site

From this first-hand report of Breuil, despite his reservations, it is quite evident that there existed at Choukoutien an industry of a nature that was far too large and advanced for it to be attributed to the small skulls of the animals which had been given the name of *Sinanthropus pekinensis*. Enormous furnaces which were kept burning for long periods, thousands of chipped and shaped stones, sometimes brought to the site from a mile or two away, and bones which had been worked and cut *all speak of modern Man, Homo sapiens, being in control*. Breuil admits that many other experts, of whom his colleague Boule was doubtless one, had reached this opinion.

The 'bolas' stones

We would consider that this viewpoint is confirmed by one particular piece of stone workmanship, which Breuil briefly mentioned in his article—we refer to the 'bolas' which he saw. It should be noted that the Professor, an expert in stone implements, unhesitatingly called them 'bolas', and did not say they were 'like bolas'. If he was correct, the implications are considerable. Bolas, as it will be appreciated, are two or three stones, secured to the ends of rope or thongs about three or four feet long. They are swung over the head and thrown at the legs of fleeing animals, and if the aim is good, they entwine themselves around the legs of the creature, which is brought down.

The stages of manufacture and use of an instrument of this sort involve very advanced techniques, such as:

(a) The shaping of blocks of stone into a sphere, which is far from easy.

(b) The attachment of the stones to the end of, say, a leather thong. This would involve perhaps the shaping of a leather bag and fastening it to the thong.

(c) Considerable skill in throwing this unusual missile to entwine the legs of fast moving animals.

Above all these considerations is the high degree of inventiveness and development of mechanical spatial concepts required to design such an effective weapon. This is surely well beyond the ability of any so-called ape-men.

The Sinanthropus skulls

As we have seen, the experts had considerable difficulty in explaining why virtually only Sinanthropus *heads* had been discovered. The total number of 'skulls' eventually found came to fourteen, but over half of them consisted merely of a portion of a cranium, or part of a jaw, *but these were still counted as a 'skull'.* [100p5]

In only five cases were sufficient bones of the cranium available to enable it to be reconstructed adequately for the volume to be measured. These were:

Skull II	Black's skull reconstructed from pieces found in laboratory	1,030 cc.
Skull III	Black's Locus E skull	915 cc.
Skull X		1,225 cc.
Skull XI	'Nellies' skull	1,015 cc.
Skull XII		1,030 cc.

Summarizing the information available regarding these 'skulls', we note that:

(a) They were always broken, generally into fairly small pieces. Only the Locus E skull was reasonably complete, and even this had the base missing and was badly damaged.

(b) They were generally found mixed up with other animal remains, most of them being deer and other animals hunted for meat.

(c) Virtually no other bones have been found. The few pieces of leg bones discovered had been badly broken and there was no real evidence whether Sinanthropus even walked upright.

(d) The skulls showed no difference between those found at the top and those at the bottom of the deposit, indicating that there had been no 'progress' or 'advancement' during the period over which the site was occupied.

Is there any common sense way of accounting for these seemingly awkward facts? The most obvious explanation is that the skulls were merely those of large monkeys, caught and decapitated in the forest. In the cave the skulls were broken so that the brains could be removed and eaten as a table delicacy. Finally, the broken pieces were thrown in with the remains of other animals hunted for food!

Clearly with such a blaze of publicity surrounding these pieces of apes skulls, the assumption that they were an important link in man's ancestry was too strong to resist. When some experts suggested the more mundane explanation that they were only monkeys decapitated by humans, the argument was refuted as being *a priori*, as no evidence of human existence had been discovered. When, in 1933, human skeletons *were* found close by, full publication of the results was delayed for five years, and the site was said to be of a much later date than the main Sinanthropus deposits. Several links between these two sites were however admitted.

We would submit that to try to interpret the evidence of the material described by Breuil as being the work of ape-men, is a reflection upon the whole science of palaeoanthropology, and simply against common sense.

Professor Boule's views

Breuil was not the only person to visit the site. O'Connell relates that Professor Boule was invited out to China, but when he saw that the only evidence provided was a battered monkey's skull, he was very angry, denounced Teilhard and ridiculed the idea that the owners of the skulls could have carried out the large-scale industry revealed. His findings [96] were that the skull was ape-like, and he calls the idea that the owners of these skulls were the authors of the large-scale industry 'a fantastic hypothesis'. In his book *Fossil Men*, he is clearly unconvinced that Sinanthropus was other than a monkey, and makes the comment:

> We may therefore ask ourselves whether or not it is over-bold to con-sider Sinanthropus the monarch of Choukoutien when he appears in its deposit only in the guise of a mere hunter's prey, on a par with the animals by which he is accompanied. [p145]

Teilhard, who could not accept this explanation, considered the idea that the scale of the industry proved that real men existed as 'pure fantasy or prehistoric fiction'!

History of the site

One would naturally like to be able to show how the site developed under the hand of the men who occupied it, to the state in which it was found by the excavators. This, however, is far from easy. A care-ful examination of the position, size and type of the various strata fails to reveal precisely how they came to be in the particular order in which they were found. In this particular instance, the normal diffi-culty of representing a complex, three dimensional site by sections and plans is further compounded by the compression and distortion of the layers of ash and debris by the fallen pieces of limestone. O'Connell considered that the site was used for a lime-burning industry for the building of the ancient city of Cambaluc, where the present city of Pekin now stands. He also suggests that the associated quarrying undermined the limestone cliff face, causing a landslide. This series of events seems to be a possible explanation of the situation revealed at this site.

The stone tool industry

In 1932 Teilhard and Pei published the *Lithic Industry of Sinanthropus deposits* [86], in which they describe some of the stone artefacts they had found. They considered it to be an old Palaeolithic, and one of the simplest stone cultures that one could imagine. Their only comment regarding the fires is:

> In the uppermost cultural zone A we include the whole (7m thick) accumulation of banded yellow, red and black sandy clay indicated as Layer 4 in the preliminary report of 1930. This entire deposit is an ashy deposit. . . .

Reviewing this article in *L'Anthropologie* [87], R. Vaufrey notes that they pass over the fires in silence and asks: 'Where are the long bones of Sinanthropus?'

1933. The 'Fossil Man in China' report

The four members of the Cenozoic Laboratory (Black, Teilhard, Young and Pei) produced the document entitled *Fossil Man in China* [88]. This is a lengthy document and covers the history of the discovery, bringing it up to date and repeating much of earlier writings. It differs noticeably from Breuil's view in that the advanced state of the stone and bone working and the size of the fires is far from evident in their account, e.g.

(a) Stone Industry—A few drawings are given of some simple stone tools, and of the thousands of stones found 'only 150 could be called implements'.

(b) Bone Industry—Despite the fact that Breuil was an acknowledged expert in this field, his views are mentioned but dismissed, as the authors consider that further evidence is necessary and it is likely that the breakages of the bones were probably due to accident! Their final judgement is: 'In view of this, we feel that further discussion of the subject here is unnecessary.'

(c) Fire—The great heap of ash is described as:

> Upper Ashy Layer, consisting of soft sandy clay layers, with their black layers of carbonaceous ash, the yellow or red colouration being due to superheating of the clay.

The layer below this, which Breuil said was charcoal reduced to particles, is described as a 'black clay'. On page 5 of the report is a view of the sites showing this heap of ash, and the description is 'sandy clay (ashes)'.

More surprising still is the section devoted to the consideration of the fires. Having spent several pages giving detailed pictures and descriptions of some of the bone and stone found, the section dealing with the fires begins with the statement:

> Traces of artificial fire in the locality 'I' deposit are so clear and abundant that they require only to be mentioned without any further demonstration!

The whole subject is dismissed in seven lines!
Such a disingenuous statement is surely unacceptable in the interests of scientific integrity. To call a heap of ash 7 metres thick as being 'traces of fire' is inexcusable, but nevertheless it is this phrase, or a similar description, which one finds in all the popular books dealing with the Pekin man. [e.g. 4p144, 5p119, 17p150, 14p89, 25p251, 8p87]. I consider that the evidence of huge fires was obvious at a very early date, and the seeming reluctance of the experts to admit its existence is considered in Appendix IV.

(d) Bibliography—This has a statement at the beginning which reads

> . . . an attempt has been made in the following bibliographical list to include therein citations of all papers which contain primary observational or historical data bearing upon the Choukoutien fossiliferous deposits or on materials derived therefrom, up to May 1933.

Breuil's paper in L'Anthropologie *March 1932 was omitted!*
It cannot be claimed that European publications would not reach China very quickly, as three other papers, published in France and Germany in 1932, *had* been included. As Vere says:

> Did Teilhard at least, who had been instrumental in bringing Breuil to China by May, 1933, not know what Breuil had found and what Breuil had written? This is simply incredible. One can only conclude that Breuil's discoveries, being inconvenient, were deliberately suppressed. The kind of creature found—or alleged to have been found—at Chou-Kou-Tien was consistent with hearths, but *not* with something uncommonly like a huge furnace.
> [33p47]

The 'Upper Cave' humans
In 1933, Teilhard wrote an article, but left it unpublished for five months. Towards the end of the season, however, W. Pei brought

into Pekin three human skulls which had been found in the 'upper cave', and Teilhard completed the article in which he describes the finds and published it in *Revue des Questions Scientifiques* in 1934, which was included in the symposium of his work—*The Appearance of Man*. [31p68]

1934. The 'Upper Cave'

At the beginning of Teilhard's article, a footnote recommends *Fossil Man in China* (with complete bibliography), which was obtainable from scientific booksellers or direct from the publishers in China.

In the article, he states that they had found in the 'Upper Cave' a true *Homo sapiens*—three adult skulls, absolutely complete (including mandible), a pelvis with two femurs', and some other small bones, totalling about six individuals, one of them being a very young child. He is quite emphatic that they were humans of modern type, but that they were found in a separate cave and were of an age long after Sinanthropus. Teilhard also mentions that they had found at another site the remains of a large baboon, and wonders if he might have inhabited the same hills before Sinanthropus drove him away. It would have been interesting to compare the skulls of the supposed hunter and his quarry.

Pei published a paper [90] in September, giving a preliminary report on the discovery of this cave (Fig.21). The 'cave' was a twisted s-shaped cavity, formed vertically in the original limestone by dissolution of the rock. It was completely filled with a grey loam and limestone pieces, in which were found some five cultural 'layers', most of them having human bones or evidence of human occupation. About the mid depth of this recess were found three human skulls of an old man, a middle-aged woman and a young woman, whilst at other levels, the teeth of animals, pierced to make a necklace, a bone needle, and burnt limestone layers were discovered.

The sequence of events given by Pei to account for the deposits is that the entrance to this natural cave was not open until long after the main Choukoutien deposits had been finished. It then may have acted as a natural trap for animals, and as the cave filled up, it was occupied by man for short periods. It is dated as late Pleistocene in view of the incomplete fossilization of the bones, the different nature of the cave filling to that of the main deposit, and the advanced culture of the ornaments, needles, etc. discovered. In a later report he considered that the lowest level, in view of the many complete animal skeletons, had been a natural trap for animals. The middle layer, he said, was a burial site, whilst the upper section had been occupied by man. [98]

He admits that some of the human limb bones attributed to one individual were (in some cases) scattered over a wide area, not only

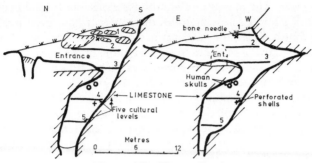

Fig.21. The 'Upper Cave'

horizontally, but vertically also. His explanation for this was that it was the work of beavers! Dr. Weidenreich, who took over after Black's death in 1934, said that they were members of one family and that the damage found on the skulls was due to their having been bludgeoned to death. Pei did not agree, saying that the damage was due to the rocks from the roof falling on the bodies shortly after being buried.

As I have already commented with regard to the main deposit, an attempt to reconstruct the sequence of events is extremely difficult with the information available and the number of conflicting factors described in the articles. The most obvious explanation of the presence of the human remains in the 'cave' is that they were one family of a group of men engaged in all the advanced works found in the main deposit, but who used this cave as their living quarters. As attractive as this solution would be, it cannot however be proved. I will therefore simply point out some of the peculiar factors discovered at this site, as I am unable to propose a sequence of events which would explain their presence.

(a) Habitation of the cave. That such a twisted, almost *vertical* shaft should have been occupied by man is difficult to imagine. Access to the lower sections was not easy. Indeed, Weidenreich refers to it as 'the *so-called* "Upper Cave" of Choukoutien' [35p86] implying that the description was not quite accurate.

(b) Human bones. Pei says these were in some cases widely distributed both horizontally and vertically. In addition, the skulls were found close underneath a large overhanging outcrop of the original limestone which is an unusual position for a burial. The damage to the skulls, which Pei attributed to the roof of the cave collapsing on them, is contradicted by the very considerable sheltering effect provided by this large area of limestone, which would have protected them in the position in which they found.

(c) Levels. The presence of animal skeletons and several pendants in the lower recess indicates that it might have been used as a rubbish dump, the pendants having been dropped accidentally. Pei's drawing of the cave showed in the upper layers a 'cultural bed' of ashes, near to which was found a bone needle. This layer is surrounded by a number of very large blocks of lime-stone which appear to have become detached from the main strata, very similar to those overlying the main deposit (see Figs. 20 and 21). Are we to believe that men inhabited the cave from which lumps of the roof occasionally detached themselves, but which they preferred to ignore?

The report clearly assumes that the entrance into the cave which they found, was the entrance used by the original men when the cave was inhabited. However, the upper cultural layers are well above the level of the entrance, and the whole cave was completely filled with the grey clay and limestone pieces.

'Upper Cave' links with Sinanthropus

One interesting bone was a fragment of a left maxilla with four teeth found in this Upper Cave in 1933, together with the skulls of the Upper Cave men. Weidenreich [100] very surprisingly (but 'with reservation') included it in his descriptions of Sinanthropus, calling it skull XIV. He thus appears to have established a link between the two separate deposits, making them coexistent.

Yet another possible link between the two caves is the few stone tools which Pei discovered in the Upper Cave [98]. Pebble tools looked 'surprisingly similar to some pieces found in the much older Sinan-thropus deposits', and vein quartz flakes and implements *exactly like those of Sinanthropus* were used by the occupants. In a footnote he makes a strange suggestion for this circumstance, for he says:

> However it is quite possible that the here described quartz implements were collected by the Upper Cave Man or introduced by natural agencies into the Upper Cave from the Sinanthropus deposits, as is true of certain fossils, including human remains.

Does he really infer that the stones and human fossils reached the Upper Cave by natural agencies (?) from the Sinanthropus deposits?

Considering all the above aspects, a fairly reasonable solution would be that when the hillside collapsed, due to the undermining effect of the main works, the cave inhabitants died at the same time, their bodies being carried into this crevice by the mass of mud and stones which filled it.

Black's death

By 1934, Black's work on Sinanthropus had received international acclaim and he had just been made a Fellow of the Royal Society in

London. On the 15th March 1934 he died from a heart attack, and was found in his laboratory, lying amongst the human fossils and his reconstruction of the Locus E skull.

Teilhard took over the running of the laboratory for the period of time required to find a successor to Dr. Black, Dr. Franz Weidenreich of Frankfurt University eventually being appointed. Weidenreich proceeded to investigate all the finds which had been made and wrote reports about them over the next few years. He issued no report on the newly discovered human finds for five years however, but when he did, it was not, as one might have expected, in either the *Bulletin* of the Geological Society or the *Geological Survey of China*, but in the Pekin *Natural History Bulletin* in 1939. [99]

1935. Further reports

Breuil visited the site again in 1934, and he and Teilhard presented separate papers [91 & 92] to the French Institute of Anthropology on 19th June 1935.

Teilhard gives a brief description of the human finds, but in a diagram of the site, which he has simplified to such an extent that it can hardly be compared with the section of the site in Fig.20, he locates the Upper Cave in a completely different position relative to the main layers.

Breuil's paper described the stone industry and he wondered if it was a little less ancient than they had at first believed, possibly middle Palaeolithic, but earlier than the Upper Mousterian and Aurignacien. He therefore left it open that it was comparable to a *middle* Mousterian culture, which would be contemporary with Neanderthal man.

Weidenreich's report
Weidenreich published *The Sinanthropus Population of Choukoutien* [93], which is mainly devoted to describing and analysing the jaws and teeth. One confusing aspect of his descriptions is his consistent use of the word 'human', when dealing with the skulls of Sinanthropus, for it gives the impression that he was keen to give a human status to the skulls which he later reconstructed.

He notes that,

> Except for skull I, locus E, (Pei's 1929 skull) all specimens were broken into more or less small pieces and partly crushed or splintered and then fossilized in this condition.

The difficulty of making a reconstruction of a brain case from such shattered pieces can be seen, and the accuracy of the final result with regard to its shape and capacity is clearly a matter of many assumptions and considerable guesswork.

He gives the total number of individuals found at the site as ten children, two adolescents and twelve adults, but over half of them are only represented by teeth, jaws or a few pieces of limb bones! Reference is made to 'the various zones with their *fire places* (charcoal, ashes and burnt bones of animals). . . .' Thus the size of the fire industry is yet again minimized.

Several pages are spent in discussing the reason why virtually only the skulls and jaws of Sinanthropus had been found, Weidenreich concluding that he must have been a head hunter, and the skulls were his trophies! He dismisses Boule's views that they were monkeys killed for their brains by saying no second hominid, the killer of Sinanthropus, had been found. To support his statement, he refers to the similar comments on this subject made by the authors of *Fossil Man in China*. But this was published in 1933, before the discovery of the human skulls in the Upper Cave. He then continues:

> I may add that also today, after two more years of excavations and new discoveries, nothing has been unearthed which point to a second hominid. All human remains from the deepest to the highest place of the cave show the same morphological type, namely, that of Sinanthropus.

Weidenreich makes not even a passing reference to the Upper Cave humans, and one cannot help wondering why he should have made such an obvious omission.

1937. Teilhard's revised assessment

Teilhard published an article in *Etudes* [97 & 31p84] in which there is again no mention of the real human skulls. The total population of the main site is given by him as about thirty individuals, of which they had five almost entire skulls, and parts of three others. He describes Boule's views of Sinanthropus as 'subtle arguments', and to refute them, mentions that they have a skull of a great *male* of *1,200 cc. capacity*, and asks 'why do we need to look for another agent?' A skull of this size, which was a reconstruction by Weidenreich, with a capacity equal to many men living today, is certainly more than adequote to account for the industry at Choukoutien.

We have clearly progressed a very long way from the 'small ape-like skull' description he and others gave of the Locus E skull, through Black's volume measurement of it of 964 cc. to Weidenreich's 1,225 cc. reconstruction of skull X.

Where they had originally thought that the main deposit was a vertical fault which gradually filled up, it was now generally accepted that it was a 'ramified cave, which became progressively bigger but was at the same time filled by the continuous disintegration of the roof'. If this is the accepted sequence of events, it only remains to comment that every time disintegration took place, the inhabitants must have been outside. Their consistent failure to be 'at home' when the roof fell in, thus leaving not one complete skeleton for future scientists to discover, can only be deplored!

1939. The bone industry

The Geological Survey published a paper (in English) by Breuil entitled 'Bone and antler industry of the Choukoutien Sinanthropus site' [July: New Series D6. Whole series 117]. In this he gives his reason for his second visit to China in 1934. He was clearly irked by the footnote appended by the editor to the paper he gave on 3rd November 1931 (see p99) for he says at the beginning of his paper that his statement did not convince the members of the Geological Survey 'who hold me responsible for my interpretation'. He was invited to collaborate with them and returned in 1934.

He gives a very detailed description of many bones which show the working of human agency, and several plates of photographs as illustrations. These photographs are given at the end of his paper, and the title page introducing them has a most surprising note added by W. C. Pei, which says:

> The specimens described herein by Professor H. Breuil have been placed at the disposal of the Museum of Geological Survey of China in Nanking for exhibition purposes, but owing to the hostilities in 1937 have become lost. It is indeed most unfortunate that these valuable objects, once so carefully studied by such a leading authority in pre-history as Professor Breuil, should no longer be available to science. I regret in particular not to be able to comply with Professor Breuil's request of supplementing various details such as the layers of origin of each specimen within the Sinanthropus site. W.C.P.

It is indeed a strange coincidence that these bones, which Breuil showed had clear evidence of human working, should suffer the same fate as later the whole fossil collection did at the time of Pearl Harbour. One would expect the loss of this valuable evidence to have been recorded by at least one or two publications, *yet this note of Pei's is the only mention I have ever seen recording their disappearance*. Furthermore, in all my reading of Teilhard's correspondence of this period, I have not seen any reference to this loss.

One further point is Pei's 'inability' to provide Breuil with details of where each fossil had been found. The excavation was supposed to have been carried out with great care, the whole site being divided into squares, vertically and horizontally, so that the position of each fossil could be accurately logged. Even if the fossils were no longer available, Pei, who was in charge of the excavations, should have been able to provide Breuil with the location of each of them from his records.

Pei's reply

In the bound volume of *The Geological Survey of China*, the paper immediately following Breuil's was by Pei entitled 'Le rôle des animaux et des causes naturelles dans la cassure des os' (The role of animals and natural causes in the breakage of bones) [March 1938. New series D7. Whole series 118]. In this, Pei makes an attempt to explain that the work on the bones was not of human agency, but he is far from convincing. On the last page of the illustrations, he shows a number of bones with small holes at one end, which he claims were due to gnawing rodents and natural causes! Nevertheless, it is Pei's views, rather than Breuil's, which are generally accepted. [26p275]

Publication dates

There are two notable points about this particular paper of Pei's. The first is that it was entirely in *French*, which is unusual for papers in this publication, whilst Breuil's paper had been translated into *English*. The second is that although it *followed* Breuil's article published in 1939, and was given the next serial number, *Pei's was published in 1938*!

As Breuil visited Pekin in 1934, why was his paper delayed for four years and translated into English, whilst Pei's was published a year earlier, presumably for circulation in France? This strongly suggests that Breuil's evidence of advanced workmanship on the bones discovered was very unwelcome to the experts in China, and his paper was deliberately delayed, whilst Pei's report was prepared for early circulation in France. This suggestion is supported by the mysterious and little publicized 'loss' of these fossils, making it impossible for Breuil's contention to be verified.

At this point, before dealing in the final section with the disappearance of the original Sinanthropus fossils, we will discuss Weidenreich's major work *The skull of Sinanthropus pekinensis* [100] and Teilhard's article *The question of Fossil Man* [101], both published in 1943.

Weidenreich's Sinanthropus skull report

Weidenreich's article was a massive tome of 506 pages, published in Pekin, but printed in America. Much of it is taken up with a very detailed technical description of the various characteristics displayed by the skulls examined, e.g.

> The squama has the form of a right angled triangle, the parietal margin representing the longer cathetus and the sphenoid margin the shorter one. This form is very characteristic of the anthropoids.

and

> The fascies temporalis passes gradually over to the fascies infratempor-
> alis so that both surfaces present a continuous curve without the sharp
> bend or strongly developed infratemporal crest which usually charact-
> erizes modern man.

In his description he notes that 'the extraordinary size of the pyra-
mid . . . and its lowness or flatness . . . is undoubtedly a simian [ape-
like] character' and that '. . . in all cases, the central portion of the
base is missing'. He deals with the first skull which Black reconstructed from fragments found in 1928, correcting Black's inaccurate
report, by saying:

> All these bones fit one another, as mentioned by Black, but he is not
> quite correct in his statement: 'No other restoration having been made
> in the skull. . . .' As Black's photographs (Figs.5–10) made from the
> original show, the exterior surface of the inferior half of the left
> parietal bone was so badly damaged that the defective region had to be
> filled with plaster in order to make the restoration at all possible.

Dealing with the 1929 skull, he simply says:

> Skull III is identical with Skull of Locus E found in 1929 by W. C. Pei.
> Davidson Black (1931) has already supplied such exhaustive descrip-
> tions of the condition and characteristics of this skull that it will suffice
> merely to refer here to that author's publication.

Thus he makes no comment on whether Black's reconstruction was
accurate or not.

Turning to the photos of Weidenreich's reconstructions of the
skulls, one is immediately struck by the large gaps between the fragments which are infilled with plaster to complete the shape. Weidenreich admits that in many cases the pieces which made up some skulls
were located some distance apart, and he had to decide whether or not
they should be allocated to a particular skull. He acknowledges that
there are visible gaps between the pieces but says they are not as large
as they appear, as some bones are touching on their inside edges,
much of the damage being on the outside. Skull bones however
usually break directly across their thickness, not as a fine angle, whilst
on Plate XV a photo of the underside of skull X shows that there is
as much plasterwork visible on the inside as on the outside of the
skull. He admits that Boule had said that these gaps might influence
the size and form of the skull 'to such an extent as to make an exact
estimation of their capacity impossible'. Weidenreich continues:

> The gaps are restricted to rather limited areas of the cranial surface.
> Moreover, in the drawing of the skulls, all major fractures and gaps are
> distinctly marked to enable the reader to form his own opinion as to the
> reliability of the reconstruction.

The skull illustrated in Fig.22 (skull XI) is the most complete of the brain cases, and was used by Weidenreich as the basis for his reconstruction of the whole skull (Fig.23), to which human features were later added. Other skulls have a larger proportion of plaster visible, and one can see the difficulty of obtaining an accurate reconstruction of the capacity from such a collection of pieces, particularly in view of the comments on this subject on p.49.

The reconstruction of 'Nellie' ·

The modelling of human features on Weidenreich's reconstruction is dealt with in considerable detail, taking several pages. Dubois's method of reconstructing the whole body of Java man from a thigh bone and a skull cap is dismissed, and McGregor's method of determining the thickness of the soft flesh parts was used, which was 'the average of well-nourished but not fat individuals'. Pins were stuck into the reconstructed skull, and cut off at the required thickness of flesh, the whole then being modelled with a woman's features (whom they called 'Nellie') by Mrs. Lucille Swann, a sculptress who was resident in Pekin at the time. Weidenreich comments on various features of the finished model, noting 'the most striking peculiarity . . . is the thickness of the neck', which was unfortunately concealed by the hair on the model! (Fig.24)

Such an elaborate procedure gave an aura of science to what was little more than a fantasy, for it was based upon the following:

(a) Skull XI, which was not complete, and consisted of a number of broken fragments.

(b) Missing dimensions were obtained from skull XII and skull II (Black's locus D skull, made up from pieces found in the laboratory).

(c) Facial bones which were mixed up with the facial bones of skull X, which was only 500 mm. (1 ft. 8 in.) away.

(d) A lower jaw, which had one tooth, found at a level over 25 m. (80 ft.) higher in the deposit than the skull! (Jaw H1 in Weidenreich's report on the Dentition of Sinanthropus [95].) Weidenreich notes:

> As was already pointed out above, I have no intention of exaggerating the primitive features of the physiognomy. I was therefore especially careful not to commit the error usually made by lay artists when reconstructing the portrait of primitive man, namely, to apply savage appearance and dishevelled headress as a sign of primitiveness. Genuine primitive traits should be sufficiently indicated without any emotional distortions of mimical muscles or disordered hair.

Such scientific objectivity in criticizing those who add ape-like features to human skulls is indeed commendable, but could he not be

Fig.22. Skull XI

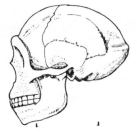

Fig.23. 'Nellie's' skull

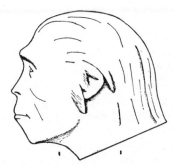

Fig.24. 'Nellie'

convicted of the opposite and equally erroneous practice of adding human features to an ape's skull?

Teilhard's article
Teilhard's article *Fossil Men* was published in Pekin in 1943. He gives the average brain capacity of Sinanthropus as 1030–1225 cc. and claims that although he has some ape-like characteristics, he is nevertheless 'as far as his mental powers are concerned' *Homo sapiens*. '*If* (italics his) we accept that Pekin man himself (and not some other, unknown inhabitant of the cave) is the author of these *traces* (italics mine) of fire and this stone industry, the conclusion is obvious.'

The consistent playing down of the great heaps of ash as 'traces' of fire, by all the responsible scientists connected with the Cenozoic Laboratory, can only raise doubts regarding the reliability of their reports, not only on this subject, but on other topics also, especially where independent accounts such as Breuil's are not available.

Teilhard again states that the site

... is nothing but a very ancient cave which has collapsed and in which a varied population of carnivores and man himself lived and died, one after another, very long ago, gradually leaving, on the floor, one after another also, their own bones mixed with those of their prey. At Choukoutien palaeontologists had been lucky enough to find by acci-

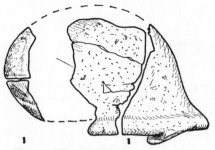

Fig.25. The 1966 Sinanthropus skull

dent a very old human habitation, that is to say, to find prehistoric man 'at home'. Under these circumstances it is not surprising that the harvest has been so rich.

His deliberate omission of the fact that only the brain case and jaws of this hominid were found, and virtually no skeletal bones, is obvious. This article was among the last to be written by a member of the laboratory and the only skeletal bones found were a semilunar bone [a small wrist-bone], a large fragment of clavicle [collar bone], two pieces of humerus [upper arm bone] and seven femoral diaphysis [parts of the *shafts only* of the upper leg bone]. Despite this, Teilhard confidently states that Sinanthropus was of upright stature and 'two handed'!

Post-war discoveries
Teilhard's article is included in the symposium of his writings, entitled *The Appearance of Man* [31p93]. The editor of this work adds an interesting footnote, in which he summarizes some points appearing in an article written by Pei, now working for the Communists, in *China Reconstructs*, 1954, in which he brings the excavation at Choukoutien up to date. He reports that in 1951 two bone fragments were found, one of a tibia (with anthropoid characteristics) and the other of a humerus (with human characteristics), and were identified as belonging to Pekin man.

One skull of Pekin man, found in 1966, was put on show at an exhibition of Chinese archaeological discoveries, held at the Royal Academy in 1973–4 (Fig.25). The height was quoted as 11·9 cm. and, as can be seen from the illustration, there is an extremely large gap between the front and rear pieces of the skull.

The Pekin man's Cave picture
I have tried to show that there was obviously a very large scale industry being carried on at Choukoutien, in view of the layers of chipped quartz and the great heaps of ash, and that the skulls of

Fig.26. The Pekin man cave picture

Sinanthropus are those of monkeys killed for their brains. On display in the British Natural History Museum is a picture (also appearing in their publication *Evolution*), which gives quite the opposite impression. I have copied this in Fig.26 and would particularly point out:

(a) The size of the cave.

(b) The extent of stone chipping being carried out.

(c) The volume of the fire.

(d) The human features of the inhabitants.

On all these points I would suggest that the picture is grossly inaccurate.

The disappearance of the fossils

We are now coming to the confused period of the approaching war years. Work at the site appears to have ceased in 1937, which Weidenreich said was due to the Japanese forces [100], when he wrote in 1943 in America. The Japanese were, however, very interested in the whole subject of Pekin man and would probably have allowed excavations to continue, but for the Communist forces in the area which turned it into a no-man's-land. The Japanese allowed all those who remained in Pekin a considerable amount of freedom. Teilhard reorganized the Geological Museum, visited Shanghai, lectured students, and published papers, whilst Speaight mentions that 'the first intelligence officers of the American forces to arrive in Pekin found him escaping from the social round and bicycling over the hills to talk with Communist guerrillas. He found their conversation much more interesting!' [p266]

In examining the available source material, it has been necessary to disentangle fact from a web of rumour and conflicting accounts. I have therefore thought it best to use only reasonably substantiated versions of the story. My own conclusions force me to raise a number of pertinent questions.

The facts regarding Dr. Foley's involvement were contained in an article in the *Observer* (19th November 1972), whilst Shapiro's book *Pekin Man* [28] gave some additional details.

Colonel Ashurst's account

During 1941, after Weidenreich had returned to America, it was decided that the fossils should be sent there for safety. Colonel Ashurst was the Commander of the American Marines in Pekin. He had been ordered to bring the detachment back to the United States, and was to meet the liner, the *President Harrison* at Chinwangtao, 180 miles away. The fossils had been removed to the U.S. Embassy for safety, but it was decided that they should be packed in some of the Marines' boxes known as 'footlockers', and, with the Colonel's name on them, travel as his personal luggage to America. Up to 1972, the usual story given, based apparently upon an account provided by Colonel Ashurst, is that the footlockers were all placed aboard a train bound for Chinwangtao during the first few days of December 1941, but the train was captured by the Japanese on 7th December, the day of Pearl Harbour, and all trace of the boxes was lost.

Ashurst, who died shortly after the war, gave to a newspaperman what appears to be his only account, in which he said:

> Perhaps they found the remains and just threw them away like canned foods. The Japanese had no use for our foods they captured so they just dumped them off the train. The Pekin relics must not have looked like much. I hardly realized what they were. Maybe the Japanese just kept what was useful to them at the time and threw everything else away.

The Japanese, however, were very anxious to obtain the fossils and subjected the staff of the Medical College to several days of interrogation, apparently to no avail.

The post-war search

After the war, the Americans searched hard for the fossils, and Dr. Frank Whitmore, a geologist in the U.S. Army, said he had found a collection of bones and artefacts from the Choukoutien site together with some documents. These, however, were said to be only what was left in the safe at Pekin. Apparently the Japanese had made complete lists of all items looted in the war, and every archaeological item was said to be accounted for.

This was the generally accepted account, up to 1951. On the 22nd of March of that year the *New York Times* published an accusation by Pei. He claimed that the Americans had found the lockers containing the fossils in Tokyo University after the war, and that they had then been sent to America and were now in the American Museum of Natural History. As Chairman of the Department of Anthropology, Shapiro issued a denial of the rumours which alleged they were in his possession. During the rumpus, a Japanese fireman said that 'he had seen Japanese soldiers taking boxes containing the Pekin man skull and other bones from the American Marine barracks in Pekin in 1942'. This was puzzling, as no mention had ever been made of any of the lockers being in Pekin at this date. After this, the dark clouds of mystery surrounding the disappearance of the vital fossils of Sinanthropus redescended, until another gleam of light broke through twenty years later.

Dr. Foley's account

In 1971, Dr. Shapiro, of the American Museum of Natural History of New York, was contacted by a Mr. Davis, an assistant to a Dr. Foley. He asked for information regarding the disappearance of the Pekin fossils, as Dr. Foley, who was writing his memoirs, had been asked to help in the transfer of these fossils to America in 1941. Shapiro immediately contacted both Davis and Foley, who gave the following account.

When Ashurst was charged with the safe transport of the fossils, he contacted his Medical Officer, Dr. Foley, who was at Tientsin. Foley was going first with the detachment to Manila, but then on to America, as he was at the end of his tour of duty. For this reason Ashurst asked him to take the fossils with him. There are conflicting reports of the precise number of boxes, but there were at least two and almost certainly more. Ashurst put some of them, marked with Foley's name, on the train to Chinwangtao for his custody on their passage to America.

Foley, who was in Tientsin, told his assistant, Davis, at Chinwangtao, to expect the lockers and keep them safe. When they arrived, Davis stored them in his room, but lost contact with the precious boxes when the Marines surrendered to the Japanese after Pearl Harbour. Surprisingly, these boxes were later delivered to Foley in Tientsin, unopened. As he was allowed a brief period of relative freedom, he distributed the boxes, still unopened, to various places such as the Swiss Warehouse, the Pasteur Institute and two Chinese friends.

Foley then claimed that while in a prisoner-of-war camp he met Ashurst, who still had one of the boxes containing what Ashurst believed to be the most important fossils. It is possible that Ashurst may have kept some of the boxes with him at Pekin. Alternatively, he may have sent some boxes, bearing his own name, as well as those with Foley's name, on the train to Chinwangtao. Foley considered that the Japanese returned to him the boxes with his name on them, due to their respect for rank. It is therefore possible that Ashurst similarly had those bearing *his* name returned to him in Pekin.

Foley and Ashurst managed to prevent the Japanese from investigating the box, through the many changes of camp, but Foley finally lost track of it when he was separated from Ashurst.

Dr. Whitmore's recovery of items

After the war, as we have already mentioned, Dr. Frank Whitmore obtained a few unimportant relics from Tokyo University, but Shapiro [p24] adds some further details. In November 1945, Whitmore wrote to Dr. Edinger at Harvard University, saying he had recovered from Tokyo University a collection of bones and artefacts, together with Davidson Black's original records, plans of the site and financial records, all of which he would be returning to Pekin Union Medical College.

Only two weeks later, Whitmore wrote an account of a meeting he had with Professor Suzuki of Tokyo University. He had made three attempts to ascertain the location of the collection. At first Professor Suzuki replied that he knew nothing about them. In answer to Whitmore's further probing he admitted that he had heard of them but did not know their location. Finally, after Whitmore's third attempt, he departed, returning five minutes later with 'the collection', which consisted of some chipped stones, blackened antlers and other artefacts. Shapiro considers that these were only items that had been left in the laboratory after the important fossils had been packed in the boxes.

The narrative above contains all the major facts bearing upon the disappearance of the fossils which I have been able to glean. There are clearly many gaps and unanswered problems. The major queries that I have, however, are not regarding what actually took place, but the surprising failure of the various authorities, who investigated the disappearance, to establish the correct sequence of events, when these facts were quite easily obtainable after the war. There appears to have been considerable inefficiency in the pursuit of the investigations, leaving several important questions without satisfactory answers.

The investigations queried

1. TEILHARD'S SILENCE

In all the various articles dealing with the disappearance of the fossils, the account of events by one person, who worked in the laboratory regularly and was in Pekin for the whole period, is noticeable by its absence. I refer of course to Teilhard. As we have seen, he had considerable freedom even under Japanese occupation and worked regularly with Pei at the laboratory on the palaeontological collection, until its closure. [30p34]

Throughout all the investigations regarding the whereabouts of the fossils, Teilhard, who had considerable responsibility for the laboratory and its collection, and lived in Pekin throughout the war, never appears to have given his account of the events. Surely he would have been told by the Americans that the main fossils had been removed from the safe and sent to Chinwangtao? In a letter written on 13th December 1940, he added a note saying that he had visited the Choukoutien site with the Japanese Captain Takata and a strong protective screen of soldiers [30p274]. The protection by the Japanese was against the 'red regulars' in the plain [30p241] who had made the site into a 'no-man's-land'. This little expedition shows that Teilhard was on good terms with the Japanese forces at that time. He should have had little difficulty in ascertaining from them the sequence of events and the location of the precious fossils. In a paper written in September 1943 [31p93], dealing with Pekin man and other fossils, he makes no mention of the disappearance of the former, whilst in the same year, he wrote to a Chinese friend wondering if they had been mislaid, and was relieved that casts had been taken for the scientific world. [29p252]

Why was Teilhard not questioned about the fate of the fossils? Even when he lived in America, he never appears to have mentioned the circumstances of their disappearance.

2. ASHURST'S RETICENCE

Colonel Ashurst's account is particularly ambiguous. The importance of the fossils must have been clearly impressed upon him by the U.S. Embassy, and Foley relates how he kept the most important box whilst a prisoner-of-war.

The Japanese fireman's account of seeing some of the fossils being taken away in boxes in 1942 from the marine barracks in Pekin, substantiates the fact that Ashurst either did not send *all* the boxes on the train to Chinwangtao with Foley's name on them, but kept some back, or else, those that had Ashurst's name on them were later returned to him at Pekin.

In his interview with the journalist, Ashurst makes no mention of this, saying that they all went on the train and were probably thrown away by the Japanese. Ashurst's version of events is clearly contradicted by Dr. Foley's account.

Why did Ashurst never submit a report of the events, and even more surprising, why was he never questioned after his release?

3. THE MARINES

At Camp Holcombe at Chinwangtao, Davis was in charge of seventeen marines in the medical unit under Dr. Foley. No attempt seems to have been made to establish what took place at the time of Pearl

Harbour. Indeed, it was only Davis's unexpected telephone call to the American Natural History Museum which publicized the events at Chinwangtao and Dr. Foley's account of the box held by Ashurst.

Questioning of all these marines would have been possible at any time after the war, for Shapiro mentions that the survivors from Camp Holcombe still meet even today at an annual reunion.

Shapiro gives a dramatic account of a mysterious woman, who claimed that her recently deceased husband, had come back from China with a box of the Pekin fossils, which he called his 'war booty'. Shapiro received a photo, which came from the woman, of several bones in a box, but he said that some of the bones of the skeleton of Pekin man in the picture had never been found at Choukoutien. Although they may not have belonged to Pekin man, could they not have been parts of the skeletons of the Upper Cave men, which were virtually complete at the time of their discovery, but which were lost with the rest of the fossils? At a later conference, one of the experts considered that the skull visible in the photo was No.XI in Weidenreich's nomenclature. This was the one on which 'Nellie's' face was modelled.

Shapiro suspected that the deceased husband was an ex-marine, and on questioning Davis, he obtained the address of one of the marines who had died recently. Shapiro then handed the information over to the State Department for further investigation. It took several months for a report to reach him which merely stated that the F.B.I. had interrogated the widow of the marine, but no link with the mysterious woman or the Pekin fossils was said to be found.

4. THE SEARCH OF TOKYO UNIVERSITY

There appear to be some strange aspects of Dr. Frank Whitmore's search of Tokyo University for the fossils, which Shapiro relates on pp. 24 and 25.

In Whitmore's first letter, he says he *had recovered*:

(a) Bones and artefacts from the Choukoutien site.
(b) Davidson Black's original research records.
(c) Original site plans.
(d) Financial records for 1927–38.

It seems clear that with a collection of material as important as this, at least one of the many boxes had fallen into Japanese hands and been transferred to Tokyo University. It would also appear that Whitmore had actually possessed them, for he said his major concern was how he could return them to Pekin. If this is correct, it must surely be asked what happened to these items? Were they returned to Pekin or are they now in America?

Whitmore's second letter, written two weeks later, describes an interview he had with Professor Suzuki. It is not clear if Whitmore is recording a meeting prior to his discovery of the items he gives in his first letter, or a second visit he paid to the University, but the impression is that it is the latter.

Whitmore says, 'I went out to Tokyo University where the collection was, and saw Professor Suzuki about it. He said he didn't know anything about it.' As we have said, it was only on a third repetition of the enquiry that the professor reluctantly produced the stones and antlers. What appears strange about the account of this interview is Whitmore's attitude. He was a member of the American forces and was specifically searching for these fossils, and he begins the meeting by enquiring of their whereabouts. Suzuki's replies, however, would have aroused anyone's suspicions, and he leaves Whitmore in the room whilst he goes to collect some of the items from another room. One would have expected Whitmore to have the authority to insist on going with him and having all storage cupboards and boxes, which might have housed the fossils, opened for his personal inspection. Did he insist on ensuring that there was nothing else in the Japanese collection? His approach was hardly that of a representative of a powerful nation intent on discovering precious relics in the vaults of a subjugated country.

Were the fossils discovered?

From all the available evidence, it is most likely that one or more of the boxes fell into Japanese hands. This is indicated by the following:

(a) With possibly five or even more of the boxes scattered in a very wide range of situations around Pekin, it is difficult to believe that every single one of them escaped discovery by the assiduous Japanese.

(b) The Japanese fireman claimed that some had been found in Pekin.

(c) From Whitmore's first letter, clearly a number of important items *were* found at Tokyo University.

(d) Pei relates that in May 1943 word came through that the boxes containing the fossils *had* been found at Tientsin, but this was later denied. [28p22]

(e) Although it cannot be cited as a supporting fact, the failure of the investigating authorities to interrogate the Marines who had been at Chinwangtao, could indicate that the fossils had already been located in Tokyo, and that no further investigations were necessary.

(f) In 1942 Teilhard declined the offer of a 'directorship of a Franco-Japanese scientific centre in Tokyo, where he was promised he could have all the newest technological instruments he needed for his work.' Was this an invitation to continue working on the fossils which were now in Tokyo?

Pei said that the fossils were shipped back to America, and there is some confirmation of this, for a sailor stated that the fossils were put on board his American ship after the war, but that they subsequently disappeared.

What possible reason could there be for secrecy surrounding these fossils? As had been seen from the consideration of the various bones and artefacts found at Choukoutien, the most likely explanation of the situation is that the skulls were only those of monkeys, brought to the site by modern men. If the original fossils and their reconstructions were ever located, put on public display, and submitted to further close examination, the nearness of their relationship to that of the apes, and any errors in the reconstruction would perhaps be very apparent. This could be a source of embarrassment to many eminent authorities. A hint that the original fossils were not particularly impressive is provided by Weidenreich's colleague, Dr. von Koenigswald who said:

We must be grateful to Weidenreich for leaving such excellent descriptions of all the material. Indeed, I believe that many people who have admired the splendid drawings and photographs in his books would be disappointed if they saw the originals. [18p55]

APPENDIX III

BLACK'S LOCUS E SKULL REPORTS

In this appendix, we will be comparing the three reports (Preliminary [72], Interim [77] and Final [80]) which Black produced on this skull. We will deal first with his problems of reconstruction and then compare the full-size photos of the skull from three views in each of the reports (Fig.27). These unfortunately do not show fine detail mainly due to the difficulty of reproducing Black's original pictures which were not high quality.

PRELIMINARY REPORT. 1929

> . . . a heavy fragment in which the glabellar part of the specimen was imbedded broke away from the main block. All details of the sutures and other surface markings are well preserved on the original though they are somewhat obscure in the photographs by reason of the shellac with which the specimen was coated. [p208]

This is unfortunate, as the sutures play a major part in the reconstruction in the final report.

INTERIM REPORT. 1930

Several photos of the base are given, showing the stages of removal of the travertine mass. In the final report he notes that in the making of the interim report, the frontal area had been repaired. Furthermore, *this portion, together with a considerable part of the parietal vault (the top part of the skull) were replaced in approximately normal relation* to permit the photos to be made.

FINAL REPORT. 1931

> Before making the cast, the frontal fragment as then prepared, was replaced upon the specimen, but to orient it in its approximately normal relations, the fragment had to be separated by an appreciable interval over the whole of its coronal arc from the travertine core. The artificial space thus formed is represented in black on the cast in contrast to the in situ reddish peripheral zone of matrix. [p(ii)3]

This procedure may well have been necessary, but what were the guiding principles he used to obtain 'normal relations' between the pieces? Was it the line of curvature he considered it should follow, or the shape taken when the broken edges butted together? He gives no indication of the method he used to ensure that his restoration was accurate.

During the removal of the hard interior material, he found a hard scale on the inside of the vault.

> When removal of this hard adherent peripheral scale was begun it became fully apparent that all the cranial sutures, in greater or lesser degree were open, each being filled with similar calcareous scale which in turn had to be removed before the natural articulations of the elements could fully be restored.

This would appear to be somewhat unusual. The sutures are the intricate line of interlock between the bones of the skull, which are said to have been cemented together by the calcareous material. It seems an unnecessary procedure first to carefully remove the hard natural cement between the bones, merely to replace them in the same position later. No description of how this was carried out is given, and one can only presume that if they were separated along the line of the sutures, it was with something similar to a fretsaw blade.

From all this, and the other quotations given above, it is clear that the skull was reduced to a number of separate pieces, and considerable care would have to be exercised to ensure that the final shape of the restored skull was close to the original as found. A comparison between them is given below. Black devotes a complete page to his method of photographing the skull, and the difficulties which this involved, with a caution on the problems of scale and perspective dimensions. This is written, he notes,

> ... since the widely divergent opinions concerning the generic status of Sinanthropus which have recently been offered and given circulation in the press, are evidently based solely upon information derived from the imperfect photographs of the skull published in the earlier reports.

He was clearly concerned at the comments made on the skull from his earlier report!

At this point we would mention that at no time was a photograph published of a scale laid alongside the skull to indicate its size. Photos are given as half or full size, and a small scale of centimetres added to the printed page subsequently. In using this scale therefore, heavy reliance is placed upon the accuracy with which the photographs, enlargements and prints were made, to which we will refer later.

In a critical review of this report in *L'Anthropologie* 1931 [82] R. Vaufrey comments that whilst there are many photos and diagrams, the photos are always unclear and difficult to use for detail work, those of the tympanal region being particularly inadequate! He also disagreed with Black's verdict that Sinanthropus was of a different type to Java man, and was at the root of the human race in a class of its own.

Brain capacity

On p.94 of *Fossil Man in China*, published 1933 [88], the volume of the skull, after repeated measurements was given as 964·4 ± ·027 cc. Presuming this is not a misprint, then it is a remarkably small variation from the average, representing an accuracy of 0·00279 per cent (or 1 in 35,800). Such accuracy would indicate that the volume was measured by a very specialized method using a high level of skill. However, when the skull capacity was remeasured by Dr. Weidenreich, he gave it as 915 cc., a difference of 5 per cent to Black's volume.

Weidenreich criticized Black's method of measuring the volume:

> To determine the cranial capacity Black filled the skull cavity with negocoll, then melted this cast and measured the melted mass in a small graduated glass tube. With Dubois I consider it very probable that these manipulations altered the volume of the negocoll which always contains a variable quantity of water. [94p11]

Weidenreich measured the volume by displacement of water by endocasts, which had been made from the skull, but these were not all equal. One endocast did fit the dimensions of the cranium and this had been made by Black himself.

> This cast shows a volume of not more than 915 ccs. This is just about the figure which Davidson Black found first (914 cc.) but rejected afterwards as he considered the water method not exact enough; and it is only 3 ccs. less than Dubois computed (918 cc.).

Black, therefore, abandoned the water displacement method and used negocoll, which was less accurate and gave a larger volume.

The reports compared

We will now compare the photographs of the skull from three different views, at the three different report stages. Photographs and overlays of the outlines are given in Fig.27.

1. PHOTOS
   (a) Top view: Preliminary: left-hand supra-orbital ridge appears to be missing. This has been restored in later reports. Damaged area to top of skull later not visible. Cracks in skull do not agree with cracks visible in intermediate report photo. Sutures clearly visible in intermediate and final report. Whole of front area appears to have been restored with a smooth, glossy material in the final report.
   (b) Front view. Preliminary report: white area of field dressings or travertine covers the area near the left supra-orbital ridge. Glossy surface of frontal section is clearly seen in the final report.

(c) Right-hand side view. Damaged area at top of skull in preliminary report seems to have been 'repaired' in later reports.

2. OVERLAYS

It is in the comparison of overlays of the three views of the skull that
a number of unexplained discrepancies become apparent.

(a) Top view. The outline of the skull in the preliminary report,
although shown here, cannot be compared with the other two
reports as the lower half was still covered by the field dressings
or travertine. However, a close inspection of this photo indicates that for some reason it may not have been taken from a
point directly above the vertical axis of the brain case. This is
not immediately obvious, as the sagittal sutures, which at the
rear are on the centre line of the skull, are not clear in the photo,
as Black mentioned.

However, by comparing the relative positions of a cracked
piece of the skull, which can also be identified in the interim
report (see Fig.27), the overlay reveals that it is displaced about
1 cm ($\frac{3}{8}$ in.) to the left in the preliminary report. Similarly, a
faint line which looks like the sutures, which should also be on
the vertical axis, has also been displaced by roughly the same
amount. Projecting these displacements on the front elevations
indicates that the plan view in the preliminary report was taken
about 10° to the right away from the true vertical position. No
explanation of this error is given in Black's text, and one can
only assume that less care was taken in the orientation of the
skull than one has a right to expect in a scientific treatise.

The discrepancy between the outline of the skull in the intermediate and final reports is very noticeable. A number of the
larger cracks in the skull have been traced, and there is a very
wide divergence in their relative positions.

(b) Front view. The difference in the outlines of the skull can be
seen. From the position of the supra-orbital ridge and the
triangular break at the forehead, again it is clear that for some
unexplained reason the photos were taken at slightly different
angles.

(c) Side view. Except for the supra-orbital ridges, the outlines of
the top of the skull are in good agreement. Tracings of the
major visible cracks, however, show that they have little in
common between the three reports.

Regarding the lower part of the skull, it can be seen that the outline
of the final report actually appears *below* the plaster encasement shown
in the photo of the preliminary report. (This plaster casing, known as
field dressing, was to protect the skull during transport.) This anomaly can only be explained in one of two ways:

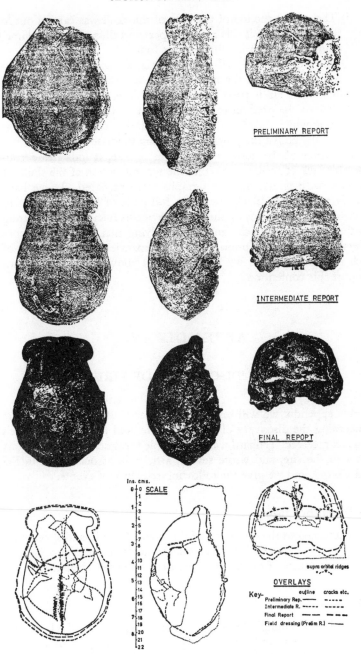

Fig.27. Black's Locus E skull illustrations

(i) The reconstruction of the base of the skull was carried out in such a way that it was made deeper (and thus a larger volume) than the position in which it was found.

(ii) All the photos, in all three reports, show the skull with no background, as if the photos had been trimmed before reproduction. This is particularly noticeable in the right-hand side view of the preliminary report, and it is possible that the line along which the photo was cut, which is not a straight line, was actually above the portion containing the base of the skull.

Whichever of the above explanations is true, it indicates a considerable lack of accuracy in either the reconstruction of the skull, or the care with which the photographs were prepared. As we have already mentioned, Black devoted a full page of his final report to discussing the problems of photography versus tracings, commenting on the differences which can arise, implying that he has used considerable care in their preparation. Discrepancies of the size and of such a basic nature as we have indicated above, however, do not support this contention.

APPENDIX IV

THE 'DISCOVERY' OF FIRE

In this appendix we will review the sequence of events and papers concerning the discovery of fire at the site, and the publicity which this fact received. Teilhard was responsible for describing the various strata of the site, and wrote several articles in association with Pei and Young, and we give the following sequence of events.

(a) December 1929

Black announced the discovery of the Locus E skull, and specifically mentions: '. . . no artefacts of any nature have yet been encountered nor has any trace of the usage of fire been observed.' [72p208]

(b) January 1930

Teilhard and Young's preliminary report on the site [75] was received at this date and covers the 1929 dig. In a diagram of a section of the site, the deep layer 4 is covered by the note: '1-10, various levels of deposits.' In the article, the reference to this layer says it was a

... very conspicuous fine grained, sedimentary zone, formed by red loam and sandy clay of various colours (yellow, reddish, brown, gray, etc.) thickly bedded and interbedded. At several levels some black layers occur which are full of rodent remains. . . . Thickness: 6.7 m.

In a footnote it mentions that in this sandy clay more than one hundred individual layers had been counted.

(c) April 1930

Teilhard wrote a paper in Pekin, which was published in *Revue des Questions Scientifiques* (Paris) in July 1930 [76]. We have already mentioned this paper on p97.. In it he says:

More curious still under these circumstances will appear another fact, that since the beginning of the excavation no trace has yet been found on the site suggesting the use of fire or any industry of any kind. Chou-koutien, it must be said, furnishes no siliceous rock capable of receiving and clearly preserving the traces of human working. Perhaps there are tools which we do not yet recognise. Perhaps, also, Sinan-thropus used wooden tools!

This paper is translated in a collection of his writings entitled *The Appearance of Man*.

(d) October 1930

Elliot Smith visited Choukoutien and, as we have seen, in his article in *Antiquity* [78] he gives a similar section of the site, but there is still no mention of fire or industry. Indeed he said:

It is a very significant phenomenon that at Chou Kou Tien, in spite of the most careful search in the caves during the last three years, no trace whatever of implements of any sort has been found. When it is considered how vast a quantity of fossil remains has been found and the scrupulous care which has been exercised in the search, it must be something more than a mere coincidence that no trace of any stone implements has been found. Not only have the various excavators been on the constant look out for such artefacts (in particular Father Teilhard has been looking for archaeological evidence), but after the materials was removed from the caves, a group of boys was put on to sift the material once more to make quite certain that no such evidence has been overlooked by the geological explorers. It must not be forgotten, however, that Dr. Andersson in 1921 found pieces of quartz in association with the fossil bones, and that in the later stages of the excavation Mr. Pei found further examples of this alien material. Those who have been searching in vain for evidence of human craftsmanship on this site are being forced to the conclusion that the Peking Man was in such an early phase of development as not yet to have begun to shape implements of stone for the ordinary needs of his daily life.

(e) October 1930

The very same month in which Elliot Smith visited the site, Teilhard entered Breuil's laboratory in Paris and placed on his desk a small stag's horn [85p1]. Without telling him where it came from, he asked for his comments. Breuil noticed:

(i) It had been *burnt by a strong fire when the bone was fresh.*

(ii) It had been hammered to make it into a shape easy for grasping.

(iii) It bore the marks of incisions *which were probably made with a stone tool.*

Teilhard then told him the horn came from the Choukoutien site and he completely agreed with his findings. He asked Breuil to visit the site as soon as possible, and when Teilhard returned to China, an invitation was duly received and accepted.

It is important to note that this burnt stag's horn, which Teilhard placed before Breuil, was the very first evidence to anyone outside China of the existence of fire at Choukoutien.

(f) Teilhard's paper

Teilhard gave a paper to the Institute of Human Palaeontology in Paris, which was published in *L'Anthropologie* in 1931 [81]. This was probably delivered during late 1930 at the same time as he visited Breuil's laboratory. This was very similar to his July 1930 paper, which we have mentioned in (c) above, many paragraphs being identical. The following two points, however, should be noted:

(i) He repeats the passage quoted in (c) above (in French) exactly, but the word 'fire' is omitted, and he begins cautiously to admit that there is evidence of it in the excavations, for he now continues:

> Finally, will the bones and antlers, which had been severely blackened (by a charcoal substance) and recovered here and there from the fossiliferous breccia, perhaps allow us to prove that fire had been used?

(ii) In his paper he gives an East-West section of the main site, similar to that shown in Fig.20, which is given as the situation 'at the end of 1929'. In the caption, the thick bed of ashes, layer 4, is again described as '1-7, main beds discovered. . . .'

In his report he refers to this layer as follows:

> A more noticeable separating surface is seen towards the middle of the deposit, at 20m depth, formed by a bed of stalagmites, above which the sediments, which up to then had been breccia-like and clayey, become sandy and finely bedded (sand carried by the wind?).

Breuil's description of this layer, as we know, was a great heap of *ash* interspersed with layers of clay. He also gave a description of the layer of charcoal and a further layer of decomposed volcanic stones beneath it.

Teilhard's tentative admission that fire might have been used, and his failure to describe the main layer of ashes, suggests that the great depth of ashes *had* been recognized, but he was unwilling to give wide publicity to the size of the furnaces which must have been used at the time.

(g) March 1931

Work restarted at the site, and Teilhard wrote to Breuil saying that as the excavations proceeded, several ashy layers, blackened and bluish bones, and an abundance of quartz fragments had been revealed.

(h) October 1931

Breuil visited the site and described for the first time the extent of the remains of the fire and industry. He published his results in his paper in Pekin on 3rd November 1931 [84], and in his article in *L'Anthropologie* 1932 [85], both of which we have discussed in detail above.

(i) 3rd November 1931. Black's announcement

At the same meeting of the Geological Society of China in Pekin, at which Breuil described what he had seen at the site, Black gave a very short paper entitled *Evidences of the use of fire by Sinanthropus* [83]. We give the opening section of this article:

From time to time *since 1929* occasional specimens of apparently charred or partly calcined animal bones have been recovered among the material excavated from the Main Deposit at Choukoutien. The physical appearance of these specimens left little room for doubt that they had been subjected at some time to the action of fire. But until the present season it has remained a question whether or not such specimens had been burned within the Choukoutien caves while the latter were occupied by Sinanthropus or were altered simply as the result of a surface fire from natural causes and had subsequently been washed within the deposit. In view of this uncertainty no report on these specimens has hitherto been published.

During the winter of 1930–31 Père Teilhard de Chardin took with him to Paris some of the specimens recovered last year, for comparison with similar ones which have been found in many of the prehistoric sites of Europe. Dr. Gaubert of the Laboratory of Mineralogy of the Paris Museum very kindly subjected to analysis some of these fragments.

He continues by giving details of the various tests carried out to ensure that the black material *was* carbon and concludes:

> It is thus clear beyond reasonable doubt that Sinanthropus knew the use of fire and it is further to be presumed on good grounds that the charred and calcined bone and antler specimens occurring elsewhere in the Main Deposit at Choukoutien, though not in immediate associa-tion with Sinanthropus material, have been produced as the result of the use of fire by this hominid.

Here is a clear admission that the evidence of fire at this site had been known for some time. It was asserted that it had not been re-ported as it may have been due to natural causes or washed into the deposit. Such an explanation, however, is so unacceptable that we can only conclude that the huge scale of the original fires was being suppressed. When Breuil first saw the stag's horn in his laboratory, he did not have to take complex chemical tests in order to recognize immediately that it had been burnt by a *strong fire* whilst it was still fresh.

(j) Teilhard's second article

Teilhard wrote a second article for *Revue des Questions Scientifiques* in 1934 [89]. In this he refers to his earlier article mentioned in (a) above, and says:

> In writing my first article here on Choukoutien three years ago, I was still able to say that 'up to now', despite certain indications, no trace of industry had yet been certainly recognised in association with the bone remains of Sinanthropus. Two months later, returning to the site with Mr. W. C. Pei, the young scholar in charge of the excavation, I gathered with him in situ incontestable fragments of flaked stone and burnt bones. These traces had hitherto escaped attention because the works have been carried on for some years in a part of the site where they would have been extremely hard to recognise. But as always, once the light had begun to shine, it spreads everywhere.

> But once we recognised the first flakes of quartz, all became clear. . . . From that moment, archaeological discoveries multiplied—the most important being the discovery (Summer 1931) of a red, yellow and black clay bed about two metres thick, extremely rich in stone and bone debris.

Zone A was 7 m. thick and was

> . . . formed of clays and ashes of mixed colours in its central mass, but passing laterally into very hard travertines, this upper part of the deposits is full of promise. But it has not been touched since the begin-ning of the excavations and, together with the untouched lower parts, constitutes the least known portion of the site. In a year we shall know

more about it. . . . Traces of fire (as is clear from what we have just said) are certain and abundant; calcined bones and burnt stones are numerous; black ash and baked clays have accumulated to the depth of several metres.

The existence of bone tools, accepted by my friend Prof. H. Breuil, remains, in my opinion, problematic. Many pieces have been notched or broken artificially. But nothing yet seems to testify to a systematic use of bones or deer antlers.

Stone tools, on the other hand, are very abundant and indisputable. Unfortunately, owing to the material used, they are also difficult to study. [31p71]

Thus Teilhard, writing *after* Breuil had published his paper, claims that the ashes and stones were recognized for what they were, only a few months before Breuil came to the site in 1931. Yet the site had been continuously excavated since 1926, and layer 4 was clearly shown in a diagram made in 1929. Furthermore, the ashes, which Breuil immediately recognized as the result of furnaces, were 7 m. thick and were in the centre of the deposit. Teilhard's feeble excuse that 'they had escaped attention' because 'they were in a part of the site where they would have been extremely hard to recognize' is an admission that they *had* been visible for some time.

SECTION V

JAVA MAN

We have seen how Pekin 'man' was discovered in a remote part of the world, to which few scientists would be prepared to travel in order to examine the exact circumstances of the excavations for themselves. Some forty years earlier, the first proposed ape-man link was discovered at an even more inaccessible site—in the 'hell' of the Javanese jungle.

An examination of the various fossils discovered in Java falls very clearly into three main divisions, which are:

1. Eugene Dubois' discoveries (1887–95).
2. The Selenka Trinil Expedition (1907–8).
3. G. H. R. von Koenigswald's discoveries (1927–41).

1. Eugene Dubois

Dubois, a Dutch physician, was particularly ambitious to find personally the long awaited missing link. Darwin had predicted that there must be an unbroken link between man and apes, although no fossils to support this had been found at the time. In 1856 the first 'Neanderthal man' skull was discovered, but this was too close to a human skull to be actually classed as *the* missing link.

Haeckel, a famous German professor, who had been Dubois's professor at Jena University, 'invented' a hypothetical ape-like man, named him *Pithecanthropus alalus* (speechless ape-man) and suggested his remains might be discovered in Southern Asia or Africa. Despite the ridicule of the famous scientist, Virchow, and others, he commissioned a painting of what he imagined such a creature would look like. The result is a rather revolting thick-lipped, pot-bellied creature, who is no credit to either apes or men! (Fig.28). The picture received much publicity and is still reproduced in some books today for its historical interest. [37p83 & 35p12]

Such was the situation when Dubois, his imagination fired by Haeckel's confident naming of the link, sailed for Sumatra in 1887, 'determined to discover the first man'. [25p219]

Dubois appears to have first approached the Dutch Government for financial aid, which was refused. He therefore went to Java as a surgeon in the Royal Dutch Army and obtained a posting to Sumatra. In 1889, he appears to have been more successful in persuading the

Fig.28. Haeckel's
'Pithecanthropus alalus'
(speechless ape-man)

Mining Authority to finance his work, for he was provided with two military mining engineers and fifty military convicts!

Once stationed in Sumatra, he investigated various caves but found little of importance. A fossil skull had been found in the neighbouring island of Java, so he travelled there, obtained the skull and found another at the same site at Wadjak (Fig.29). Both skulls were fossilized, but too much like modern man to fulfil his search for half-ape specimens. He therefore said nothing about these finds, and continued his explorations.

In November 1890 at Kedung Brubus, some twenty-five miles from Trinil, the site of his major finds, he found a portion of a jaw con-

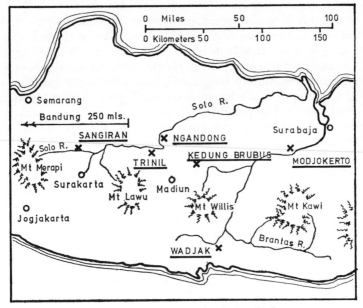

Fig.29. Map of principal fossil sites in Java

taining a root of a tooth. At Trinil, on the Solo river, a number of fossilized animal bones had been found, and Dubois commenced excavations on this site. In September 1891, he discovered a very large upper right molar tooth in a cave on the banks of the Solo river. The following month he found the famous skull cap of an ape-like creature, and in August of the following year, 14 m. (46 ft.) away, he found a human femur; both were completely fossilized (Fig.30). Later, another molar was found 3 m. (10 ft.) from the skull cap. He also discovered various portions of four more human femurs and a human tooth, but did not publicize them until many years later. Dubois carefully considered these finds. Moore writes [p221]

> He did not hurry, for a momentous decision was forming in his mind.
> . . . Then he startled the world: he had decided that the skull and the leg bone belonged to the same creature.

Carrington adds some further information regarding Dubois's decision, for he says:

> Dubois was at first inclined to regard his skull cap and teeth as belonging to a chimpanzee, in spite of the fact that there is no known evidence that this ape or any of its ancestors ever lived in Asia. But on reflection, *and after corresponding with the great Ernst Haeckel,* Professor of Zoology at the University of Jena, he declared them to belong to a creature *which seemed admirably suited to the role of the 'missing link'.* [p83]

From this, it would appear that Dubois was keen to know if the discovery of these few fossils could in any way be claimed as the 'missing link' and receive their due meed of recognition and support from such an eminent authority. Haeckel was enthusiastic about the finds, and immediately telegraphed back—'From the inventor of Pithecanthropus to his happy discoverer!' [37p167]. The fossils received considerable publicity, and moreover, were discovered at a particularly opportune time, for at that period the controversy over Darwin's theory of evolution was raging, and the lack of fossil evidence of any links between the major classes of animals or between man and the apes was particularly damaging to the theory. The discovery of the Java fossils and the subsequent publicity given to them was greatly used by enthusiastic proponents of the theory to turn the tide against the opposition. Von Koenigswald, who followed Dubois's footsteps in Java, excavating there in 1930–41, mentions this aspect in his autobiographical book *Meeting Prehistoric Man*, saying:

> Dubois' find came at just the right moment: at a time when the conflict around Darwinism was at its height. For the scientific world it constituted the first concrete proof that man is subject not only to biological but also to palaeontological laws— [18p26]

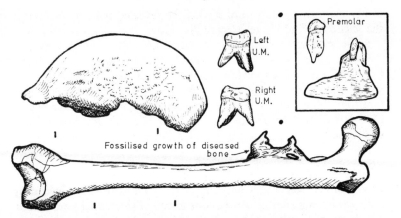

Fig.30. Dubois' Java man fossils—skull cap, femur and two molars, with the premolar and Kedung Brubus jaw fragment

Dubois thus joined a human femur to an ape-like skull, thereby making a hybrid form, an 'upright (walking) ape-man—*Pithecan thropus erectus*'. He claimed that the stratum was Pliocene, which gave a very early date for his discovery. Von Koenigswald, however, points out:

> When Dubois issued his first description of the fossil Javanese fauna he designated it Pleistocene. But no sooner had he discovered his Pithecanthropus than the fauna had suddenly to become Tertiary. He did everything in his power to diminish the Pleistocene character of the fauna. . . . The criterion was no longer to be the fauna as a whole, but only his Pithecanthropus. [18p38]

The distance of 12–14 m. (45 ft.) separating these bones, however, is considerable. This factor is often minimized by many writers, saying the femur was found 'less than fifty feet away', or that the finds were separated 'by a few yards'. Dubois's own explanation of the distance between the fossils was that the bodies had floated down the river, and been eaten by crocodiles. Vere comments that it must have been a well harnessed river to have kept its course for half a million years!

While still in Java, Dubois published a paper in 1894, entitled *Pithecanthropus erectus, a Human-like Transitional Form from Java*, and on his return the following year, bringing with him 215 packing cases of fossils, he displayed only the skull cap, femur and teeth and gave lectures on them in various cities in Europe. Controversy raged over the fossils which he exhibited, *but he said nothing whatsoever about his discoveries of the Wadjak skulls, the Kedung jaw, the premolar and four more human femurs, keeping them quite secret!* Some writers admit that he deliberately withheld the Wadjak skulls, in order to ensure acceptance of his ape-man combination, for had he revealed them at this stage, the scientists would have rejected his views.

Some authorities completely accepted his views, others remained sceptical. Moore says that some were 'suspicious that so significant a find should have been made in such an out-of-the-way place as Java, where others could not easily investigate all the circumstances'. Grafton Elliot Smith wrote, 'The amazing thing has happened. Dubois had actually found the fossil his scientific imagination had visualized.'

Haeckel's 'evidence'

Professor Haeckel, a very fiery supporter of Darwin, said it 'was truly a Pliocene remainder of that famous group of the higher Catarrhines, which were the pithecoid ancestors of man. He is indeed the long-searched-for Missing Link.' Haeckel's commendation, however, should be considered to be of doubtful value. He was the zealous proponent of the well known, but now discredited, Theory of Recapitulation, which claimed that the stages in the development of an animal's embryo trace the animal's evolution through its ancestral predecessors, e.g. the gill 'slits' in the human embryo are a relic of its fish ancestry. To support his theory, however, Haeckel, whose knowledge of embryology was self taught, faked some of his evidence. He not only altered his illustrations of embryos but also printed the same plate of an embryo three times, and labelled one a human, the second a dog and the third a rabbit 'to show their similarity'. He also drew the four-weeks-old embryos of a dog and a human which I have copied in Fig.31A. In Fig.31B I give correct drawings of these embryos at the same age, and the extent of Haeckel's 'alterations' can be seen.

All these inaccurate drawings were pointed out by L. Rutimeyer, Professor of Zoology and Comparative Anatomy at Basle University, when he criticized two of Haeckel's books in 1868 [*Archiv fur anthropologie, dritter band, Braunschweig,* pp.301–2]. He was charged with fraud by five professors and, when convicted by a university court at Jena, admitted that he had 'altered' his drawings. One writer reports him as saying:

A small per cent of my embryonic drawings are forgeries; those, namely, for which the observed material is so incomplete or insufficient as to compel us to fill in and reconstruct the missing links by hypothesis and comparative synthesis. I should feel utterly condemned and annihilated by the admission, were it not that hundreds of the best observers and biologists lie under the same charge. The great majority of all morphological, anatomical, histological, and embryological diagrams are not true to nature but are more or less doctored, schematized, and reconstructed.

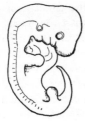

Fig.31A. Haeckel's drawings of the four weeks old embryos of
a dog (left) and a human (right)

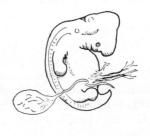

Fig.31B. Drawings of the four weeks old embryos of a dog (left)
and a human (right)

Regarding Haeckel's theory, Sir Gavin de Beer of the British
Museum (N.H.) has said:

> Seldom has an assertion like that of Haeckel's 'theory of recapitulation',
> facile, tidy, and plausible, widely accepted without critical examination,
> done so much harm to science. [2p159]

Biographies of Haeckel usually gloss over this affair, but occasional
references are made, such as in the *Biographical Dictionary of Scientists*
(Black, London, 1974), which says:

> His enthusiasm for his theories led him into attempts at forcing ob-
> served facts to fit into his schemes of evolution rather than allowing the
> facts to test and if necessary modify them.... (He) sometimes allowed
> his artistic skill to replace scientific accuracy in the illustration of his
> monographs.

The *Dictionary of Scientific Biography* (Scribners, New York, 1972)
refers to:

> ... Haeckel's far too schematacised illustrations of various embryonic
> stages. Concerning these 'forgeries', many distinguished anatomists and
> zoologists ... explained in 1909 that while they did not approve of
> Haeckel's methods they nevertheless refused to attack him since the
> concept of development 'cannot suffer any damage through some
> incorrectly rendered embryological illustrations'.

Clearly, these professors considered the concept of development (i.e. evolution) to be more important than the 'facts' produced to support it. It is a strange comment upon the times that, despite the acknowledgement that Haeckel had faked some of his evidence, the theory (which he called the Biogenic *Law*) was widely accepted and quoted for decades afterwards, until it was eventually disproved.

One would have expected that Haeckel's falsified illustrations would have been quietly forgotten, yet Wendt, who writes at length about Haeckel's contribution to biology, actually reproduces, with no hint of criticism, one of his 'schematized' illustrations on p.81. This shows the 'similarity' of the embryos of a pig, a cow, a rabbit and man, but these pictures are gross distortions of the actual embryos which are different at very early stages.

The theory has been succeeded by the theory of Paedomorphosis, which says that the modern *adult* is like the young of its *ancestors*, e.g. the skull shape of man is like those of Neanderthal children. Although discredited, overtones of Haeckel's Theory of Recapitulation still appear in museums and books. It is of interest that Virchow, who had been Haeckel's professor at university, considered his former pupil a fool. [120]

The debate on the finds

When Dubois exhibited his skull cap and thigh bone in Berlin in 1895, Virchow refused to chair the meeting, and having pointed out the deep suture in the skull which was characteristic of apes, he said, 'In my opinion this creature was an animal, a giant gibbon, in fact. The thigh bone has not the slightest connection with the skull.' [37p168]

Although he had only found a skull *cap*, Dubois estimated the capacity to be 900 cc., half-way between man and apes, and proceeded to make a model of the complete Java man, which received considerable publicity.

Debate on the significance of the finds continued in both scientific and popular press, until one could virtually say that Pithecanthropus generated an industry, numerous pictures and articles being published about this famous 'ancestor of man'. It was this outpouring in the national press and periodicals which prompted G. K. Chesterton's remark quoted on p.46. Similar views to his are given by Boule and Vallois in *Fossil Men*, who say, 'Painted models of a complete Pithecanthropus such as have actually been made are pure flights of fancy' [p123]. This comment would of course apply to the slouching figure of Java man to be seen in our museums and books today.

There is little debate today in scientific journals on whether the skull and femur belonged to the same individual, the general assumption being that they did. Indeed it is considered surprising that some scientists of the day should have doubted this. With the massive publicity which followed in the wake of the discovery, few scientists today are prepared to risk their status by contending that these bones were from different individuals.

In his book, *History of the Primates*, published by the British Museum (Natural History), Sir Wilfrid Le Gros Clark makes no mention of the distance between the finds, and says, 'Dubois discovered in Central Java portions of a skeleton. . . . They included a skull cap and a thigh bone.' From this, any uninformed reader would assume that a significant proportion of Java man's skeleton had been found, of which two bones were of particular interest. The fact that these were virtually the *only* bones of the skeleton found is far from obvious.

Following his discoveries in Java, Dubois, although qualified in the field of medicine, was nevertheless made a Professor of Geology at Amsterdam University. However, in view of the very strong criticism which his opinions received, he locked his specimens away, allowing no one to see them for some thirty years. Such conduct is surely inexcusable in a scientist of any repute. Dubois's action is never questioned on this basis however, it usually being ascribed to either a sensitive or a volatile nature, which resented criticism.

This situation continued until 1920, when Professor Smith of Australia claimed he had found the first fossil man in Australia. Dubois, probably provoked by this announcement, revealed to a startled scientific world that he had found two fossil skulls at Wadjak thirty years before. Under considerable pressure to display these skulls and any other finds he had made, he eventually allowed Dr. Hrdlicka to inspect the collection. Moore quotes Hrdlicka as reporting:

> We found Professor Dubois a big-bodied, big-hearted man who received us with cordial simplicity. He had all the specimens in his possession brought out from the strong boxes in which they are kept and demonstrated them to us personally and then permitted me to handle them to my satisfaction.

Moore continues: 'Having opened the door, Dubois continued gracious. Other scientists also were permitted to see the long hidden bones. . . .' This is a very generous interpretation of his conduct!

Hrdlicka, however, was wrong. He did *not* see *all* Dubois's discoveries, for several years later he publicized some other fossils which he had found in Java.

In 1924 he gave details of the small fragment of a jaw (Fig.30) he had found at Kedung Brubus, which was over 40 km. (25 miles) away from Trinil [103]. He had briefly mentioned it in two articles in 1891 and had considered it 'human', but he now claimed that it was part of the jaw of a *Pithecanthropus erectus*. In the same paper he gave details of the premolar tooth he had found. Von Koenigswald's view of the

Trinil teeth were that the premolar was from a *true man*, and regarding the left and right molars, he did not 'hesitate to ascribe them to an *orang*, a diagnosis confirmed by *the discovery of other orang teeth in the same level*'. [4p121]

In 1932 Dubois claimed that he had recognized part of a second femur in the collection which he had brought back from Trinil [104]. He said his assistant had put the specimen on one side, thinking it was a deer's horn. When Dubois recognized it, he said that he searched further and found the upper end that fitted it, and a further six pieces to compose two more shafts of femurs! In December 1934 [105], he said he had found another shaft of a femur! Dubois's failure to disclose *all* his material after forty years is surely inexcusable.

Referring to Dubois's collection, von Koenigswald remarked that some of the items were very inadequately distinguished, *because some of the labels got lost*. [18p36]

It will be found that books describing Dubois's discoveries either made little or no reference to his secrecy, as the following examples show:

Kenny:

> ∴ in the early nineteen twenties, Dubois reissued his specimens. Their reception this time was more favourable, . . . [p147]

Leakey:

> In order to understand why this material was not made available at the time of its discovery, it is necessary to look at the circumstances surrounding his first announcement of the Java skull cap, femur and teeth. Dubois . . . believed that these specimens belonged to single individual, and he had released them first as being the most important of his finds. [22p107]

Moore:

> Long delays in describing and publishing were frequent, but Dubois secretiveness passed all bounds. [p224]

Sir Arthur Keith:

> . . . if on his return in 1894, he had placed before the anthropologists of his time the ape-like skull from Trinil side by side with the great brained skulls from Wadjak, both fossilised, both from the same region of Java, he would have given them a meal beyond the powers of their mental digestion. Since then our digestion has grown stronger. [16p441]

von Koenigswald:

> Dubois then took the Wadjak finds to Europe, but did not work on them till 1920. [p124]

Boule and Vallois in *Fossil Men* comment on the four femurs:

In 1932 he added four incomplete femurs, originating from the excavations carried out at Trinil in 1900 (sic) but only just freed from the
gangue that concealed their true nature. [p116]

One can only comment that forty years is rather a long time for simply
cleaning up a few bones!

Reference to other publications will show how this topic is either
ignored or briefly mentioned in passing. In all accounts I have read of
Dubois's late admissions of finds, not one ever looks beyond the
incident to question his motivation in deliberately withholding
damaging counter-evidence. Strangely enough, Dubois himself
doubted if the skull was from an ancestor of man, and finally, a few
years before his death in 1940, he admitted that *it was the skull of a
large gibbon*. This admission was *not* accepted, however [107], and it
was generally dismissed as yet another idiosyncrasy of this tempera-
mental scientist, whom Moore describes as 'brilliant, unaccountable,
stubborn, pioneering and secretive'.

Criticisms of Dubois's conduct are very infrequent. Millar considered him mentally unqualified for his position as Medical Officer
in Sumatra, and comments:

> His many scientific biographers say as much but in a different way . . . .
> But everything written about Dubois has been so highly charged with
> reverence that it gives rise to the suspicion that romance has been pre-
> ferred to fact. [p86]

Dubois's concealment with regard to his Java finds is referred to by
Professor W. R. Thompson, F.R.S. in his interesting introduction to
the 1956 edition of Darwin's *Origin of Species*. The publishers, J. M.
Dent, decided to republish this work in their Everyman Library
(No.811) on the event of Darwin's centenary, and invited Professor
Thomson to introduce it. He pointed out that it would not be the
usual 'hymn of praise' to Darwin, but the publishers made no objection. In the course of his critical assessment, Professor Thompson
says:

> The success of Darwinism was accompanied by a decline in scientific
> integrity. This is already evident in the reckless statement of Haeckel
> and in the shifting, devious, and histrionic argumentation of T. H.
> Huxley. A striking example, which has only recently come to light, is the
> alteration of the Piltdown skull so that it could be used as evidence for
> the descent of man from the apes; but even before this a similar instance
> of tinkering with evidence was finally revealed by the discoverer of
> Pithecanthropus, who admitted, many years after his sensational report,
> that he had found in the same deposits bones that are definitely human.
> Though these facts are now well known, a work published in 1943 still
> accepts the diagnosis of Pithecanthropus given by Dubois, as a creature
> with a femur of human form permitting an erect posture.

Criticisms such as this have obviously had no effect upon those who write school textbooks and articles for the general public.

2. The Selenka-Trinil expedition

This German expedition was mounted by Professor Emil Selenka, who unfortunately died before it set out. However, his wife, Lenore Selenka, a professor in her own right, took over the project and provided most of the finance for this expedition which was thorough and costly. The Trinil site was searched during 1907–8 for further remains of Dubois's Pithecanthropus. Scientists were engaged to investigate the finds on the spot, and up to seventy-five coolies were housed in the midst of the inhospitable conditions of the Javanese jungle. Over 10,000 c.m. of earth were moved, reaching a depth of 40 ft. below the surface, on the exact location of Dubois's discoveries. Forty-three large boxes of fossil remains were found and later distributed amongst seventeen specialists in Europe for their examination and report. Despite all this effort, *not a single bone, which could be attributed to Pithecanthropus, was found.*

The report of the expedition, published in Leipzig in 1911, is a model of its kind, with clear diagrams and illustrations, no translation into English having been made however. Keith briefly reviewed it in *Nature* (13th July 1911) [102] and we give the following summary of the main findings in the report.

(A) GEOLOGY AND VOLCANIC ACTIVITY

The report says that, in view of the considerable activity of the nearby volcano, Mt. Lawu-Kukusan, the strata cannot be identified by their organic contents. This statement completely upsets the normal means of identifying the age of the different layers. Bright shells were found embedded in volcanic material, and the main fossil bearing stratum appears to be the result of a very large lava flow. Considerable geological activity is further indicated by local tradition, which said that at one time the Solo river flowed on a different course, probably nearer Mt. Lawu.

Eruptions were said to have occurred at about thirty year intervals —1864, 1875, 1901. This volcanic material seems to have produced complete fossilization of any animal relics. This would explain the fossilized state of the skull cap and femur, which is therefore no indication of great age. Bones showed no abrasion due to being carried to their position by water, and no complete skeletons were found. All the evidence points to the bones of already decomposed animals being brought to their present positions, as a result of volcanic activity of comparatively recent ages. Three experts, dealing with the geology, marine life and plants, considered that the deposits were

Pleistocene (the geologist even considering it *recent* Pleistocene), but two other experts, who studied the fossils of mammals, leaned towards Dubois's estimate of Pliocene. Frau Selenka, however, considered that 'the decisive layers are geologically younger than were previously accepted for the most part'.

A footnote in the report describes the effect of a disastrous flood which occurred in East Java in 1909. Fourteen inches of rain fell in one day, over 500 men died and whole villages were swept away and buried beneath volcanic ash and mud.

(B) FOSSILS, ETC.

As we have said, numerous animal bones were found at Trinil, but no remains of Pithecanthropus. Two miles away from the site, however, was found the cap of a large molar tooth which was human. This tooth was one of the more interesting finds by the expedition and was known as the Sondé tooth. Professor Selenka showed this tooth to Dubois, who subsequently circulated a printed note, saying it was a 'quite recent and white-looking human molar from a lower jaw, with, on the rootless underside, adhered sand as if from Trinil . . . this sand could not have been brought by natural causes'. Frau Selenka protested against the idea that the sand had been made to adhere, saying that it had been discovered by a reliable European and later tests showed that it was fossilized.

It is a strange comment on the attitude of Dubois, that he should accuse another colleague of fraud at a time when he still held secret the Wadjak skulls and other fossils.

(C) HUMAN EXISTENCE

The most surprising feature of the report was some evidence of human existence in the same stratum as Pithecanthropus had been found, consisting of some splinters of bones and tusks, and traces of hearth foundations and wood charcoal. On the strength of these remains, and the Sondé tooth (evidence which Keith considered 'slender'), Frau Selenka considered that man was a contemporary of Pithecanthropus and that the latter was an abberant.

Today, most authorities consider the Trinil layer to be middle Pleistocene, and not Pliocene as Dubois contended. Summarizing the results of this large expedition, Keith said, 'So far as Pithecanthropus itself is concerned, the expedition was a failure.' Those writers who do briefly mention it refer to it as 'unsuccessful' or 'disappointing'.

The editor of the report, Professor Max Blanckenhorn, said the expedition was 'fruitless', and he gives an interesting account of the delays experienced in publishing the final report. In 1905, before the expedition left, it was agreed with Dubois that his report on the 1891

Trinil expedition, as yet still unfinished, would be given a three year 'precedence' over the Selenka report. This he fully accepted, as he was quite certain that he would publish his report within one year. After the expedition, Dubois had still not made his report and on two occasions asked for the Selenka report to be delayed, which was agreed. In view of publication dates which had to be met however, a third request for delay from Dubois was overruled, and the report was finally printed.

3. G. H. R. von Koenigswald's discoveries

The complete failure of the Selenka expedition to find any supporting evidence for Dubois's *Pithecanthropus erectus* clearly damaged his claim that it was the missing link, and further evidence was needed to solve this 'puzzle'.

Kenny says [p147] that it was Dubois's 'reissuing' of his specimens which prompted the Geological Survey of the Netherlands East Indies to send von Koenigswald to Java to search for further remains of Pithecanthropus in 1930. Von Koenigswald was clearly convinced that further evidence of Java man *would* be found, for he says:

> Thus, despite the discovery of Pekin man, it remained necessary to find a further Pithecanthropus sufficiently complete to prove the human character of this disputed fossil. [18p55]

Von Koenigswald spent many years in Java in an effort to discover such a 'sufficiently complete' fossil. We shall see later what degree of success he achieved. He arrived in Java in January 1931 and was stationed with the geological team at Bandung. He began his searches for fossil man 40 miles away from Trinil on a high level bank above the Solo river. A number of skulls were found, which came to be known as the 'Solo' or 'Ngandong' skulls. They were very similar to Neanderthal man; in addition to this, some artefacts were found with them. For these reasons, they were considered to be too advanced to be a 'missing link'.

Discussing one of the skulls, von Koenigswald makes a very strange comment, for he says:

> Despite its solidity, this particular skull had been smashed, and by a mighty blow with a blunt instrument—perhaps a wooden club. . . . *Unfortunately, on orders from above, the skull was entirely taken apart during preparation and put together in its original shape,* so that the fragment of bone that had been knocked in is no longer recognisable as such. [p72]

He does not say who these higher authorities were, but one is left wondering whether they gave any other instructions regarding the fossils found in this country.

In 1935 he began explorations in the area of Sangiran using native collectors, and in the first basket of fossils he received, there was a large 'human' lower jaw (Mandible 'B'. Fig.34). He published the discovery saying it was from *Pithecanthropus erectus*. This provoked Dubois to reply that it was from *Homo soloensis*. Von Koenigswald later amended the strata from which he said it came, which showed it must have belonged to an older form than Pithecanthropus. This late change of strata to which this fossil was attributed was one of several factors in the considerable confusion of naming and classification, to which many of von Koenigswald's fossils were unfortunately subjected. Professor Le Gros Clark was very critical of the variety of names given to the fossil fragments found by von Koenigswald, and furthermore in a footnote he said:

> . . . although I have a high regard for the judgement of my friend von Koenigswald (which is, of course, based on quite considerable experience), I am not persuaded that such a distinction is valid on the fragmentary material so far available. [7p95]

When the jaw was first brought to von Koenigswald, it was partially embedded in a conglomerate and his first impression was that it had been rain washed into the black clay strata in which it was found, and he dated it accordingly as a 'Trinil' fossil. He later changed his mind and considered that it did come from the clay strata, although why it should then be encased in a conglomerate is not clear.

Teilhard de Chardin
In 1935 von Koenigswald invited Teilhard de Chardin to visit him and inspect his discoveries. This was accepted and Teilhard arrived in January 1936. Teilhard was delighted to meet von Koenigswald, whose invitation he was only too willing to accept, as he 'guessed that von Koenigswald's discoveries would supply entire new evidence for his theory of the origin of man' [29p221]. Teilhard in fact expected to find a connection between Java and China, and this appears to have been the whole purpose of his visit, as Cuénot makes clear:

> In short, Java, because of its geographical position, seemed to present a crossroads where two Palaeolithic currents met: one, a north-western current probably derived from India . . .; the other, a north-eastern current rising from China (with Pithecanthropus—Sinanthropus, orang and buffalo). From these facts the point of Teilhard's trip is clear. Java seemed to be a hinge between India and China; . . . and finally, it was of importance to attempt to establish a satisfactory connection between Pithecanthropus and Sinanthropus [p192]

Although he made only a brief ten-day visit, Teilhard was successful in establishing links with both these Continents. He had just finished an exploratory journey in India, during which he had found a number of stone tools in the Narbada Valley. Regarding von Koenigswald's discoveries, Teilhard wrote:

> ... V. K. had just made some extraordinary finds which he wanted to clarify with me: in particular a magnificent Chellean industry that no-one had even suspected. I thought myself back in India, on the Narbada. [30p221]

The link with India having been made, it only remained to establish a link with the Chinese mainland, and here they appear to have been particularly fortunate. Fossils of orang-utan had been found in China but not in Java, and von Koenigswald seems to have instructed his native helpers to search particularly for such remains [18p95]. At the time of Teilhard's visit, still no fossil links with China had been discovered. From all accounts, however, whilst in the area of Patijan, where the stone tools had been found, he and von Koenigswald entered a cave and discovered on the floor an 'abundance' of teeth, from not just one but *three* animals which had existed in China.

As Cuénot describes it:

> To crown these efforts, just above the valley in the limestone of this southern part of the island he and von Koenigswald discovered a cavern floor with an abundance of isolated teeth—orang, large gibbon, bear, and so forth—'absurdly' similar to the fossilbearing deposits of Kwangsi. For the first time, orang, gibbon, and bear were found in Java. A correlation was thus established with Southern China [p192]

Quite how the presence of these teeth on the *floor of a cave* can be said to form a link between the Pithecanthropus *strata*, said to be some half a million years old, and the Sinanthropus discoveries, over 3,000 miles away, is difficult to understand.

Cuénot records an almost uncanny fulfilment of another prediction made by Teilhard just before he left Java on the 15th January 1936:

> ... von Koenigswald had been hard at work. In the karst lands of Patjitan, south of the Solo basin, he had found Stegodon in the limestone fissures, thus establishing a connection between the Solo basin and the Kwangsi fissures. Teilhard had almost had a presentiment of this discovery when, on 14 January 1936, speaking of these karst formations, he wrote:
> 'Stegodon or hippopotamus will have to be found here for a connection to be made with the Solo basin. Let's hope that some will be found. Deposits of this kind ought to abound in the karsts.' [12p200]

On board ship as he left Java, Teilhard wrote about the discoveries that had been made during his brief visit:

> I have taken advantage of this long voyage to get down my travel-notes and write a number of letters aimed at passing on to discreetly-chosen quarters what I saw and what is not even suspected by any prehistorian in Europe. [30p222]

It may be asked, what was so very important about these discoveries which Teilhard saw that the information has to be passed on only to 'discreetly-chosen quarters'. Palaeontological discoveries are hardly likely to cause governments to fall or rioting in the streets. Indeed, the discoverers are usually keen to publicize the importance of their finds as widely as possible. Did Teilhard perhaps sense that with the energetic von Koenigswald scouring the island, Java would once more provide further important fossils some forty-six years after Dubois had made his very controversial discoveries?

Teilhard was very conscious of his good fortune in making important discoveries, for he said:

> ... I pitched most opportunely on two of the hottest sectors on the prehistory front—and just at the moment to take part in decisive offensives. This is proving a great addition to my experience and another valuable plank in my platform. [30p218]

His arrival at this opportune moment to see these fossils and confirm von Koenigswald's views caused him to reflect:

> ... it seems somehow providential that I should arrive in Java just at the right time to give my opinion on and to some extent place definitely what von Koenigswald has unearthed. I am sometimes a little disturbed when I think of the uninterrupted succession of such strokes of luck that runs through my life. What does it mean, and what is God expecting of me? [30p221]

Speaight comments upon Teilhard's good fortune in making archaeological finds, saying:

> Indeed throughout the life of Teilhard de Chardin we find this contrasting pattern. Where his scientific researches were in question, the luck came all his way. He met the right people; was on the spot at the right moment; and received his due meed of recognition. [29p222]

Teilhard visited Java twice, first in 1936 and again in 1938. His first visit was at a particularly critical time in the progress of von Koenigswald's search for fossil man. Because of the depression von Koenigswald had lost his post with the Geological Survey, and had to rely upon his Dutch colleagues to support him. Teilhard advised him to write to John C. Merriam, the President of the Carnegie Institution in Washington. Von Koenigswald did write at length, setting out his palaeontological and personal difficulties. He was optimistic of finding further Pithecanthropus remains, for he said, 'I have found a new fossil locality here in Java; if a Pithecanthropus is to be found anywhere, it will be here.' [18p92]

Cuénot says Teilhard took a great interest in von Koenigswald, writing a long letter to Merriam in his support, widely broadcasting his discoveries and arranging for Weidenreich to visit him in September 1938 [p162]. (Von Koenigswald returned the visit by going to Pekin in January 1939.)

Teilhard's international contacts were growing and became so extensive that Cuénot says:

> One has the impression of a vast web, of which Teilhard held in parts the threads, where he served as liaison agent, or better still, as chief of staff, able, like a magician, to make American money flow, or at least to channel it for the greatest good of palaeontology. [p163]

As a result of Teilhard's support, von Koenigswald was invited to attend a Symposium on Early Man, held in March 1937 in Philadelphia, under the sponsorship of the Carnegie Institute. Here he met many other experts in this field, amongst them Teilhard, Broom, De Terra, and Dorothy Garrod, Breuil being unable to attend. Cuénot says the meeting was not large, consisting of a select few, but surprisingly for a symposium on this important subject, no record of the meeting was available to him. The purpose of the meeting was apparently to form an executive committee for the Carnegie Foundation for financing explorations in Asia.

Von Koenigswald was made a Research Associate of the Institute and granted a considerable sum of money for pursuing his search for fossil man, and he immediately wrote to his Javanese assistant to continue the search. Returning from America, he visited Pekin and looked around the site at Choukoutien. Arriving in Java, von Koenigswald engaged hundreds of natives to search for fossils, offering a reward for every piece they found.

The Search

Two aspects of von Koenigswald's discoveries of the fossils should be considered at this point. The first is the fact mentioned above, that he paid his native collectors for any fossils they found. It is understandable that he should want to use the local population in the search for important fossils, but such a practice is open to abuse and deception by tribesmen who were not noted for their honesty. This was to have unfortunate results in the discovery of one fossil at least.

The second and more important aspect is that he remained at Bandung, which was over 200 miles (300 km.) from the main sites of Trinil and Sangiran. Consequently, whenever an important find was made by a collector, a lengthy journey had to be made both by the collector and by von Koenigswald to reach the site. Here again, there was considerable scope for error or oversight in obtaining from the native the precise details of the position, level and other factors concerning the fossil when discovered. As one can appreciate, an inaccuracy of only a few feet in the recording of the level at which a fossil was discovered, could affect the stratum to which it was allo-

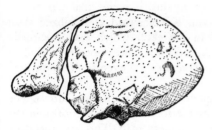

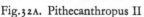

Fig.32A. Pithecanthropus II   Fig.32B. Pithecanthropus III

cated, considerably altering its dating. This heavy reliance upon natives to discover such important fossils is in contrast to the normal means of exploring a site, such as that of the Selenka-Trinil expedition, where experts were on the spot to record the exact situation of each fossil as it was unearthed.

In 1936, at Modjokerto, a large part of the brain case of a child was discovered in strata which were earlier than those of Pithecanthropus. Von Koenigswald considered it to be a forerunner of Pithecanthropus, naming it *Pithecanthropus modjokertensis*, but Dubois contested it was not an ancestor of Pithecanthropus, and von Koenigswald renamed it *Homo modjokertensis*.

Pithecanthropus II
In September 1937, he received a thick piece of fossilized cranium, and immediately travelled out to the site. He gathered together all the native collectors, showed them the skull piece, and offered 10 cents for every piece of the skull which they found, which was considerably higher than the ½–1 cent usually paid. They began hunting up the hillside and found a number of very small pieces. Von Koenigswald then says that he realized too late *that the native collectors had broken the skull up into small fragments to increase the total reward.* Thus the combination of monetary reward and poor supervision reduced this fossil to a mass of fragments. [18p96]

Von Koenigswald, far from being dismayed by the tactics of his 'opportunist brown friends', threw a feast to mark the occasion, complete with village orchestra and dancing girls!

Von Koenigswald mentions [18p97] that *forty* fragments were found during the search, from which an almost complete braincase was reconstructed (Pithecanthropus II—Fig.32A). In the report of the discovery of the skull, however, he says that the skull was made up from *thirty* fragments [106]. This discrepancy of ten pieces is confirmed by Moore, who says: 'When the inch by inch search ended, von Koenigswald had forty fragments, thirty of which proved later to belong to the skull' [25p228]. From this, it seems that ten pieces, which had been identified by von Koenigswald as fossilized skull fragments, were not included in the skull which was eventually reconstructed! One may well ask, did these pieces not fit the skull—were they part of another skull—were they not even skull fragments? No clue is given.

The braincase was more complete than that found by Dubois. The general shape was similar, whilst the formation of the bones in the region of the ear was like that of modern man. This was therefore taken to prove that Dubois's skull was human after all, and von Koenigswald wrote to Dubois privately with a photo of the pieces as found and of the reconstructed skull.

Dubois, as unpredictable as ever, promptly published the photos, and indirectly accused von Koenigswald of faking the skull [108]. He had measured the separate pieces from the photograph, and claimed that the skull formed from them was 10 mm. and 18 mm. smaller than it should be! It is difficult to follow Dubois's arguments in his paper, but he clearly considered the shape of the skull's outline had been altered by the reconstruction.

Von Koenigswald's protest in reply to Dubois was not published, but Dubois modified his statement, saying that he did not wish to insinuate that von Koenigswald had intentionally altered the shape of the cranium in putting it together. Von Koenigswald considered this accusation to be sheer nonsense, for the pieces could be fitted together easily, as they were more than 1 cm. thick. With this thickness of fossilized bone, clearly the natives must have had some difficulty in breaking the skull into such small fragments.

Close inspection of photos of the skull shows few gaps between the many pieces, except the right front portion, which was completely missing. One very large discontinuity, however, is clearly visible on the left-hand side near the front. This gap, which was commented on by Dubois, is so large and irregular that the front and rear portions are effectively separated at this point. In addition, the whole of the base is missing, again making accurate measurement of the capacity impossible, with volumes ranging from 750–850 cc.

In an article in *Nature* [107], Weidenreich considered that in view of von Koenigswald's discovery of the Pithecanthropus II skull piece, the Modjokerto skull and the Mandible 'B', 'the human-like characteristics of Pithecanthropus found by Dubois are definitely proven beyond doubt'. In the same issue, the columnist writing in 'News and views' agreed that Dubois's final conclusion that he had only found the remains of a giant gibbon 'was now definitely disproved' in the light of the new evidence. The writer also says, 'It is interesting to note that Professor Weidenreich's view as to the close relationships existing between Pithecanthropus and Sinanthropus are fully in accord with P. Teilhard de Chardin, who on the Palaeontological evidence holds the flora and fauna of China in the early Quaterney period were derived at least in part from the South.'

In 1938, three pieces of a skull of a juvenile Pithecanthropus were found and designated as Pithecanthropus III (Fig.32B). [109]

The skulls of Pithecanthropus were very similar to those of Pekin man, and accordingly von Koenigswald arranged to visit Dr. Weidenreich in January 1939, so that the two skulls could be closely compared. Weidenreich and von Koenigswald considered the characteristics of the two types of skulls, and were convinced that they were closely allied forms [110]. Von Koenigswald says that this completely confirmed Davidson Black's original conjecture that they were closely related. This is surprising, for Black went to considerable lengths to prove that, whilst they appeared to be similar, 'they differed sufficiently to give a generic distinction' [80p104]. Black considered that Pithecanthropus had evidences of archaic specialization, whilst Sinanthropus had evidence of archaic generalization, and was a progressive type. To put this into plain English, Black was saying that Java man was a blind alley, whilst progress continued through his Pekin man!

Pithecanthropus IV

Shortly before von Koenigswald left for China, he was handed a thickly encrusted upper jaw. Surprisingly, he considered that it had links with the Australopithecus of South Africa, and wrote to Teilhard in Pekin giving his views [30p254]. When he later arrived in Pekin, he examined it with Weidenreich and they noticed that *it had recently been broken* and therefore sent back to the collector for further pieces [35p49]. A large block duly arrived. When they had chipped off the hard encrustation, before them lay several skull pieces. One would of course expect that they would be a part of the skull adjoining the upper jaw which had been found earlier, but, strangely enough, the bones formed only the *rear* half of a braincase! There was thus no point of contact between the two sets of fossilized bone.

As the jaw was freshly broken, the question naturally arises regarding the adjoining piece(s). If it was discovered by a native collector, who recognized it as a fossil, he would naturally dig around the immediate vicinity in the hopes of discovering more, particularly in view of the reward offered. Finding this part of a braincase was of great value, but the failure of the collectors to retrieve the adjacent portion of the jaw should surely have prompted von Koenigswald to commission a closer search of the area, or to ask for an explanation from his collector, but no further mention is made of this particular aspect.

The jaw and the portion of the skull were given the same designation—Pithecanthropus IV. As it came from a similar 'Djetis' layer to

the Modjokerto infant cranium, which was earlier than the original
Pithecanthropus 'Trinil' layer, von Koenigswald named it *Pithecanthropus modjokertensis*. The jaw had human features, but was said to
possess an ape-like characteristic in the gap between the canine and
the adjacent incisors. The skull pieces were crushed while still fresh,
fossilized, and then crushed again, which must have made the reconstruction particularly difficult. [35p49]

Von Koenigswald's description of the two fossils which he and
Weidenreich inspected in Pekin is particularly optimistic, for he says:
'We ended up with the major portion of a thick, coarse skull, of which
only the frontal section and the upper part of the face were missing.'
One would assume from this, that it was only a minor portion of the
whole skull that they had failed to discover. Fig.34 shows how little
of the skull had actually been found, the lower jaw having been
added from another site (Mandible 'B'). When Weidenreich returned
to America, he made a complete reconstruction of the skull from the
fragments which von Koenigswald had collected and called it *Pithecanthropus robustus*. This made the classification very confusing, as von
Koenigswald had already named it *Pithecanthropus modjokertensis*.

The reconstruction
Fig.33 shows the reconstructed skull whilst Fig.34 gives the relative
sizes of the fossils actually discovered. There was considerable difficulty in obtaining a scaled picture of the right-hand view of the skull
piece, whilst the scale of illustration of the whole skull in Weidenreich's publication was 'about half' [112]. It can be seen that the rear
skull portion is reasonably in proportion, but that the actual jaws
found appear to be somewhat larger than those in the reconstruction.

As no bones were found connecting the rear skull piece to the
jaws, their relative disposition is heavily dependent upon the assumptions of the reconstructors, and to emphasize this, I show in Fig.35
the same fossils positioned on the outline of the skull of a female
gorilla. This is not to say that these fossils *were* of a gorilla, but
simply to show how these same few fossils can be rearranged to give
an ape-like appearance if required.

Vallois in *Fossil Men* (Boule died during the war) uncritically
accepts the model as being an accurate reconstruction, for he says:

> Although the reconstruction made with the aid of these new evidences
> cannot be absolutely guaranteed—since certain parts, such as the as-
> cending ramus of the mandible, and the regions of the nose and cheek,
> are still unknown—it must at least be pretty near the truth. The half
> human, half simian appearance of Pithecanthropus stands out with
> particular clarity. [4p124]

Dubois, yet again, disagreed with von Koenigswald's description

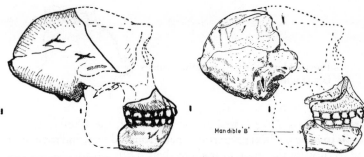

Fig.33. Weidenreich's reconstruction of Pithecanthropus IV (robustus)

Fig.34. Pithecanthropus IV and Mandible 'B'

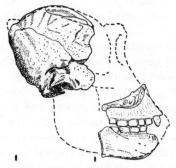

Fig.35. Pithecanthropus IV on the outline of a gorilla

of this fossil, which he considered to be another specimen of *Homo wadjakensis*. [111]

In 1939 a small fragment of a jaw was found with two teeth, but in very poor condition. In view of the cusps in the crowns of the teeth, von Koenigswald considered it to be different from the *modjokertensis* jaws he had found earlier.

In 1941, another fragment of a lower jaw was brought in, with three teeth in place. It had certain human characteristics, but was much larger than usual. He carried it around in his pocket for over a week, looking at it again and again to make sure that he was not mistaken! He named this fragment *Meganthropus palaeojavanicus*—'The Great Man of Ancient Java' (Fig.36), and sent a cast of it to Weidenreich, now in America, just before Pearl Harbour.

Gigantopithecus

We will here consider von Koenigswald's other source of fossils, from which he collected a number of fossilized teeth. This was not, as one might expect, from any particular locality or strata, but, of all

Fig.36 Meganthropus palaeojavanicus
jaw fragment

places—*Chinese Drug Stores!* As we have said, the Chinese consider
fossils to have medical properties when ground down, and fossil bones
and teeth were the stock in trade of their 'Drug Stores'.

Von Koenigswald visited such shops, searching for unusual
'human' teeth wherever he was travelling, whether it was Java,
China, or even San Francisco's Chinatown or New York! In Hong
Kong in 1935 he found a very large molar which he considered to be
'human', and named it *Gigantopithecus blacki* in honour of Davidson
Black. His friends, however, did not believe him, considering it to be
the tooth of a pig or bear! Weidenreich records that two years later,
von Koenigswald found another similar tooth and two years later
still, yet another (Fig.37). Weidenreich did 'not know whether all
three teeth came from the same drawer and the same shop', but
nevertheless proceeded to estimate the size of the whole jaw, giving
its outline for comparative purposes in his book [35p60]. Von Koenigswald also drew his version of the jaw [18p62]. A comparison of these
two drawings of the jaw, based on the same teeth, and an actual jaw
discovered later [113p83], is given in Fig.38.

Weidenreich's theory
In studying the large Meganthropus jaw, and noting the great thickness of the *Pithecanthropus robustus* skull, Weidenreich arrived at the
concept that man had descended from a race of giants. When he had
reached this conclusion, he remembered the very large teeth which
von Koenigswald had found in the Chinese shops. He wrote a book,
in which this thesis is reflected in its title, for he called it *Apes, Giants
and Men*. He devotes pp.55–66 to putting forward his justification for
this proposition. His arguments, however, are most difficult to follow,
for his line of logical steps follows a most tortuous path. In the course
of his arguments, however, he makes some surprising statements. The
first is that although the fossils came from the 'Trinil' beds, it does not
mean they were all living at the same time! This is because '*all the
bones came from secondary deposits*'.

   . . . there were devastating torrents and mud streams which swept down
   from the slopes of the volcanoes and scooped up large masses of soil,
   transporting them with all their contents *to geologically different places!*

Fig.37. Left third lower molar of Gigantopithecus blacki (Most complete of Von Koenigswalds collection)

Fig.38. Reconstructions of jaw of Gigantopithecus blacki . . .

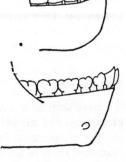

. . . as drawn by Weidenreich [35p60]

. . . as drawn by von Koenigswald [18p62]

. . . as later discovered [113p83]

Clearly, these vast soil movements, described in the Selenka report, are used by Weidenreich to support his arguments at this point. Elsewhere, both he and von Koenigswald appear to ignore this factor.

The second is the very unconvincing evidence which was used to date these teeth. When von Koenigswald bought these teeth at the Chinese Drug Stores, *in the drawer with them* were teeth of Stegodon, tapir and orang-utan. These animal fossils are considered to be Middle *or even* Lower Pleistocene, according to Teilhard and Young, and are generally found in the yellow loess in caves. Some of this same yellow soil was said to be in the crevices of the giant teeth which von Koenigswald found and Weidenreich considered that this was suffi-cient evidence in itself to date the giant teeth as being contemporary with the animal fossils found in the drawer with them, i.e. Middle or Lower Pleistocene. Weidenreich gives a map of the hypothetical route, by which man's ancestors arrived in Java from India, with a branch going up to Pekin!

Thus, simply upon the teeth found in the same drawer with those of Gigantopithecus, we have a whole chapter of man's geneology constructed and publicized by an eminent authority. Had evidence of this nature been relied upon to prove the early existence of *Homo sapiens* in that section of this book, it would have been rightly rejected out of hand.

I did not find Weidenreich's logic fully convincing, and today, few experts accept his theory of man's ancestry. With regard to von Koenigswald's Gigantopithecus teeth, over one thousand have been discovered, together with four lower jaws, but no other remains of the animal. Despite the great interest generated by the teeth and the various papers produced, it is now considered that they are merely those of a very large ape. [113 & 114]

Conclusion

We have seen how Java has been searched by no less than three explorations, and the very fragmentary nature of the evidence supporting the existence of Java man which these provided. We have also examined some of the less satisfactory aspects of the earliest and most recent explorations. It is possible that, had these been carried out with the scientific objectivity of the Selenka expedition, 'Java man' would not be gracing our museums and textbooks in this day and age.

SECTION VI

NEANDERTHAL MAN

The discovery of Neanderthal men poses a considerable problem for anthropologists. Over the period of the last 100 years, several skulls and skeletons, very similar to those of modern men, have been found. In view of the low forehead, prominent eyebrow ridges and the stooping posture he was said to possess, which gave him a primitive ape-like appearance, he was considered for some time to be man's near ancestor, and appeared as such in many early books on the subject. Further investigations, however, have shown that the true situation is not as simple as was once thought.

The story begins with the discovery in Germany in 1700 of a portion of a skull at Cannstadt, and in 1823 of the brain case of a child at Engis, both of which were seen to differ from normal skulls. Then in 1856, the skull cap and some limb bones were found at Neanderthal, which was to give the classifying name to all the skulls of this type to be discovered subsequently.

For many years little notice was taken of these finds, but with the publication of Darwin's *Origin of Species* in 1859, the search for man's ancestors began, and the possible significance of these fossils was hotly debated. Some considered them to be a forerunner of modern man, others that they were sufficiently like us to be classified as only a variety. Virchow maintained that the skull was that of a 'pathological idiot' suffering from rickets and arthritis. As further Neanderthal type skulls were discovered, his views were ignored and even treated with contempt. *Fossil Men*, which mentions Virchow's views of the Neanderthal type skulls, comments, 'It is hardly necessary to point out that they are now only of historic interest' [4p212]. Ottaway, writing an appreciation of Virchow, lamented, 'Virchow's name will always be linked with his refusal to admit that the Neanderthal skull, and similar fossil remains found later, could have belonged to a species other than *Homo sapiens*.' [120p106]

Over a period of time, portions of the skeletons of over sixty individuals were found, most of them in Europe, with some in Africa and Asia. There are several particular features which characterize this race of men. These are—prominent eyebrow ridges, low forehead, long narrow brain case, protruding upper jaw, and a strong lower jaw, but without a chin. The skeleton was short, deep chested, with curved, heavily built leg bones which possessed large joints.

In 1908, the skeleton of La Chapelle-aux-Saints was discovered, and Professor Boule of the Institute of Human Palaeontology in Paris submitted it to a close investigation.

He concluded that the head was thrust forward and the spinal column was curved. The femur was strongly bowed and the knee joint was angled, all of which was taken to indicate that Neanderthal man shuffled along with his knees slightly bent, and his head thrust forward in an ape-like gait. Based upon this interpretation, various 'reconstructions' of Neanderthal man appeared, depicting a savage brute complete with a covering of shaggy hair, and posing in the attitude which is popularly expected in a cave-man ancestor.

Further evidence, however, began to accumulate, which was to cast doubt on whether Neanderthal man was our immediate forerunner. This was as follows:

1. BRAIN CAPACITY

The volume of the La Chapelle-aux-Saints skull, which was at first thought to be small, was remeasured by Boule to give a surprising 1,600 cc., which is significantly above the present day average. Boule ignored this factor and emphasized the ape-like characteristics of the skull and skeleton.

Measurement of many other Neanderthal skulls, however, showed that their brain capacities were on average at least as large, if not slightly larger than *Homo sapiens*. Naturally an explanation for this was sought, for a race of men with larger brains, and presumably therefore more intelligent, should not have been superseded by one with a smaller brain.

When dealing with this problem, authors of popular books either comment that it is quality of brain, not quantity which counts, or point out that the whale possesses the largest brain, and therefore size should be related to body weight. We have already discussed on p.48 this dubious change of arguments, one being used when dealing with large capacities, the other being used with small capacities.

2. LA CHAPELLE-AUX-SAINTS SKELETON

Boule's description of this skeleton, with its primitive ape-like posture, set the pattern for the popular image of Neanderthal man for many years. This view was challenged in 1957 by two anatomists, W. Straus of the John Hopkins University and A. J. E. Cave of St. Bartholomew's Hospital Medical College, who re-examined this skeleton [115]. They considered that Boule was incorrect on a number of points:

(a) The individual had suffered from severe arthritis, which affected the vertebrae, which would not have been so badly curved in a normal individual, and the jaw also had been affected.

GLACIAL PERIOD	NEANDERTHAL—HOMO SAPIENS		HOMO-SAPIENS
WURM	[Classic Neanderthal] Mt Carmel		
	Saccopastore Ehringsdorf Krapina		Fontechevade
RISS			
	Steinheim		Swanscombe
MINDEL		(Pekin & Java)	Vertesszöllos
	Mauer jaw (= Heidelberg)		
GUNZ			

Fig.39. Datings of mixed Neanderthal and Homo sapiens types

(b) The big toe was not 'prehensile' as Boule claimed.

(c) The pelvis was not ape-like.

Normal Neanderthal man was thus shown to be fully upright and remarkably like modern man. In their report, they commented:

> If he could be reincarnated and placed in a New York subway—provided that he were bathed, shaved and dressed in modern clothing—it is doubtful whether he would attract any more attention than some of its other denizens.

3. HOMO SAPIENS

The discovery of Neanderthal man with his primitive appearance probably explains why many of the discoveries of *Homo sapiens* in earlier strata were dismissed or ignored. However, some skulls were found with a mixture of modern and Neanderthal features, whilst three discoveries of portions of the brain case (Swanscombe, Fontéchevade and Vertesszöllos) were fully *Homo sapiens*. The importance of these skulls is that they pre-dated or were contemporary with the era of the 'classic' Neanderthals (Fig.39). We will briefly describe these fossils and the circumstances of their discovery.

(a) *Swanscombe*

In 1935, A. T. Marston, who regularly searched a gravel quarry at Swanscombe in North Kent for fossils, noticed a bone protruding from the side of the excavated face. Knowing well that the discovery of an unusual fossil could create a storm and be subject to much criticism, he took great care to obtain a verification of his discovery [24p193]. As he was alone, he decided to remove the fossil, which was the occipital bone of the brain case, as it was likely to be covered in the shifting gravel, but he marked the spot and brought a quarry mechanic to see the site. He then sketched and photographed the location. He continued the search and the following year found the left parietal bone of the skull, and again photographed the spot. The

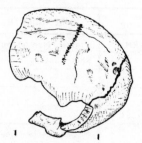

Fig.40. The Swanscombe skull

later piece fitted the other exactly. With such precautions there could be little suggestion of the fossil being a 'plant'. In 1955 a further piece of the brain case, the right parietal, was found which fitted the others (Fig.40).

The bones formed a considerable portion of a thick *Homo sapiens* brain case, whilst the fossils found with it clearly placed it in the Mindel-Reiss Interglacial. The existence of *Homo sapiens* at such an early date presented a major problem to the anthropologists, for what is rarely appreciated is that this early period makes Swanscombe man exist not very long after Pekin and Java man. As these are the fossils which are presented as the main primitive links with man, Swanscombe man was an embarrassment, and not readily accepted by some experts.

It is also somewhat unexpected that the immediate successor to these fossil men of the Far East should be a modern type Englishman, whose remains had been found close at hand in the Kentish countryside. In addition, no intermediate links have been found between these two locations, which fit into the short time interval, separating the periods to which they are attributed.

Marston's caution prevented any charge of a hoax and the skull is now accepted as a genuine fossil. Such acceptance was not without considerable investigation. Galley Hill man, another example of early *Homo sapiens*, had been subjected to the Fluorine test. As it contained much less Fluorine than fossils at the Swanscombe site and others—as we have said, over half a mile away—it was rejected as being a late or intrusive burial, and could therefore be safely removed from its awkward position in the line of man's ancestry. These tests included the Swanscombe skull, but as it contained the same Fluorine content as the adjacent fossils, as one might have expected, it could not be rejected on *this* account.

Swanscombe man was therefore accepted into the missing-link 'club', but not without considerable reluctance, as can be seen from a footnote by Le Gros Clark, which says:

It will be agreed that, however sound the evidence for the antiquity of the Swanscombe bones may appear to be, this isolated discovery pointing to the existence of *H. Sapiens* in Europe during the second interglacial period needs to be confirmed (just because it *is* an isolated discovery) by the accession of further, and more complete, material. [7p68]

A further investigation on this fossil was carried out by Weiner and Campbell in 1964, who made numerous measurements of the skull [116]. After comparing them with a number of Iron Age skulls from Lachish in Palestine as a reference for *Homo sapiens*, and various Neanderthal skulls, they came to the conclusion that Swanscombe possessed more Neanderthal features than was generally realized, and was not therefore completely *Homo sapiens*. The use of complex measurements and statistics, to show that what most experts had considered as a perfectly human skull was half-way to being Neanderthal, is difficult to accept.

In their paper they quote a number of experts who also considered Swanscombe to have Neanderthal characteristics. One of them is Weidenreich, of whom they say, 'Weidenreich (1940, 1943) finds grounds for aligning Swanscombe not only with Steinheim, but also with the classic Neanderthal group.' They quote an extract from his 1940 paper, in which he mentions that the occipital torus of Swanscombe is like Steinheim and the Neanderthal group. When one goes to his 1943 paper, however, one finds that Weidenreich says:

> The Swanscombe skull is not a primitive hominid skull but has all the characteristics of a modern human skull—so far as those cranial bones which have been preserved permit of judgement. If it could be proved that the missing frontal bones had a frontal torus, the skull could be placed in the same group with the Steinheim skull or the Skhul population of Mount Carmel. As long as this proof is *not* brought forward, the nature of the skull remains doubtful. [100p273]

The *frontal* torus he refers to are the eyebrow ridges, the bones of which have not been found for the Swanscombe skull. He seems clearly convinced that the skull is more human than anything else.

(b) *Fontéchevade*
In 1947, whilst excavating Upper and Middle Palaeolithic deposits in a cave, Mlle. G. Henri-Martin reached a thick layer of stalagmites which overlaid 20–30 ft. thick older deposits. In these deeper layers she found a skull cap very similar to *Homo sapiens* (Fig.41). A number of crude stone tools, which became more simple with depth, together with animal fossils, indicated a Riss-Wurm Interglacial period for dating the skull. Although this is later than the Swanscombe dating, it still makes it contemporary with, or even before, the period during which the 'classic' Neanderthals lived.

Fig.41. The Fontéchevade skull   Fig.42. The Vertesszöllos skull
fragment

(c) *Vertesszöllos* (*Homo sapiens Palaeo-hungaricus*)
This fossil, found in Hungary in 1965, consists of the occipital part of
a *Homo sapiens* skull (Fig.42), with an estimated brain capacity of
about 1,400 cc. The most significant facts about this discovery are,
firstly, the very early date of the *Mindel* Glaciation, to which geological and radiometric tests attribute it, and secondly, that at this level,
simple stone tools, fire, burnt bone and human teeth had also been
found. From this, *Homo sapiens existed, made stone tools and used fire at
the same time as Pekin and Java man, who could not therefore be his ancestors!*

This striking conclusion, which is simply deducible from the time
charts given in Fig.14 is most damaging to the status of these well
established fossils, but this fact is not made apparent in any of the
textbooks on the subject.

As with the Swanscombe skull, Vertesszöllos did not conform to
the accepted sequence. A comparison of this small portion of a skull
was made with that of *Homo erectus* (Java and Pekin man) by Wolpoff,
who subjected it to numerous measurements, and concluded as
follows—(V2 is the reference number to the Vertesszöllos occipital
skull fragment).

> In sum, it seems likely that V2 is the occipital of a *Homo erectus*. V2's
> similarity to the Swanscombe material is not surprising in view of the
> strong possibility that the English cranium is a member of the same
> lineage somewhat later in time. [119]

As we have already noted, Weiner and Campbell, using a similar
approach to Wolpoff, had concluded that the Swanscombe skull had
affinities not to *Homo erectus* but to Neanderthal man!

Turning now to the skulls which show a mixture of modern and
Neanderthal characteristics of varying degrees, we will briefly mention the principal finds.

(a) *Mauer jaw* (Heidelberg man), Germany. Gunz-Mindel Interglacial. A very large jaw, but with small modern type teeth. There
is considerable debate on its position relative to *Homo sapiens*, some
considering it to be a form intermediate between Pithecanthropus
and Neanderthal.

(b) *Steinheim skull*, Germany. Has a mixture of Neanderthal and human characteristics with the emphasis on the latter. This skull is interesting in view of the Mindel-Riss Interglacial date to which it is now ascribed. This makes it contemporaneous with the human Swanscombe skull, with which it is often compared.

(c) *Saccopastore skulls*, Italy. Two skulls were found, with mixed characteristics. They are given a Riss-Wurm Interglacial dating.

(d) *Krapina*, Yugoslavia. Portions of five skulls, which had some Neanderthal traits, and numerous modern skeletal bones, comprising a total of about twenty individuals. Some of the bones had been burnt by fire. Mousterian artefacts were found with them, and they are dated as Riss-Wurm Interglacial.

(e) *Ehringsdorf brain case, and two jaws*, Germany. These fossils possessed mainly Neanderthal characteristics, but the shape of the forehead was modern. The brain case was badly damaged and there are considerable gaps between the pieces in the reconstruction. The fossils were found with Mousterian type artefacts, and are dated as Riss-Wurm interglacial.

(f) *Mt. Carmel* (Tabun and Skuhl caves—Palestine). The Tabun skeleton was of a woman with marked Neanderthal characteristics. The skull was badly broken and there are large gaps in the reconstruction.

The Skuhl cave, which was adjacent to the Tabun cave, contained the remains of about ten individuals, six of them being fairly complete skeletons. All appear to have been buried, as the bones were in proper relation to one another. No grave furniture was found, however. These fossils were quite modern, but with a wide range of Neanderthal characteristics, some of which were not unlike the adjacent Tabun skeleton. Mousterian artefacts, identical to those found in the Tabun cave, were found with them and the fossils are given a similar Wurm glaciation date.

Whether the occupants of these two caves were contemporary is debatable, but the discoverer, Miss D. Garrod, considers they were closely associated. This conjunction between *Homo sapiens* and Neanderthal has led some to suggest that there was intermarriage between them, but this is disputed by others. Clark considers that 'it is probably more appropriate to regard them as representative of early types of Homo not completely diversified specifically' [7p73]. Had these fossils been found in very early layers, this proposal would have been acceptable. However, they are virtually contemporary with the classic Neanderthal period, and had been preceded by all the Neanderthal-Homo and pure *Homo sapiens* types which we have given above.

The Neanderthal problem

It is generally accepted that the emergence of Neanderthal man was as a variety of *Homo sapiens*. A slightly different explanation is that there was a common ancestor, from whom developed the Neanderthal men on one hand and *Homo sapiens* at the same time. There is also little disagreement regarding the sudden disappearance of Neanderthal man from the scene, to be replaced by Cro-Magnon man (who is almost identical to *Homo sapiens*) after a definite gap in time, and with much more sophisticated equipment for hunting and very cultured ornaments and sculptures. This gap between the two periods is seen in many of the excavations where both cultures have been found. Often, between the Neanderthal layer (Mousterian) and the later *Homo sapiens* types (Cro-Magnon, Grimaldi or Chancelade men— Magdalenian or Aurignacian cultures), there is a distinct layer containing no fossil evidence of man, known as 'sterile' layers.

Constable makes every effort in his book *The Neanderthals*, in the beautifully illustrated Time-Life series on 'The Emergence of Man', to show that man evolved from the Neanderthals with no real break between them. He nevertheless has to admit:

> Fossils might provide a more direct line of inquiry than tools into the fate of the Neanderthals—provided enough could be found. If there were a complete series of fossils from all over the world dated from about 30,000 to 50,000 years ago, any amateur could study the remains and tell what happened to the Neanderthals.
>
> Regrettably, the trail of humanity through this period is not at all well-marked by bones. No Neanderthal fossil has been given a reliable date more recent than 40,000 years ago. The oldest securely dated modern men come from Czechoslovakia; they lived about 26,000 years ago. A few other fossils may belong in the intervening millenia, but their dates have not yet been fixed. There is a fossil gap, and it holds secure the Neanderthal mystery. [11p127]

He considers various explanations for the gaps between Neanderthal man and *Homo sapiens*, but puts forward as the more persuasive one of the Lieberman-Crelin theory of the development of the vocal chords of the pharynx. By studying the *bones* of the neck vertebrae and the base of the skull of La Chapelle-aux-Saints skeleton, which they later extended to other Neanderthal fossils, they came to the conclusion that the pharynx of Neanderthal man was small. He could, therefore, possess only a very limited vocabulary, perhaps only 10 per cent compared with modern man, which would have put him at a severe disadvantage in competition with a more advanced invader.

Constable also gives an account of the extension of this theory by Pilbeam, who, by studying the development of the pharynx of *newly born infants*, considered that Neanderthal man could have very quickly evolved full speech by the lowering of the voice box and the underside of the skull arching upwards to form a larger resonant cavity

These changes could have affected the whole of the skull, transforming the low browed, muzzle-like face of Neanderthal man into the high-domed skull of Cro-Magnon man!

Constable admits that the Lieberman-Crelin hypothesis has been 'vigorously disputed' and 'widely challenged', which is understandable, for to attempt to reconstruct a voice box, which has long disappeared, by examining the adjacent bones, must clearly involve a very large number of unprovable assumptions. Similarly, the acceptance as a fact that the development of the pharynx in man is paralleled by its development in newly born infants, sounds remarkably like the theory of recapitulation, which as we have already pointed out, is now discredited. It even contradicts the theory of paedomorphosis (or 'Peter Pan' evolution), which says that some modern adult forms resemble stages in the development of the young of the ancestors, the development having been 'arrested'. Pilbeam, however, claims that Neanderthals developed in the same way as the young child of modern man!

These theories have been heavily criticized as there is little real supporting evidence which would allow them to become 'proven facts'. Unfortunately, some hypotheses tend to become accepted as 'facts' after a time, and the speculative nature of the evidence makes them difficult to disprove!

A POSSIBLE SOLUTION

Thus far we have set out the situation, as it is presented in the various books and publications. The generally accepted view of Neanderthal man is that he evolved from an earlier *Homo sapiens*-like stock, only to disappear suddenly from the scene, to be later replaced by Cro-Magnon man (who differed little from modern man), with a noticeable gap in time between the two cultures, certainly as far as Europe is concerned.

We would now, however, like to refer to two papers published in *Nature*, which, whilst they do not basically contradict the main sequence of events given above, do throw quite a different light on the whole question of the origins of Neanderthal man.

Evidence of rickets

The first of these papers is by F. Ivanhoe and bears the intriguing title of 'Was Virchow right about Neanderthal?' [117]. His opening paragraph says:

> Nearly a hundred years ago Virchow diagnosed rickets in the Neandertal bones, accounting so for their peculiar simian cast. Though this was not the first time such an opinion had been published, it was the first authoritative statement by one expertly acquainted with the disease who was also personally familiar with the fossil material. As other

diluvial hominids of the same type turned up in Belgium and France and the day was carried for Darwinism, however, Virchow's carefully argued and factual diagnosis concerning the earlier finds became discredited—by association, if never objectively. But the growth of knowledge since, anthropological as well as medical, suggests that Virchow's view may have been essentially correct.

He then considers the strong evidence of rickets in Neanderthal man. We summarize briefly the main points of this paper as follows:

1. Rickets are caused by a lack of vitamin D in the body. This vitaman can be obtained by exposure of the body to direct sunlight, as the ultra-violet rays produce it in the skin. Also fatty fish and egg yolk are rich in vitamin D, whilst there is little in fats and milk and virtually none in meat and vegetables.

2. Neanderthal characteristics can be related to two factors:
   (a) Latitude. In general, those skulls found in the more northerly latitudes have strong Neanderthal characteristics, whilst for those nearer to the equator, this is much less conspicuous.
   (b) Palaeoclimate. Skulls found at the same latitude show variations between them which can be related to the climate during which they existed. Those living during cold periods, again, were more 'Neanderthal' than those during warmer periods.

3. Examination of a number of Neanderthal skulls and skeletons showed ample evidence of rickets. (These are bowing of the legs, enlargement of the joints, curvature of the spine, 'squaring' of the head and other skeletal and dental deformities.) In addition, direct evidence of a deficiency of vitamin D was obtained by the laboratory examination of sections of teeth and bones.

   Furthermore, it has long been accepted that 'the Neanderthal child is a small replica of the adult—a situation unique among primates. . . .' Rickets is most active between six and twenty-four months of age, and *every* Neanderthal child skull examined showed evidence of severe rickets.

4. Cro-Magnon man, who succeeded Neanderthal, had a regular supply of vitamin D, as evidenced by the fishing tools which he is known to have possessed.

5. From this, Ivanhoe concludes that Neanderthal man was evolved 'from an advanced *Homo erectus* (=pre-sapiens) of the Ehringsdorf/Fontéchevade/Saccopastore/Rabat or similar stock, whose thick bones have been deformed by rickets in childhood and perhaps various grades of osteomalacia in adulthood'.

   He considers that Neanderthal man was deficient in vitamin D due to:
   (a) Unsuitable diet. He had abundant meat but there is little or no evidence of the consumption of fish or eggs.
   (b) Inadequate ultra-violet light. The cold, overcast climate in

the more northerly latitude would severely limit the penetration of these rays, and furthermore, the low temperatures would force him to shelter in rock caves. In the lower latitudes, whilst there would be adequate ultra-violet light from the sun, this would not suffice in conditions of over-crowding or if the custom of purdah was practiced. (Purdah is the complete covering of women in clothing, which is still carried on in some Middle East countries even today.)

Thus, despite the scorn with which Virchow's views of Neanderthal man was treated, it now appears that he was probably right all the time!

Evidence of syphilis

The second paper is by D. J. M. Wright [118] entitled 'Syphilis and Neanderthal man', in which he points out that many of the symptoms of rickets are similar to those of congenital syphilis. He mentions that it was the curve of the long bones, and particularly the backward curve of the femur, which made Virchow consider that Neanderthal man was *Homo sapiens* with rickets. These symptoms could be due to syphilis, which might also account for the bones being so short and stout. He says:

> In societies with poor nutrition, rickets and congenital syphilis frequently occur together. The distinction between the two is extremely difficult without modern biochemical, serological and radiographic aids. The degree of confusion can be gauged by Parrot's untrue aphorism 'without hereditary syphilis, there is no rickets'.

That Neanderthal man was an aberrant form of modern man is supported by the authors of *Fossil Men* who say:

> In the Mousterian period it represented a belated type existing side by side with the direct ancestors of Homo sapiens; its relation to the latter was similar to that which exists at the present day between the races we call inferior and the superior races. Perhaps one might go so far as to say that it was a degenerate species.

From these two papers there seems to be good evidence that as far as European history is concerned, Neanderthal man was a degenerate form of existing *Homo sapiens*, suffering from malnutrition and rickets, possibly living promiscuously, which allowed the widespread infection of syphilis. The whole race appears to have been swept from history, to be later replaced by modern man with a higher culture from the East.

SECTION VII

THE AFRICAN APE-'MEN'

Since 1925, a number of ape skulls and bones have been recovered from two areas of the African continent—South Africa, around the Transvaal area, and East Africa, at the Olduvai Gorge, around Lake Rudolf, at Hadar in Ethiopia and at Laetolil. It is claimed that these apes show a number of 'human' characteristics in certain details of their teeth, skull, etc., and are therefore the primordial offshoot from the ape line, which eventually developed into man. This theory has received criticism from a number of experts, particularly when the first discoveries were made, and there is still considerable debate on the precise position which these fossils should occupy in the ascent to man.

It is also acknowledged that dating of these fossils, relative to the European periods (glaciations, etc.) is difficult, due to the very different climatic conditions to which the African continent has been subjected. Periods of considerable rainfall (Pluvials) and drier periods between them (Interpluvials) are said to be correlated with the glacial and interglacial periods in Europe. The correlation which appears in many books is:

Gamblian pluvial	—	Wurm Glaciation
Kanjeran pluvial	—	Riss Glaciation
Kamasian pluvial	—	Mindel Glaciation
Kageran pluvial	—	Gunz Glaciation

Professor E. S. Wayland, Director of the Ugandan Geological Survey, was said to be obsessed by the need to find a correlation with European glacials, and first proposed this sequence, whilst Leakey was keen to find similar evidence in Kenya [9p56]. Professor R. F. Flint of Yale visited Kenya in 1957 specifically to investigate this subject, and in his report [142] accepts that there was some evidence for the last pluvial. He dismisses most of the others due to inadequate evidence and suggests that the normal stratigraphic methods (strata, fossils and cultures) should be adopted, using Olduvai as a basis.

Some authorities still use the pluvial correlation for dating, but at the Third Pan African Congress in 1955 it was agreed that Pluvials dating layers should basically only be used in the area in which they have been recognized and indexed, and applications outside East Africa required further corrobation [26p118]. In addition it was acknowledged that the Pluvials were not even synchronous throughout the Continent. [26p141]

174

Leakey mentions [22p100] that Dr. Max Schlosser had reported the discovery of jaws and teeth of a primate from Egypt, just at the turn of the century, which Leakey says was the fossil evidence needed to support Darwin's theory that Africa was likely to be the continent where man originated. As we have seen in the Pekin man section, Professor Schlosser also predicted that man's ancestors would be found on the continent of Asia.

I would contend that all the fossils discovered on the African continent (which are known as the *Australopithecines*), and that are claimed to be ancestral to man, are simply those of different types of apes. It is only by a close examination of, say, the teeth, shape of a jaw, or minor bones of the skull that any 'human' characteristics can be imputed, for they are all very ape-like.

Do these small features prove that these animals were the precursors of man? I would suggest not. With so many different species, extinct and living, there is a very wide range of possible forms which any particular feature of the skeleton may take, and some of these are bound to be more like those in humans than others. For example, seen from above, the shape of the jaws in some apes is almost rectangular, whilst in others it is more curved. As the human jaw is curved roughly in the shape of a V or a parabola, those apes possessing the more curved jaw are considered to be 'progressive prehominids'. A similar line of reasoning is used for other features, whilst the fact that the animal is only one of a wide range of apes is ignored.

We have already considered the unacceptably heavy reliance which is placed upon slight differences of the jaws and teeth. Just how confused and contradictory the whole situation is can be illustrated. One writer in *Nature* said in discussing the African fossils, 'The size relationship between the teeth and the mandibular structure is particularly relevant.' In an issue only a few months later, however, another writer said, 'Mandibular robustness is notoriously variable in living hominoids, and has little taxonomic value.' He states that the right characters must be chosen to show that the hominids are taxonomically distinct. He also mentions as a further indication of variability that, 'Even in the normally large crested gorilla, smaller females have no crest.'

This whole question of wide variability was considered by Schultz in a section entitled 'Age changes, sex differences and variability as factors in the classification of the primates' [34p85]. In this he demonstrates the wide range of characteristics which exist in members of the *same species*.

Another feature is that many of these South African fossils were broken into pieces and sometimes found mixed up with the fragmented skulls of baboons and other primates and animals. Clearly we have here a repetition of the Pekin man skulls, which were also broken open and mixed with the remains of other animals. Most of these South African fossil sites similarly consisted of a mixture of animals and looked uncommonly like a kitchen refuse dump. The Australopithecines are surely just simply animals who were hunted for food, either by carnivores or by true men.

The view that the Australopithecines are nothing more than apes is supported by Sir Solly Zuckerman, an expert on these animals. In a symposium edited by Sir Julian Huxley, he says:

The apparent hiatus in man's evolutionary history between the early Miocene and the earlier part of the Middle Pleistocene has so far been filled not by the hard facts one would prefer, but mainly by speculation.

After an evaluation of the features of the Australopithecines, he concludes that they were 'predominantly ape-like and not man-like creatures'.[15p347]. In his book, 'Beyond the Ivory Tower' he summarises the very extensive investigations he and his assistants carried out on a comparison of the Australopithecines with apes and man. They found that their brain capacities were no bigger than the brain of a gorilla, and indeed mentions that their volumes 'were highly overestimated', and more important the evidence was very clear that *they did not walk upright*.

He bewails the fact that his results have been virtually ignored by the experts and comments:

Once Dr. Robert Broom, one of the group of wise men who had never doubted 'that the Piltdown mandible belongs to the same individual as the associated brain-case', had endorsed with his authoritative voice the original assertions of Professor Raymond Dart, and as soon as Professor Sir Wilfred Le Gros Clark added his support to their views (at the start he was a 'disbeliever' or at least an agnostic), a host of lesser known anatomists and anthropologists fell into line, and the Australopithecines automatically became members of the same family. the Hominidae, as ourselves . . .

More recently, Oxnard made a detailed examination of these fossils, and summarized his results in an article in *Nature* [4th December 1975, v.258, p.389–95] with the intriguing title of 'The place of the Australopithecines in human evolution: grounds for doubt?' In this he shows the very wide gap between these two lines. and admits that:

it is rather unlikely that any of the Australopithecines, including Homo habilis and Homo africanus can have any direct phylogenetic link with the genus Homo . . . but adds: . . . except perhaps at earlier times.

Bearing all these considerations in mind, it is obvious that all the Australopithecines are varieties of apes. This should be clearly borne in mind when reading the rest of this book, for *all* the fossils discovered—except 1470 man and the Kanam jaw—are apes whose claim to possess human characteristics is based upon flimsy and unconvincing evidence.

SECTION VIIA

SOUTH AFRICA

Fig.43 shows the location of the main fossil sites.

Taungs (*Australopithecus africanus*) 1924. (Fig.44)

Front of the face and lower jaw with a natural cast of the brain of a six-year-old ape. Found with numerous remains of other animals, often with the marks of blows having been inflicted.

These fossils are found in hillocks, which consist of masses of bones which have become cemented together. The fossil was handed to Dr. R. A. Dart, Professor of Anatomy at Witwatersrand University at Johannesburg, who had worked under Grafton Elliot-Smith at University College, London. Keith, who recommended him for the Witwatersrand post, was nevertheless concerned by Dart's '. . . flightiness, his scorn for accepted opinion, the unorthodoxy of his outlook.' [24p180]

On examining the skull, Dart considered that the human features it possessed were of considerable importance and rushed a notice to London announcing his discovery [122]. However his view that the fossil was a link with man was treated with great scorn by the scientists of the day, who considered the skull to be a variety of chimpanzee and called it 'Dart's baby'.

Dart appears to have ceased hunting for fossils until 1945, when he was tempted to take it up again in the Makapansgat area, and discovered the remains which he called *Australopithecus prometheus*.

Sterkfontein (*Australopithecus transvaalensis*, or *Plesianthropus transvaalensis* or *Australopithecus africanus*). 1936 and 1947–8. (Fig.45)

A skull, several jaws and numerous teeth, portions of a pelvis, fragments of long bones.

When Dart was being criticized for his assessment of the Taung's skull, he was visited by Dr. Broom, a medical practitioner, who was also living in South Africa at the time. He was convinced that Dart was correct, and eventually began his own investigation at Sterkfontein in 1936.

Broom, who had been born in Scotland, had lived in Australia and now lived in Cape Town, his main interest being to search these continents for the fossil links between mammals and reptiles. Broom's first estimate of the brain capacity of the skull he found at Sterkfontein was about 600 cc., but this was later reduced to 435 cc. Following his discoveries at this site [123], he made a lecture tour of America, describing his fossils.

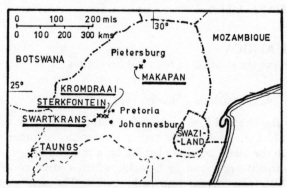

Fig.43. The main South African fossil sites

Moore describes Broom's strong personality at some length, mentioning his quick fire judgement, his forthright nature and the rapidity with which he publicized the fossils he discovered. He roused the opposition of the authorities, and at one time he was only allowed to work in collaboration with 'a competent field geologist' and not at Sterkfontein. He ignored this order and soon found a skull at the forbidden site. This site had always been a rich source of fossil apes' bones ever since the 1880's (when it had been mined for gold), so much so that an advertisement said 'Come to Sterkfontein and find the missing link'!

Later in the excavations, a bone tool was discovered, worn smooth with use and, in a layer above the fossil strata, about two hundred simple stone tools were recovered.

Kromdraii (*Paranthropus robustus* or *Australopithecus robustus*). 1938 and 1941.

Small portion of left side of skull and upper jaw and right half of lower jaw. Ends of a few limb bones. A juvenile lower jaw.

These discoveries were originally made by a schoolboy, who took Broom to the site, which was only two miles away from Sterkfontein [124]. Broom searched further at this location, but found little more at that time. Three years later, however, a juvenile lower jaw was found.

Swartkrans (1. *Paranthropus crassidens*. 2. *Telanthropus capensis*). 1948–52.

One fairly complete skull, several incomplete skulls. Upper and lower jaws and teeth. A few ends of limb bones. Part of a pelvis. None of

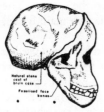

Fig.44. The Taungs skull

Fig.45. The Sterkfontein skull

Fig.46. The Swartkrans skull
(Paranthropus crassidens)

Fig.47. The Makapansgat skull

the skulls (named *Paranthropus crassidens*—Fig.46) was sufficiently complete for the brain capacity to be checked.

This site, which was only one mile from Sterkfontein, was searched by Broom and Robinson, and yielded the remains of a number of fossil apes [126]. As they were larger than those found at the other sites, it was considered that there were two parallel lines of progress, one being of a small 'gracile' type, the other being a 'robust' type. There is much controversy not only about the relationship between these two types, but also their correlation with those fossils found in East Africa.

At this site, Broom found a lower jaw, a fragment of another jaw and an upper jaw, and small fragments of a radius and a metacarpal, which he classified as *Telanthropus capensis*. They were found in a small pocket of breccia, cut into the main strata, which contained the jaw and a few remains of very small mammals [127]. These fossils differed from any of the other bones found in the area, and they were later attributed to the species *Homo erectus*, who may have preyed upon the Australopithecines. This classification was rejected by Le Gros Clark after he had visited South Africa and inspected the fossils. [7p129 & p170]

Makapansgat (*Australopithecus prometheus* or *Australopithecus africanus*). 1947–62. (Fig.47).

A considerable quantity of fossils was recovered, including a cranium, parts of others, jaws and long bones.

Dart took up field exploration again in 1945 and began work at the Limeworks Cave site [125]. Almost all these bones came from the dump of rejected material at the entrance to the quarry. They were able, however, to correlate the finds with the two main bone bearing strata in the excavations.

Dart found many bone tools, which he said had been used as clubs, daggers, saws, choppers, etc. and numerous baboon skulls were discovered, most of them having clearly been smashed open by heavy blows. Clark suggested to him that they may have been broken open by the ape-men, and after further investigation, Dart considered that a number of long bones of animals had been used as the blunt instrument [128 & 133]. However, some of the skulls of the Australopithecines are also broken in a similar fashion, and Dart presumed that the blows had been inflicted by their fellow creatures!

The Limeworks Cave was only one of several at Makapansgat which gave evidence of fire, which was not discovered at any other hominid South African site. The association of fire with his hominid fossil prompted Dart to name it *Australopithecus prometheus*. The accepted sequence of events is that Pekin man, a much later and more advanced pre-human, was the first to know the use of fire. Obviously its appearance in conjunction with such a primitive ancestor at Makapansgat was a matter of considerable significance, and we examine in Appendix V the discovery of the evidence, and the investigations which led to its later rejection as proof of the existence of fire.

Teilhard de Chardin

Teilhard de Chardin's view of the Australopithecines was rather cautious. He considered at first that they were a branch of development which, however, did not continue to progress up to Man. He twice visited the fossil sites in Africa in 1951 and 1953. His first visit was financed by the Wenner Gren Foundation (originally named the Viking Fund), and on his return, he was made a 'research associate'. His prestige as an expert on human origins had grown considerably, and on his second visit he was given the task of organizing anthropological research in the whole of Africa, south of the Sahara. Some of the diggings were directly financed by the foundation, and his control of considerable funds resulted in his being courted by various friends and colleagues. [29p316]

According to Speaight, Teilhard considered Asia was an abortive attempt, as it had not led to *Homo sapiens*, from which one presumes his Pekin man was included! Neither did he consider the Australopithecines as leading on to man, but now thought it probable that the true roots of human ancestry would be found in the Uganda–Kenya area. This area is now such a rich source of fossils, that one writer was prompted to say, 'Today, Africa, particularly East Africa, is turning out human fossil remains with the despatch of an assembly line. . . .' [14p64]

APPENDIX V

THE EVIDENCE OF FIRE AT MAKAPANSGAT

The first reference to this site was by Dart as early as 1925 [121]. Workers at the Limeworks quarry had driven a 50 ft. deep tunnel and throughout its length there was a 4 ft. thick bone bed. Some of the bones had a *blackened and charred appearance*, and tests carried out by the Government chemists showed that free carbon was present. From this, Dart considered the bone bed 'was a kitchen midden result of human occupation at a remote epoch', and suggested that the cave should be investigated further.

In 1948, in his paper reporting his discovery of *Australopithecus prometheus* at the Limeworks site [125], he mentioned his earlier 1925 paper with regard to the evidence of fire at this site, and continued:

> Detailed chemical analyses of glassy and ashy materials and microscopic examination of these fluxes, *ashes and charred bones* during the past two years have furnished Dr. V. L. Bosazza with ample corroboration . . . about the systematic use of fire by these primitive troglodytes.

Thus at this stage there were two independent investigations, both of which agreed fire *had* been used.

In 1950, Broom, in his book *Finding the Missing Link* [p73], referred to Dart's 1925 claim and said:

> He does not appear to have examined the breccia to any extent, but he found in it some black particles which proved to be carbon. Dart therefore assumed that the bones were collected by an early type of man who knew how to make fire.

On page 74, dealing with the 1948 finds, he says

> . . . and he thinks it knew how to make fire. I unfortunately do not agree with him that there is any satisfactory evidence that he made fire . . .

Broom does not give any reason why he rejects Dart's inference of fire following the tests which were carried out, neither does he give an explanation for the presence of carbon.

It was suggested that the glassy material may have been generated by a naturally occurring bat guano fire [130], as evidence for such an occurrence had been found at the nearby Cave of Hearths in the same valley. The situation and strata at this site, however, are so different from those at the Limeworks site that it is difficult to see the relevance of this evidence.

Further tests [131] indicated that the blackening of many of the bones was due to oxides of iron and manganese. The suggestion is made that the free carbon found by the earlier investigators was possibly due to the blasting charge used in the quarry, but it is difficult to imagine how enough could have been collected to obtain the positive results they reported.

Even if the staining was due to manganese, it could not explain why some bones were *charred* and in an *ashy* material, which contained *carbon*, as Dart described in 1925.

Dart, writing in his book *Adventures with the Missing Link* in 1959, said it had been questioned

> whether Australopithecus prometheus ever did use fire because up to now we have not been able to repeat finding *large amounts of carbon* reported by the chemists in 1925.... *Minute traces of carbon have been found* but not enough to be regarded as diagnostic of regular hearth making.

When one remembers that by the 1950's the limeworks had been worked out, a possible explanation for the absence of large quantities of ash may be that they had been disposed of in the large dump of rejected material at the mouth of the cave, which was the source of the later bone discoveries. [132]

I would submit that there is good evidence for the existence of fire at the original site. If this is correct, it would further support my contention that the sites are simply the refuse dumps of modern men, the ape skulls being one of many remnants of animals hunted for food.

SECTION VIIB

OLDUVAI GORGE

This site is 100 miles west of Mt. Kilimanjaro (Fig.48), and consists of a 300 ft. deep gorge shaped like a shallow V, which has been cut through five main strata. These strata are horizontal beds which were numbered 1–5 upwards, overlying a basalt layer. Fig.49 gives a diagrammatic section and plan locating the disposition of the main fossil finds which occur in Beds 1 and 2.

The gorge was first explored in 1913 by Dr. Reck, who discovered fossils of giant forms of animals (including apes!), and more important, a modern human skeleton at the top of Bed 2. This latter find was critically examined in view of the early date ascribed to this stratum, and the ensuing correspondence is considered in Appendix VI.

Reck revisited the site in 1931 and with him was Dr. L. S. B. Leakey, who continued exploring this site and others in the area for over thirty years. He was financed by the Wenner-Gren Fund, the National Geographic Society, and Mr. Charles Boise, and as a tribute to the latter, named his first discovery after him.

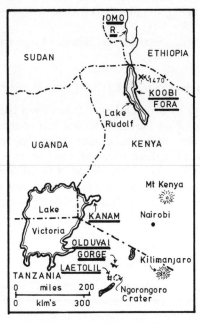

Fig.48. East African fossil sites

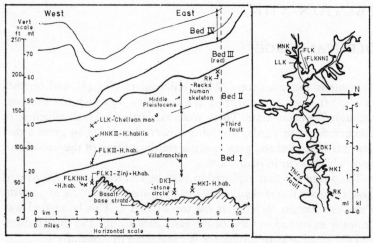

Fig.49. The Olduvai Gorge strata. Plan and stratigraphic section along centre of gorge

In 1932 Leakey discovered fragments of a modern human skull at Kanjera and the front of a lower jaw at Kanam, which he claimed were from early Pleistocene strata. Again, such early dating of *Homo sapiens* resulted in their being submitted to a close investigation, which is reviewed in Appendix VII.

Leakey's main discoveries in the Olduvai Gorge were as follows:

Zinjanthropus boisei. Site FLKI [141]. (See frontispiece)

Discovered in 1959 by Mrs. Leakey, this skull was badly broken, and consisted of much of the face and the rear half of the brain case, but the section between them was almost completely missing. It was accompanied by the fossilized bones of many animals, including pigs and antelopes, which had been deliberately broken up for their marrow. Numerous stone tools, two leg bones, some additional teeth and skull fragments of another individual (later named *Homo habilis*) were also found.

Homo habilis. Site FLKNNI [145] (Fig.50)

250 yd. from the Zinjanthropus site, and 2 ft. lower, some skull fragments, some teeth, two clavicles, a large part of a foot, six finger bones and two ribs were discovered in 1960, and later a lower jaw. With them was a bone tool which Leakey considered to be a 'lissoir'

Fig.50. Homo habilis (site FLKNNI)

Fig.51. 'Chellean' man

for working leather. If this was correct, it would indicate a very advanced culture for this site.

Homo habilis. Site MNKII [148]

Parts of skulls, teeth and jaws were found of two adults in 1963, together with portions of the cranial vault of a younger individual.

Homo habilis. Site FLKII [148]

Skull fragments and teeth were found washed out of the ground and trampled on by cattle. Four hundred pieces were eventually recovered and used in the reconstruction.

Homo habilis. Site MKI [147]

At the very lowest level of Bed 1, part of a jaw was found. On the same level and 1 mile away, however, a rough circle of loosely piled stones was found, possibly forming a wind break. As these stones were discovered in the oldest stratum, this construction is surely unexpected for such an ape-like ancestor.

Based on the various pieces of skulls, etc. of *Homo habilis* which had been discovered, Leakey considered that they were a new genus [147]. This started a heated discussion which is still continuing, but it is overshadowed by the finds at Lake Rudolf. (See Section VIIC.)

'Chellean Man.' Site LLK [146]. (Fig.51)

Fragments of a large skull were found in 1961. This was not unlike Pithecanthropus but bore considerable resemblance to the Steinheim (Neanderthal) skull. Here again, the skull and the 'Chellean' implements found with it are surprisingly advanced for the early Villa-franchian stratum in which they were discovered.

Bolas stones

Reviewing all these fossil apes, we would comment on one particular aspect. In both Beds I and II, numerous spherical stones were found, roughly shaped in the lower layers and almost perfect spheres in the upper strata [149, vol.3, p266]. Leakey considered that they were likely to have been used as bolas. We have already discussed, in the section on Pekin man, the skill which the manufacture and use of this artefact would require. To expect this level of ability in such near-ape ancestors is difficult to accept, and we consider these bolas stones to be yet further proof of the early existence of man.

At Olorgesalie, Leakey found a number of isolated stone balls, and at least twelve sets were in distinct groups of three. Clearly these were bolas stones, but this grouping was said to be probably fortuitous [26p186].

One surprising aspect of Leakey's main report on his discoveries [149] is his rejection of the geological survey, which was originally carried out by Dr. R. Pickering of the Tanganyika Geological Survey. Leakey disagreed with his conclusions and said that much of his report did not fit the visible facts. Leakey subsequently called in an American, Dr. R. Hay, to carry out a fresh survey. Leakey's own geological assessments of his sites have been criticized by others (see Appendix VI and VII), and it is therefore strange that he should have dismissed the report of a highly qualified expert in this field. His detailed reasons for this would have been of interest.

APPENDIX VI

RECK'S HUMAN SKELETON

During his exploration of Olduvai Gorge in 1913, Professor Hans Reck discovered a complete human skeleton in a stratum which contained many fossils of extinct animals. He realized the importance of the discovery, and it is clear from the report [135], which he wrote on his return to Germany, that he took great care to check that it was not an intrusive burial.

His report, which we summarize below, is remarkable for the way in which he investigates even very unlikely possibilities, which could have caused the skeleton to be situated as he found it.

A. *The strata at the site of the skeleton*
As we have seen in the section dealing with the discoveries at Olduvai, the sides of the gorge are basically divisible into five different strata. Reck says that the Red Bank layer (which figured prominently in the ensuing arguments) was almost, but not completely, eroded over the top of Bed II just above the place where the skeleton was found. This layer was continuous with the normal depth on the upstream (west) side of the gorge, whilst downstream (east) it appeared in its full thickness 20 m. lower on the other side of a fault. (Fig.52.)

B. *Fossils*
Reck does not give a detailed description of them but says that fossils in the lower strata were mainly of forest types, whilst those in the upper strata were of a dry, steppe-like type, and that although they were similar to present-day forms, there were nevertheless marked differences. As we have seen (Fig.49), the present date given to the top of Bed II is Middle Pleistocene.

C. *The situation of the skeleton*
The skeleton was virtually complete, lying horizontally, parallel with the layers in the strata at the top of Bed II, and had been slightly dislocated and compressed by the earth pressure. It was cemented into the surrounding strata so strongly that it had to be removed with the aid of a hammer, chisel and nail, *exactly as the animal fossils were removed*. The layers on all four sides were of the same hardness and continuous with the layers in the main strata. This would not be the case if the skeleton had been buried, for they would clearly show signs of disturbance, but on the contrary they were found to be identical to the surrounding material of Bed II.

187

D. *Alternative explanations*

   (i) Reck considers various possibilities, one being the unlikelihood of the skeleton having been buried from the present level of the top of the gorge, as this would have required a dig of 3–4 m. (9–13 ft.) depth. As he points out, erosion is continually making the edge of the gorge recede, and in past times, it would have been several metres further into the gorge.

Other possible explanations for the situation of the skeleton were:

  (ii) That it had fallen to its position with the collapse of rocks which were at a higher level, along some parts of the gorge.

 (iii) That it had been brought to its position by the 'flowing' of this strata when soft.

By examination of the strata, however, he produced evidence which dismissed these possible explanations. Reck's final conclusion is that both the skeleton and the strata were laid down simultaneously at some time in the remote past.

Professor Reck travelled back to Germany, taking the most important part of the skeleton, the skull, with him in his personal baggage, the remainder following in packing cases. The interest which the discovery aroused was considerable, and the *Illustrated London News* of 4th April 1914 carried an article with several pictures.

Leakey's interest

Louis Leakey was very interested in the fossil and visited Germany three times in order to inspect it and talk to Reck. On return from one of his visits he wrote in *Nature* (31st March 1928, v.121, p.499) that Reck said the skeleton was covered by 3 m. of undisturbed alluvial strata, and that no trace of even a shallow grave was found. Leakey, however, doubted if it was as old as Reck claimed.

Due to the First World War, Reck was unable to revisit the site, but when Leakey was arranging to explore the gorge in 1931, he invited Reck to go with him. Accompanying them on the exploration were A. T. Hopwood, Donald MacInnes and a geologist from St. Johns— E. V. (Bunny) Fuchs, who was later to become the famous Sir Vivian Fuchs. When they revisited the exact spot where Reck had discovered the skeleton, Leakey and Hopwood were completely convinced by Reck's evidence and wrote a letter to *Nature* (24th October 1931, vol. 128, p. 724). In this they confirmed that after very careful examination of all the evidence on the spot, it was considered that:

  (a) The skeleton came from Bed II and not Bed IV, as Leakey had earlier suggested.

  (b) Beds III and IV overlay Bed II conformably.

  (c) The skeleton was *Homo sapiens*, who lived during the Upper

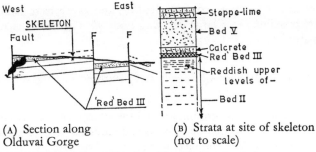

(A) Section along Olduvai Gorge

(B) Strata at site of skeleton (not to scale)

Fig.52. Geology of the site of Reck's human skeleton

Kamasian period. (This would date it in the Mindel-Glacial period, roughly contemporary with Pekin and Java man.)

The criticism

As can be imagined, this sparked off an exchange of correspondence in *Nature*, which culminated in a final letter in 1933. It would be too tedious to give a summary of every item raised in the seven or more letters which appeared in the columns of *Nature*, but I give below the references, together with a summary of the major points upon which I would comment.

1932—27th February—Forster Cooper and Watson

The discovery of a complete skeleton surely indicated an intrusive burial?

1932—14th May—Leakey

He claimed that Bed III, which was a brilliant red colour, was laid down *after* the skeleton became embedded in Bed II, which was yellow, and any admixture of these two different soils if the skeleton had been buried would be immediately visible. Leakey said he saw the skeleton in Munich, whilst it was still embedded in the matrix *and could detect no admixture or disturbance.*

1932—18th June—Forster Cooper and Watson

They point out that any red pebbles from the red Bed III, which may have been included in the returned material around the body may have been discoloured either by the normal methods of bandaging and hardening, used to remove the skeleton, or due to contact with a decaying body. (With regard to this last possibility, one cannot help noticing that in their letter it is very tentatively suggested the first time, for they say: 'It is quite conceivable that their colour *might* be materially altered by contact with a decaying body.' The second reference states more confidently: '. . . and as we have pointed out, mere proximity to a large decaying body *often* alters the character of a matrix'!)

1932—15th October—Leakey's reply (written 14 August at Olduvai Camp)

Measurement of the ground around the stumps of the hut erected by Reck in 1913 indicated that *the site* had eroded 15 cm. (6 in.) between then and 1931. The cliff face, however, had receded 45 cm. to 60 cm. (1 ft. 6 in. to 2 ft.) since 1913.

1932—August

Hopwood wrote an article in *Man* (Article 226, p.192–5) strongly supporting Reck's contention that the skeleton was not intrusive. He says:

> Examination of the site in 1931 confirmed the observation that the bed in which the skeleton lay was undoubtedly, Bed II. The cliff at that point shows the the full thickness of Bed I followed by Bed II, which is reddish in colour at the top. Over the red top of Bed II lies a narrow band, a few inches thick only, of bright red material, the residuum of Bed III. This material is sharply demarcated from the reddish top of II, and forms a continuous conglomeratic layer. It is succeeded by a softer, but still hard bed, the loess-like Bed V, here locally compacted, and by the steppe-lime. Direct evidence bearing on the question of an intrusive burial was not found; for that had been destroyed in the original exhumation, and must now be sought in the original descriptions by Professor Reck. Since there seems to be some danger of Reck's statements being overlooked, the relevant extracts are here reproduced in full.

He then gives some extensive quotations in the original German from Reck's 1914 paper, a 1926 paper, and an unpublished manuscript.

Hopwood concludes: 'It is clear that Professor Reck, when he found the skeleton, thought it possible that he might be dealing with an intrusive burial, that he was careful to look for evidence for this, and that he failed to find it.' Hopwood dismisses the possibility that pebbles from Bed III would have been discoloured by decomposition of the body, and proves that the skeleton was not buried by one of the local Masai tribes. He gives impressive evidence of the hardness of the strata overlying the skeleton, for he relates how their native helpers, working for two days with heavy crowbars, failed to dig a hole 60 cm. sq. × 90 cm. deep (2 ft. sq. × 3 ft. deep).

He repeats Leakey's evidence regarding the rate of erosion and estimates that it could be as high as 3 m. (10 ft.) per century. Two diagrams accompany the article, the main details of which are given in Fig. 52. This was not drawn to scale in Hopwood's article, but from other reports the skeleton appears to have been buried in the main yellow layers of Bed II, and not in the slightly reddish upper layers of that strata. Hopwood (and presumably Leakey) is very definite that the bright red pebbles of Bed III are very distinguishable from the reddish upper layers of Bed II.

1932—13th August

We now come to an important letter by Professor P. G. H. Boswell of Imperial College, London, who was later to figure prominently in the rejection of the human Kanam jaw, which had also been found in early strata. (Appendix VII.)

He had received from Professor Mollison of Munich a sample of the material from around the skeleton and he, Hopwood and Dr. Solomon had analysed it. They found it contained:

(a) *Pea sized bright red pebbles like those of Bed III.*
(b) Chips of limestone like material from Bed V.
(c) A relative abundance of a material not found in Beds II or III but present in Bed IV.

The fact that the sample contained bright red pebbles the size of a pea, which would be easily visible to the naked eye, is very unexpected. Reck was adamant that the skeleton was surrounded by pure Bed II material, and Leakey had actually inspected the matrix whilst it was still round the skeleton, and could detect no admixture. The possibility that the sample from Mollison had become accidentally mixed with other material, or some similar explanation, must surely be considered.

One wonders whether this thought occurred to Boswell, for he specifically states that he was 'assured' about the sample, saying: '. . . Prof. Reck, at Mr. Hopwood's request, persuaded Prof. Th. Mollison of Munich to send us a sample of material which, he assures us, was part "of the material in which the Oldoway skeleton had been embedded".' Was his caution perhaps prompted by the thought that the sample was *not* typical, or by concern lest others should arrive at the same conclusion? Unfortunately, whether the phrase he quoted was made by Reck or Mollison is not clear, as 'he' could refer to either of them.

Cole records [p93] that Leakey made yet another visit to Munich in 1934, where Mollison had examined the skeleton under ultra-violet light to determine the organic content. He had found that the results differed from those obtained from the fossils of animals also from Bed II, which indicated different dates of burial. These tests appear to have convinced Leakey that he was wrong, but in a paper in 1974 [153] Protsch dismissed these tests, saying that 'they later proved invalid', and also mentions that Mollison had found the organic content of the skeleton was identical to those of the animal remains. Cole, however says they differed.

These misleading tests may also have been effective in convincing Reck that he too was wrong in his opinion of the fossil, for both Leakey and Reck, together with Boswell, Hopwood and Solomon signed a final letter of agreement regarding the discovery, which appeared in *Nature* in:

1933—18th March

This letter, far from clarifying the whole situation, only seems to make confusion worse confounded. Leakey had brought back many samples from the Olduvai strata, which had been analysed by Boswell and Solomon, and the results of their examination and conclusions were signed by all the five experts I have mentioned.

The letter is very difficult to follow, for some statements are made which appear to contradict much of what had gone before. I will therefore only summarize a few points made in the letter which are of particular interest to this section, as follows:

(a) Beds II and III have a very similar mineral constitution, both being clearly distinguished from Beds IV and V.

(b) The thin red layer near the site of the skeleton is a 'hillwash' material containing minerals from Beds IV and V.

(c) Samples collected from Bed II 'differ very markedly from the samples of the matrix of the skeleton which were supplied by Professor Mollison from Munich.'

(d) In considering all the data, '... it seems highly probable that the skeleton was intrusive into Bed II ...' and took place just before the deposition of the main depth of Bed V.

Thus, on the basis of laboratory tests on material from the red 'hillwash' material above the site, and on the sample from Professor Mollison (both, incidentally, carried out twenty years after the discovery of the skeleton), the earlier evidence of Leakey's inspection of the original skeleton, and Reck's detailed description of the undisturbed nature of the strata around the skeleton, are swept aside.

I find this final letter very unsatisfactory and I can offer no adequate explanation for Reck's and Leakey's agreement to its contents, for it flatly contradicts all that they had consistently maintained up to that time. One is left to conjecture whether other evidence was provided and discussions took place which went unrecorded, that resulted in Reck and Leakey being prepared to sign this letter.

Protsch's report

To close this section, one further report on the skeleton was made by

Protsch in 1974 [153]. He carried out some dating tests on the fossil, but only the skull could be found at Munich, *for all the rest of the skeleton had disappeared*! Protsch comments:

> Mollison's usage of ultra violet fluorescence to estimate the organic content was one of the first attempts to get some idea of relative age on bones but the method later proved invalid. *He obtained identical results for the organic content of the hominid and the fauna of Bed II, but in fact both are far apart in time.*

Protsch then gives the results of C14 tests which dated the 'hominid' as 16,920 years old. I have already commented on the difficulty of obtaining a reliable C14 date from fossilized bone in section III whilst extra doubt must surround these results, as only 32 per cent of the counter used in the test could be filled, there being only 224 g. of bone available.

Furthermore, a footnote says:

> Several other radiocarbon dates were run, but could be contaminated by either recent or old radiocarbon, since these sample materials were mostly calcrete or fresh water shells.

No information is given on what criteria were used to determine whether a dating result was acceptable or not.

In this report (in which the human skeleton is relegated to the status of 'hominid'), Protsch admits that 'all evidence points to the indigenous position of the skeleton in the stratum in which it was found'. On the basis of his tests, however, he claimed that the burial took place not before Bed V was laid down, as the 1933 letter concluded, but from the middle of this bed.

Conclusion

Reck's original evidence showing that the skeleton was contemporary with Bed II is far more convincing than the doubtful tests which are accepted as showing it to be intrusive. I would contend that this is yet one more fossil proving that *Homo sapiens* existed in very early ages, and I consider that the unsatisfactory way in which this skeleton was dismissed raises more questions than it purports to answer.

APPENDIX VII

THE KANAM JAW

Leakey's discovery of the *Homo sapiens* type Kanam jaw (Fig.53) and Kanjera skull pieces in such very early strata was sufficiently important to warrant the convening of a committee of twenty-seven experts, who examined the evidence from a number of aspects, the results being duly reported in 1933 [136]. The committee largely agreed with the early dating of these human fossils (equating the jaw with Bed I, and the skull pieces with upper Bed II of the Olduvai strata), and congratulated Leakey on his discoveries. This Middle Pleistocene date for the skull pieces would make them contemporary with the Swanscombe skull, but the jaw came from the Lower Pleistocene layer, and therefore was the subject of most of the ensuing correspondence. The committee noted the exceptional thickness of the jaw and the conformation of the parts about the chin, but could see no details which were incompatible with *Homo sapiens*.

Sir Arthur Keith (who was unable to attend the committee) in a review in 1935 of Leakey's book, *The Stone Age Races of Kenya* [138], said that the rear of the chin had a rare bony tumour, which had spread and obscured the normal features in this area, but that the fossil was, however, quite certainly a human jaw such as is often found in primitive humans living today.

Professor Boswell, a member of the committee, visited the site in 1935 for the Royal Society, and his letter in *Nature* [137] was highly critical of Leakey, for he said:

(a) The exact sites could not be found and had not been marked, nor shown on a map.

(b) Leakey had provided an incorrect photo of a different sector in his evidence to the committee.

(c) The clayey beds had frequently suffered much disturbance by slumping and therefore the dating of these bones was doubtful.

(d) Had the committee known of these facts, it is likely that they would have submitted a different report.

Leakey was furious, but his lengthy reply was not accepted by *Nature*. A shorter letter appeared later [139] and in this Leakey said that he had shown Boswell the precise location, and due to malfunctioning of his own camera, had unfortunately used a photo taken by a colleague. This was only provided to give a very general idea of the area to the committee and was not used as evidence. Cole also mentions [p101] that Leakey had marked the spot with iron pegs, as Boswell knew, but they had been stolen by the local natives.

(Boswell had also held that the deposits, said to be clays, were

194

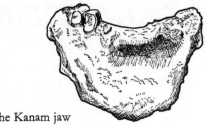

Fig.53. The Kanam jaw

really volcanic agglomerate, which certainly made it look as though Leakey was so incompetent that he was unable to tell the difference between them! Leakey protested and Boswell agreed that this statement only referred to the strata shown in the incorrect photo.)

Despite Leakey's reply, it appears that this single letter by Boswell, completely unsupported by any evidence whatsoever, was sufficient to have these human fossils ignored in subsequent publications for many years. Boule and Vallois in *Fossil Man* [p443] admit that the jaw was fully human, but uncritically accept Boswell's letter as being sufficient for its rejection, and make no mention of Leakey's reply.

Boswell's most damaging assertion that the slumping of the *clay* beds had cast doubt on the dating of the jaw was apparently quite unjustified. The area *is* fissured, but the jaw was found in a mass of *concretionary* bed material [19p48]. Leakey referred to the absence of any proof by Boswell in the 1953 edition of his book *Adam's Ancestors* [p202], and blamed the dominance of the Piltdown fossils (which Boswell strongly championed) for the unacceptability of the evidence for the early existence of man. [22p145]

One aspect of the jaw which received further criticism was the manner in which it was discovered. One of Leakey's most experienced and reliable natives dug out a lump of conglomerate, which was found to contain the jaw. Leakey was called to the spot and they searched for other pieces, but nothing more could be found. It was claimed that *as it was not actually seen in situ by a scientist,* its exact situation must be in doubt, as it may have been washed down to this position. This judgement seems rather harsh, and if it were to be applied to all the accepted fossils, many of them would fail on this score, *including every single discovery made by von Koenigswald's native collectors.*

With further discoveries in East Africa of early man in old strata, Professor Oakley was asked if the Kanam jaw should be reconsidered. In his letter to *Nature* in 1960 [141] on this subject, he mentioned that Tobias had re-examined the jaw (his letter followed Oakley's), and that Sir Arthur Keith had changed his views in 1948, for he then considered that the small front teeth of the Kanam jaw indicated a relationship to Dart's (Australopithecine) fossils rather than to early man. Surely, the fact that Dart's fossils had small front teeth does not make the Kanam jaw any less human, and Keith appears to have ignored the fact that they did not possess a chin.

Tobias, in his letter, said the 'chin' was only a bony reaction to a pathological lesion, and therefore the fossil may be placed somewhere between Atlanthropus and man, but might possibly be Neander-thaloid. As we have seen, this peculiar feature of the tumor had been noted by the 1933 committee and by Sir Arthur Keith, and all these highly qualified and eminent gentlemen had nevertheless accepted it as fully human. Even if it was considered to be Neanderthalian (which as we have seen is an abberant offshoot from *Homo sapiens*), a Lower Pleistocene date would still be too early for such types.

Tobias later submitted the jaw to radiometric tests [20p180]. Uranyl ions, like fluorine, can be gradually absorbed by bone over a period of time. Tests on the jaw gave results of 4–12 parts per million. (A surprising range of 3:1 within the *same* fossil it should be noted in passing.) Tests on eleven other fossils from the Kanam beds, however, gave the much higher range of 60–214 p.p.m. suggesting a greater age, but how near in position these fossils were to the jaw is not given. In this article Tobias quotes from an unpublished report by Oakley (which we have already given in the section on the Galley Hill skele-ton). In this he admits that '*the distribution of uranyl ions* in ground water, like that of fluorine ions, *is subject to very considerable variation from place to place*'. It is submitted that these tests for fluorine and uranyl ions, which rely upon factors acknowledged to be so variable, as we have shown elsewhere in this book, are thus rendered virtually useless.

Although Leakey should have taken more care with his presenta-tion of his finds to the Cambridge committee, Boswell's attack does seem to have been unnecessarily sharp and a little unjustified, and it considerably damaged Leakey's career. Ironically Boswell, in his turn, was also made to appear incompetent. Cole says [p103] that one of his papers was so heavily criticized that he resigned his professor-ship and never recovered from a nervous breakdown.

I have given this account of the Kanam jaw as a further indication of the critical examination and rejection which awaits these early *Homo sapiens* fossils. Boswell's letter in 1935, which lacked any evidence whatsoever, provided sufficient excuse for this fossil to be cast into comparative oblivion, where it is seemingly destined to remain.

SECTION VIIC

EAST RUDOLF

The highly publicized discoveries in this area have been made by Richard Leakey, the son of L. S. B. Leakey. Although he never attended university and had no academic training, he took over from his father the directorship of the Kenya National Museum at the early age of twenty-three, and now has control of all excavations in Kenya [151].

As the leader of the Kenya contingent on the large international Omo expedition in 1967, Richard Leakey considered he would not receive the credit for any finds he made and objected to 'turning over the goodies to the Ph.D.'s', as he put it. He therefore left to start searching the Lake Rudolf area on his own. In an interview he said, 'With no degrees, it was either spend years studying at universities or stick my neck out and gamble on these lake deposits.'

Hiring a helicopter from the American contingent of the Omo Expedition, he landed near Lake Rudolf (now called Lake Turkana). He had walked not more than 50 yd. when he saw what he considered to be a simple stone tool, and near it a fossilized pig's jaw. Geological experts had said the area was of volcanic ash. But Leakey found sedimentary deposits which were a museum of fossilized bones, amongst which he 'hoped he would be lucky and find something important'.

Having found his potential fossil field, it now required a considerable sum of money to explore it. Cole gives a revealing account of Leakey's approach to the National Geographic Society, and their reaction. She says he accompanied his father to a meeting with the Board of Directors. In due course they spoke to Richard himself.

> At last Dr. Grosvenor asked if he had anything to say. 'Yes', said Richard, 'I don't want to go to Omo at all. I would like the money to work my own area at East Rudolf'. There was an appalled silence . . .
> The research committee returned to consider their verdict and found in favour of Richard. 'You can have the money,' Dr. Grosvenor told him, '*but if you find nothing you are never to come begging at our door again.*' [9p296]

With such an injunction, the pressure upon the young, twenty-three year old Leakey to find something, indeed anything that was 'newsworthy', would be enormous. What chance would there be of any fossil being examined in a cool, scientific atmosphere to determine its precise nature, if the existence of the whole expedition

197

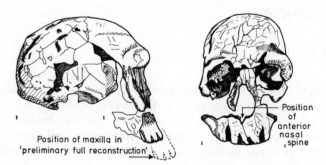

Position of maxilla in
'preliminary full reconstruction'

Position
of
anterior
nasal
spine

Fig.54. '1470' man

depended upon some 'startling' evidence being discovered? Such
pressures give added point to Richard's quote referring to '. . . the
Leakey tradition, that you look and look *again until you find what
you know must be there.*' [152p106]

Motivation is extremely important, and this needs to be borne in
mind when considering the various fossils discovered and the considerable publicity which they engendered.

Now having the very substantial support of the National
Geographic Society, he returned in 1968, accompanied by several
qualified scientists, and set up a camp at Koobi Fora on the east
shore of Lake Rudolf (Fig. 48). Little was found that year. But in the
following year, whilst walking along a dry river bed, Richard and his
wife saw a domed grey skull sticking out of the ground. It proved to
be a fairly complete cranium of an Australopithecus, and the
resultant publicity focussed considerable interest on the discoveries
of this young man. Such was his rise to fame that many felt that he
must have inherited a full measure from his father of what was
termed 'Leakey's Luck'.

The size of the team grew to seventy people, who stayed for
various periods. Richard himself, who now left much of the searching to his native helpers, travelled up in his plane from Nairobi at
regular intervals. One member of the large team at the base camp
was an artist who was available to make pictorial reconstructions of
any fossil fragments discovered.

1470 man

In the course of the search, numerous stone tools and 40 specimens
of Australopithecines were discovered. Then in August 1972 one of
the native helpers noticed bone fragments being washed down from
the side of a gulley. Richard was contacted and he immediately flew

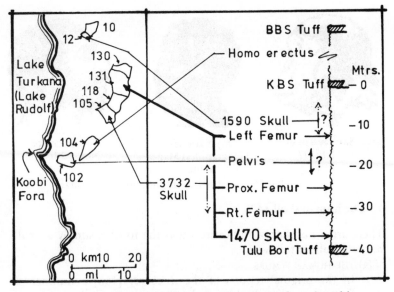

Fig.55. The Lake Rudolf discoveries. Site plan and stratigraphic section

up to the site in his Cessna plane, returning with a bagful of pieces. Even before their reconstruction, he was '. . . already convinced that they were extraordinarily important.'

The reconstruction of the bones was undertaken by his wife, Meave, who has a Ph.D. in Zoology and specialized in bones. Within six weeks enough had been reconstructed to confirm 'the enormous importance of the finds'. Worldwide publicity ensued of the skull KNMER 1470—the number being its registration at the Kenya National Museum, East Rudolf (Fig. 54). The capacity of the brain in the reconstruction was measured as 800 cc, much larger than most ape-men skulls discovered in Africa. Even more important, a volcanic tuff some 36m (118 ft.) above the skull was dated by Potassium Argon as 2.6 million years old. From this, the age of the stratum in which the skull was found was estimated at 2.9 million years old (Fig. 55). The combination of a large brain in a very early stratum was said to prove that this was the most advanced hominid ever discovered. This sparked off worldwide publicity. As is customary on these occasions, the usual rash of pictures appeared in various publications, depicting 'what our ancestors looked like', and some of these are illustrated in Fig. 56.

What is skull 1470? And how accurate is the dating? It is my conviction that the skull is quite human and that there are many discrepancies regarding the dates. These are two quite distinct subjects which will be considered separately.

 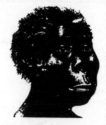 

a.) Sunday Times   b.) National   c.) Observer
Nov. 12th 1977.   Geographical Mag-   Nov. 12th 1977
                              azine

Fig.56. Some artists' impressions of 1470 Man

1. The human skull 1470

There are a number of indications that the fossil is simply a small
human skull, as follows:

(a) THE HUMAN FEMURS

In the original reports of the discovery [153] a number of
features are listed which indicate its 'humanity', e.g. small
eyebrow ridges, no crest, domed head, etc.

In this same paper, Leakey reports the discovery of two complete femurs, a part of a third femur, and parts of a tibia and
fibula. They were all above the skull level, but still below the
2.6 million-year marker bed. He says they share many features
of a modern Homo sapiens femur, and actually admits,

> The postcranial elements cannot be readily distinguishable from
> H. sapiens if one considers the range of variation known for this
> species.

In his account in the National Geographic Magazine [154],
Leakey said that he could not be sure if they belonged to 1470
man. But the caption to a drawing of them in the same article
states that Leakey believed that the femur belonged to the
same species as the 1470 man. If nothing else, we have here a
perfectly normal human femur being associated with a very
human-like skull. Leakey, however, cautiously refuses to
classify the skull, calling it 'Homo sp. indet.' (Homo species
indeterminate).

(b) THE MOUTH

One characteristic of apes is the projection of the mouth in
front of the face (prognathic), whereas in man it is almost
vertically below (orthognathic). This angle in 1470 is uncertain, for the report says:

The face is less complete and although there are good contacts joining the maxilla through the face to the calvaria, many pieces are still missing. The orientation of the face is somewhat uncertain because of distortion of the frontal base by several small, matrix filled cracks. [153]

The writer, Hammond Innes, was shown the skull by Leakey and he reports:

> Only the front of the face is not attached. Richard leaned forward holding the nose section to the skull, first almost straight, then slanting. 'If we fixed it on to the skull, there would be endless arguments.' He smiled, that boyish enthusiasm lighting his face. 'Sooner or later we shall find another skull which will give us the angle—proving, I hope, that it is orthognatic (as in man), not prognathic as in Australopithecus.' [151]

Clearly, the front could have been fixed at an angle which would have made the skull look very human. However, Leakey stops short at this point. In Fig. 54, copied from Leakey's report, the mouth is shown in a fairly prognathc position. It is indeed unfortunate that from the several hundred fragments discovered, none of them are in the position which would determine this important angle. Some of the problems raised by Leakey's *two* reconstructions however will be considered later.

(c) THE NOSE

The face which Leakey's artist, J. H. Matternes, drew on the reconstructed skull is a perfectly normal face of a woman (Fig. 56), except for the nose, which is short and broad and similar to that of a gorilla. Leakey says, the—

> Narrow nasal aperture of the original skull and a lack of bony support beneath the nostrils might indicate a rather gorilla-like nose. This characteristic is perhaps the most strikingly human feature in a physiognomy that displays an intriguing mix of the primitive and the advanced. [154]

Leakey is wrong here. The nose aperture in the skulls of gorillas is *wide*. But in 1470 it is comparatively narrow, as in humans, and therefore flatly contradicts the evidence. The average reader of the *National Geographic Magazine*, however, is unlikely to realize this.

Furthermore, his statement regarding the '. . . lack of bony support beneath the nostrils . . .' is rather misleading. He is referring to the anterior nasal spine which is a small bony point projecting forward to support the base of the nose. In the reconstruction of the skull, it is not a case of the bone in this area showing no sign of a forward projection, but that this particular piece *is missing from the reconstruction* (see Fig. 54). As this evidence is missing, then on the basis of the narrow aperture alone, the picture of the full face should have been given a human nose, not the grotesque looking gorilla nose appearing in the illustrations of the *National Geographic Magazine* (Fig. 56).

Had this small tell-tale bone been found, it would have indicated immediately whether or not 1470 possessed a human-like nose.

(d) A HUMAN SKULL?

Probably the most convincing evidence, as it comes from an independent source, is the assessment of the skull given by A. Cave. Cave was formerly emeritus professor of Anatomy, London and Barts, and was co-author of the paper which showed that Neanderthal man was a form of Homo sapiens [115 and see p164]. On seeing the skull when exhibited in London by Glynn Isaac (Leakey's co-investigator), Cave's opinion was, 'as far as I can see, *typically human* . . .'. [155] With all his experience in dealing with the human skeleton, Cave's testimony is highly significant.

(e) OTHER HUMAN SKULLS?

Leakey found two other skulls which he said were similar to 1470. As so few details of these skulls are given in the reports he makes in *Nature*, it is difficult to say whether these are human or not. However, I give details as they may be relevant, particularly as they were both found below the KBS tuff (as was 1470).

The first was No. 1590, found in 1973 [156]. It was noted that although the cranium was immature, the brain capacity was as large as that of 1470. Although he gives no indication of the owner's age, it is possible that its mature capacity might have been larger than 1470's, and surely therefore of greater interest. Several times in his report, Leakey classes these two skulls together when comparing them with other skulls. He does report that the skull's parietal bones 'suggest that the cranium was wide with a sagittal keel'. If it did have a sagittal keel, this would certainly indicate it was the skull of an ape. However in another report [157] he gives only a plan view of the cranial fragments, and there is no mention of it possessing a keel.

The second skull (No. 3732) was found in August 1975. In

March 1976 he said it was a 'dead ringer' for 1470, i.e. almost identical. In his report in *Nature* in June 1976 [158], he admits that it is 'strikingly similar' to 1470, and it was found in the same basic stratum. This report of a skull similar to 1470 is remarkable, for it is only briefly referred to in a few lines and no pictures are provided.

The reason why both these seemingly important fossils should receive so much less publicity than 1470 will, however, be examined at the end of this section.

(f) THE PELVIS

One further human-like fossil was also discovered. In June 1976 [158] Leakey reported the discovery of a right pelvic bone (innominate). This bone must have seemed remarkably man-like for he said:

> The position and orientation of the ischial tuberosity is similar to that observed in a sample of modern H. sapiens, as are a number of other morphological characteristics . . . there are few resemblances to the material referred to as Australopithecus.

and

> the essentially modern appearance of this fossil require that it be attributed to Homo. [158]

He claimed this pelvic bone should be considered together with the very man-like femur found at the same time as the large 1470 skull. He concludes from this that they reflect '. . . the mechanical requirements of a large brained, striding biped'. This is actually an accurate description of a normal human being. But had Leakey admitted this, he would have been on the verge of committing professional suicide!

(g) THE SKULL RECONSTRUCTIONS

In his first 1973 report, Leakey mentioned:

> The skull is not fully reconstructed. Many small fragments remain to be included, and it may be some time before the task is completed. [153]

From this, one would expect a final model to be produced in due course. Surprisingly, however, no complete reconstruction has ever been made, even four years later. This can be seen from a careful inspection of illustrations in Leakey's book, 'Origins', published in 1977.

In this book, on pages 86–7, four pictures of the reconstructed skull are given. The first one is called the 'first reconstruction', and is very similar to the illustration in his 1973
report, except that the upper jaw now appears to be completely detached from the face bones. Details of some other
bones seem to indicate it was taken prior to 1973.

The other three pictures are of a *preliminary* full reconstruction', in which the gaps are now filled with plasticine,
and these show some interesting features as follows:

(i) Compared with the upper jaw in the earlier versions, *it is
now made 2.4 cm (1 in.) longer*, thus making it more
ape-like (see Fig. 54).

(ii) Allied to this, no further fragments have been used in
this reconstruction, such fragments which would, of
course, actually determine the position and angle of the
face.

(iii) The fragment of bone, which would show whether 1470
possessed the anterior nasal spine below the nose, is still
missing.

I could detect no additional bones used in this reconstruction
compared with that appearing in the 1973 report, which mentions that 'many small fragments remain to be included.' Can
we infer from this, and from the fact that this later full reconstruction is *still* called preliminary, that many pieces are yet
unused? Perhaps the vital bones we have mentioned above,
which would have shown whether 1470 was human or not,
may be lying amongst them, still 'unrecognized'. This raises
the question as to whether the Leakey motto of 'look and look
again' was fully applied on this occasion.

These rather doubtful aspects of the reconstruction of skull
1470 emphasize a major problem facing anyone wishing to
make valid criticisms of the models presented for publicity by
the experts. First, the pieces are already made up into a skull,
shaped according to the reconstructor's preconceptions.
Secondly, the photographs or drawings of the reconstructions
appearing in magazines are only small pictures. This is all that
is made available for comment. Thus criticism can be made
only on material which is at least two or three stages removed
from the original pieces. Had access to the original fragments
been available, quite different results from those produced by
the discoverers would probably have been achieved.

It seems certain that, despite the small brain capacity (which
might be owing to the bad fitting of the very small fragments),
Leakey had found at least one human skull, human femurs
and a pelvis in strata given a very early date, all of which quite

contradicted the established view of how man emerged from his ape-like ancestry. As might be expected, his views were criticized, and we can trace the subsequent decline of 1470 man. Before doing so, however, we will first consider the various dates which the experts gave to the stratum above the 1470 skull.

2. The stratum datings

Most of the fossils were found between the upper KBS tuff stratum and the lower Tulu-Bor tuff. These two marker beds could be traced over a distance of several miles, enabling fossils found in different areas to be correlated. (See Fig. 55.)

In 1969 samples of tuff were sent to Cambridge for Potassium-Argon dating and, as we have mentioned, three tests gave average dates of 220 million years! This was quite unacceptable. 'Extraneous argon' was blamed for this anomaly and less calcified samples were requested from this site.

Exploratory tests now gave dates of 2.37 and 3.02 million years which were considered to be 'most encouraging' and full tests were then carried out. The final results, however, still varied widely, the pumice fraction giving 2.25–4.62 million years, the crystal fraction having a minimum age of 2.37, with the well known dating of 2.61 million years being put forward as 'the best and most acceptable estimate . . .'!

I will not criticize in detail the paper in which these results appeared [159] or a later paper [160] that gave various explanations of why results are so diverse and also highly technical reasons why 2.61 million years should be the most likely date for the strata. In reading these papers, one has a distinct impression that even the experts are very much in the dark in their efforts to explain these discrepancies and make suitable corrections. For example, they say:

> . . . each may contain two small inherent geological errors of opposing sign and of amounts that cannot be estimated (but are unlikely to be greater than the quoted experimental errors which are themselves large because of low potassium content and high atmospheric contamination). [159]

With the minute quantities involved, experimental errors become important '. . . because they are frequently of a similar order of magnitude to that of the date required'. With regard to the last word of this quotation, it is rather intriguing that a certain date is *required*. Perhaps this was a Freudian slip of the pen!

It is not easy to identify where this dated tuff was located as it was only later designated KBS. The actual location from where the samples were taken was site 105, whilst Skull 1470 was found at site 131, a distance of 10 km (6 miles) away. Leakey admits that the tuff at site 131 gave datings which were 'inconclusive', but he had received a personal communication from V. A. Miller, one of the authors of the paper giving the 2.61 million years that '. . . there is no reason to suspect the validity of that date . . .' Once again a series of tests on a strata have been run. But when they failed to give the 'right' ages they were ignored. The dates which were ultimately used were actually obtained from the stratum several miles away from the 1470 man site. Possibly these discrepant results are the ten dates (ranging from .52 to 2.64 million years) which were briefly mentioned in passing in the later report in 1974 [160].

Despite the variety of the results and the assumptions used in obtaining this date in the original paper, Leakey nevertheless claims that the KBS tuff was '. . . securely dated at 2.61 m.y.', and points to paleomagnetic results and fossil evidence as corroborating this date [153].

The American datings

This very early date did not go unchallenged. G. H. Curtis, with others in the University of California, re-tested the KBS tuff in 1976 and obtained much younger ages [161]. The reasons they gave for checking these dates were that pig fossils below the KBS tuff were better correlated with those in the Omo area (100 miles—160 km away!) which had been dated at 2 million years. Furthermore, they repeated the tests, 'Because of the great interest in the dating and the question of reliability, raised by the scatter of results . . .'. These seem inadequate reasons, for rarely does one group of radio-metric dating experts challenge the results of another. In view of this, the possible influence of the discoveries by Johanson in Ethiopia will be considered in section VII D.

In their criticism of the Cambridge tests the Americans made some interesting statements, such as:

. . . it assumes that all non-radiogenic argon in the sample has the same relative abundance as in the atmosphere, an assumption demonstrably wrong in some cases. [161]

Their interpretations rely on oversimplified and unproved models for the diffusion of argon in solids, both in nature and in the laboratory procedure necessary to make an age determination. For this reason we feel that their results, even when they are reproducible to high precision, may be an artefact of experimental procedure, and thus not geologically meaningful. [161]

One is tempted to add: 'so much for this "scientific" method of dating rock'! This devastating criticism is actually also an indictment of the American's methods.

For the tests carried out in California, the specific minerals required were carefully selected from the crushed samples and cleaned before testing. The results, however, ranged from 2.01 to 6.9 million years and were discarded. The material was inspected closely and 'K-spar . . . probably derived from ancient bedrock' was seen. It proved too difficult to exclude this material, so they were reduced to picking out minute individual grains from the crushed material with tweezers under a microscope! Clearly no effort was spared to obtain an acceptable date! The final results were 1.6 million years for the KBS tuff in areas 105 and 10, and 1.82 million years in area 131 (the site of skull 1470). On this basis they claimed that the 131 tuff was 'distinguished' from the other areas, by which one presumes it was laid down 220,000 years later. This, however, contradicts the general geological report [162] which is confident that this tuff was laid down rapidly over a large area, hence its use as a 'marker bed'.

On this question of accuracy of radiometric reports, it is noticed that they are always quoted together with a very small value of ± error. For example in the paper we have just considered [161] the rejected results were quoted as 2.01 ± .03 and 6.9 ± .05. These ± figures are simply an indication of the inaccuracy due to the air Argon contamination, however, and are not an indication of the true accuracy of the actual result. In other words, it does *not* mean that the sample has an age with an upper limit of 6.95 million years and a lower limit of 6.85 million years, for identical tests invariably give results well outside the ± range. The quoting of these small dating ranges gives an air of extreme accuracy to the results. This impression, however, is quite spurious.

I have already pointed out (p65) the very large *assumptions* used in obtaining a date from all the radiometric dating methods. In addition it is obvious from all these quoted tests, ranging from 223 to 1.5 million years on the same strata, that there are also enormous variations entirely due to the *technique* that is used. With both these factors in mind, I would consider the method to be quite worthless and any dates based upon them to be unacceptable.

These younger dates considerably reduced the importance of Leakey's 1470 skull. Leakey himself did not accept them, for in a report he made in 1976 [158] he says they raised important questions and admits that the dating for the area '. . . may need a complete re-examination . . .'. He goes on to say, however,

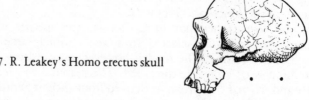

Fig.57. R. Leakey's Homo erectus skull

Alternative dating methods such as fission track will be given close attention in the future and may offer, together with studies of certain taxa, useful indications about the reliability of isotopic age determinations. [158]

From this it would appear that if Potassium-Argon dating does not give the results he wants, he will go to other methods to get them!

Leakey continued to ignore these unacceptably low dates, for in his book, 'Origins' [152p86], he says that 1470 '. . . lived at least two million years ago, and possibly nearer to three.' This is a clear example of a 'scientist' (although in this particular case an untrained and unqualified one) accepting and publishing only those results which are conformable to his views. Leakey, however, is not alone. Hunters of fossil men seem particularly prone to succumb to this failing.

The Homo erectus skull

We will briefly digress to consider this skull—No. 3733—(Fig. 57) which was also given considerable publicity. It was found in 1975 in many pieces. Following its reconstruction Leakey said, 'In all its features the cranium is strikingly like that of H. erectus from Pekin' [163]. It was found in strata dated 1.3 to 1.6 million years and Leakey said it was about 1.5 million years old.

On the problem of what angle the face-bones should be set (which we have met regarding 1470 man, p201), he says:

The facial skeleton is flexed under the calvaria and in the preliminary reconstruction is set at about the same angle as that reconstructed for a female H. erectus by Weidenreich. [163]

Here indeed is a classic example of much supposition being eventually accepted as a fact. As we have shown on p116, Weidenreich's reconstruction of Nellie was from a number of broken pieces of apes skulls from widely different parts of the Pekin

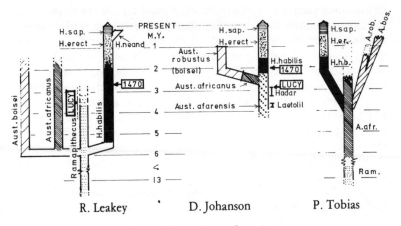

Fig.58. Three views of man's ancestry

site. So despite the grave, scientific aura with which he tries to invest his reconstruction, it is clearly piecemeal and arbitrary. Leakey, seeing that his skull was similar to Weidenreich's, set the face-bones at the same angle.

It would appear to me, on the one hand, that Weidenreich gave the *ape's* skulls a face at a *human* (orthognathic) angle (which enabled Weidenreich to make 'Nellie' look very modern), whilst on the other hand, Leakey, as we have seen, has given the *human* skull 1470 an *ape-like* angle (prognathic) (p201). In this fashion do we see the intermediate stages between man and apes occurring not in real life but in the minds of their reconstructors.

The classification of Homo erectus is nowadays given to both Pekin man and Java man. As we have demonstrated, the former consists of broken skulls of apes, whilst the latter is a giant gibbon's skull cap, and it is upon this shaky foundation that the classification of Homo erectus was constructed. This should always be borne in mind when this important classification makes its invariable appearance in diagrams of man's 'family tree', such as Leakey's [152p84], Johanson's [167] and Tobias' [164], which are illustrated in Fig. 58. These charts were all made within recent years and based upon virtually the same fossils. But the discrepancies are so obvious that no comment is necessary, except to note that they are a clear demonstration of the complete unreliability of this field of research.

The Homo erectus skeletons of Kow Swamp

At this site in Australia, some thirty skeletons were found, and several of the skulls were said to have the characteristics of Homo erectus [165]. It would appear to me that they are only a Neanderthal-like variety of Homo sapiens. At one end of the range there is a close similarity to present day aborigines, whilst two of them are likened to the Neanderthal La Chapelle cranium. Furthermore, the skeletons were found in *graves* furnished with stone artefacts, ochre shells and marsupial teeth, clearly signifying human burial. This would be far too advanced for Homo erectus. The most interesting fact, however, is that Carbon 14 datings gave age ranges of only 8-10,000 years! It is admitted that Homo sapiens was in existence in the area before then, and therefore this dating is so embarrassing to the experts that one can be certain that no reference will be made to them in the future. As far as I can see, I think it is possible that the Homo erectus skull found by Leakey was of a similar type to those found at Kow Swamp, i.e. a degenerate Neanderthal-like form of earlier Homo sapiens.

The 1½ million year camp fire

The Homo erectus skull was not the only interesting discovery dated 1½ million years. A television programme in April 1975 gave details of the discovery in 1973 of evidence of fire, tools and broken bones, etc., which were admitted as indicating a camp site. A jaw, said at first to be like 1470, was also discovered at the site. However, later it was 'disappointingly' classed as an Australopithecus.

The importance of the evidence of fire was recognized, and the statement made, '. . . as you know, we can't be too careful about this, because if it is confirmed that these are traces of a humanly-made fire, these are, at 1½ Myrs, the oldest known fire anywhere in the world.' A further comment was made that evidence of fire had been found the previous year also.

I tried to discover further details of this site, but was unable to find its location. Additionally, there is no mention in the report of the 1973 discoveries, of fire being found. Surely the earliest dated evidence of fire should have been given considerable attention. The fact that no further mention is made suggests to me the possibility that the evidence of human occupation has been suppressed. If so, such suppression of evidence may well occur more frequently than the public are aware.

Leakey's 'Origins'

Richard Leakey, in association with Roger Lewin, has written a book [152] in which he claims that man evolved by co-operation and not by his aggressive instincts, a view popularized by Dart, Lorentz and Ardrey, which he says is 'fiction—dangerous fiction'.

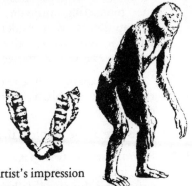

Fig.59. Ramapithecus jaw and artist's impression

In this well illustrated book, he uses a bewildering array of types of 'evidence' to support his thesis. These range from finger manipulation in humans through maturing ages of babies and apes, teeth adaptation, and fossil discoveries. Finally the reader is taken on an imaginary time trip (complete with Land Rover!) during which he can watch four types of 'humanoid' apes collecting their food by different methods. The actual fossil evidence, however, is no more than a mere handful of bones.

Often, when wishing to prove a point, the authors relate one incident which occurred to one member of an ape tribe that was noticed by one observer. Upon this one single incident a complete rule of human behaviour and development is then set forth as fact. This technique of placing heavy reliance upon one small incident was used to a considerable extent by Desmond Morris in his book 'The Naked Ape', and many other 'social biologists'.

A fossil ape frequently referred to is Ramapithecus. Yet, as we have seen, the only fossils they have of this creature are upper and lower jaws and teeth of some thirty individuals. Despite this, the reader is presented with the usual picture of the complete ape, although the authors admit that it is very tentative '. . . because so few remains have been found'! (See Fig. 59.) The reason why Ramapithecus has become very prominent is because it is the only possible ancestor of '1470' man, which has been dated at 2.6 million years old.

The lack of evidence is occasionally admitted as the following statements reveal:

p12   'If we are honest we have to admit that we will never fully know what happened to our ancestors in their journey towards modern humanity; the evidence is too sparse'.

p67   'Compared with the fossil remains from Montana of the pioneering primate, the evidence concerning Ramapithecus is considerable—though in absolute terms it remains tantalisingly small . . .'! [An interesting example of strange logic.]

p84   '. . . inescapably it is a matter of faith and this makes the whole problem more challenging—and more exciting'.

p84   'The core of the problem then is the fossil record . . .'

p117   Having spent two pages taking the reader on an imaginary time trip watching four groups of ape ancestors and their feeding habits, the authors conclude by admitting, 'All of this is, of course, a complete fairytale, a fabric of more or less inspired guesses. The truth is that no-one knows exactly how the hominids lived'.

We have seen how Johanson demoted 1470 by redating the strata. Leakey, in his turn, only briefly refers to Johanson's work whilst his caption to Lucy's picture (which is printed round the wrong way!), says she was possibly 'a late form of Ramapithecus'.

Despite the prestigious name of the author, this book nevertheless has received poor reviews in the press.

The Decline and Fall of 1470 man

Returning now to the subsequent fate of skull 1470, we have shown how the early dating of the skull was reduced by the American tests, but there still remained the problem facing the experts that it was a *very* human-like skull that had been found in an early stratum. This combination completely upset the accepted view of the development of man.

As we have seen in Section III, the usual method of 'disposing' of early Homo sapiens fossils was to say that they were either,
(a) an intrusive burial, or
(b) they had slipped to the position due to earth movements, or,
(c) they had been put there by a practical joker.
In the case of 1470 man, however, none of these could be made to apply. A fourth method was therefore used for this fossil, which was to 'bury' it scientifically, i.e. to call it by another name. In this case, one already existing was chosen, that of 'Homo habilis', discovered by Richard's father (p185). Thus it would be included with fossils of a different type, and after a time the human character of the original skull would eventually be forgotten. We can trace the

decline and fall of 1470 in three very clear stages.

STAGE 1—THE UNIQUE SKULL

When it was first discovered, Leakey made some sweeping claims regarding the importance of the skull. Newspaper reports claimed that all of man's ancestry would have to be reconsidered, whilst scientific magazines admitted that it made some ape-men into evolutionary offshoots which became unsuccessful 'dead ends'. Leakey himself, in a meeting in San Diego, said that what he had found destroyed all that we had ever been taught about human evolution, and that he had nothing to offer in its place!

Hillaby, a columnist for the *New Scientist*, however, was unwilling to accept that it was really 'different from all other forms of early man' and suggested it was only one link in man's long ancestry. He gives a rather unflattering account of L. S. B. Leakey's temperament and says:

> Now I'm not for one moment suggesting that Richard has stuffed a remote corner of Rudolf with bits pillaged from a Bantu boneyard. He is, as far as I am aware, a man of the utmost integrity. Nobody could possibly doubt that the bones were found exactly where he said. [155]

He finishes, however, with the almost libellous comment that 'Richard, I am told, has inherited none of his father's negative qualities except, I suspect, a thirst for publicity.'! [155]

Leakey's tendency to bypass all the work done by other experts over many years was further apparent when he discovered the Homo erectus skull in 1976 (p208). He said, 'The specimen is very similar to the Homo erectus material from China . . . and is therefore assigned to H. erectus.' The main reason for Leakey's giving his discovery widespread publicity was that he claimed it was found in a stratum dated 1.5 million years old. As Pekin man was supposed to have existed only 500,000 years ago, he boldly said at a meeting held at the *National Geographical Society*'s headquarters:

> The Chinese must develop a new, different way to date their sites for more accuracy. Upon examination, they'll probably find these fossils to be a million years older than now dated. [166]

Thus in one stroke Leakey sweeps to one side all the years of patient work by many experts in providing a 'reliable' date for this classification.

As we have noted, Leakey was careful never to call the 1470 skull 'Homo sapiens', for he was well aware of the possible repercussions. He did, however, consider existing types to see if it was just another specimen. He rejects the possibility of it being an Australopithecine in view of their small brain capacity and as for it being a Homo erectus skull, he claimed that no example had been found at such an early date and furthermore 1470 was quite distinctive from it.

Considering Homo habilis, he points out that its brain capacity was only about 650 cc and that it had been found above a basalt dated at 1.96 million years. He therefore states,

> At present therefore there does not seem to be any compelling reason for attributing to this species the earlier, larger brained, cranium from East Rudolf. [153]

STAGE 2. THE 'GRAVE' IS DUG

Although he had rejected the possibility of 1470 being the same as Homo habilis, in a report published the following year [156] in a very roundabout way he now suggests they *are* alike. First he says a jaw, No. 1802, could be considered as belonging to the same species as 1470. Then he points out the striking similarities between this jaw and that of Homo habilis, thus establishing a tenuous link, and eventually he makes the passing comment,

> My suggestion here, that H. habilis may have affinities with KNM-ER 1470 and 1590, refers only to OH 7 and OH 16. [156]

He now considers that the small brain capacity of Homo habilis was inaccurate, '. . . due to the fragmentary material upon which the former estimates were made' and makes no reference whatsoever to the younger date they have compared with 1470.

STAGE 3. THE SKULL IS 'BURIED'

Having now established the link with Homo habilis, all the human characteristics of 1470 could now be ignored, for the former fragments have always been classed as one of the many ape-men ancestors.

This is the classification which Leakey gives to 1470 in his book, 'Origins', in which the human features are not mentioned. In fact Leakey makes a complete somersault from his first statement, for he now says,

> Indeed, there is every reason to classify it as Homo habilis. [p86]

So keen are the experts to ignore it that it is only briefly referred to in the N.H. Museum's exhibition 'Man's place in evolution' (see Appendix VIII). This playing down of the human features of 1470 would now explain why the two other almost identical skulls, No. 1590 and 3732, found in 1973 and 1975 (see p203), were only briefly referred to in Leakey's reports.

Johanson, in constructing *his* version of man's family tree (Fig. 58), also classes 1470 as Homo habilis, but has successfully demoted 1470 by using the *American* date of 1.8 million years.

This, then, was the process by which 1470 man was 'buried'. What do we make of the sequence of events we have outlined above? Clearly, the young, inexperienced Leakey had found a human skull and proceeded to announce his find in a blaze of publicity. This doubtless aroused the establishment to the dangerous situation, for the boat was so badly rocked that it was in peril of overturning and all being lost. However, older and wiser counsel appears to have prevailed and the danger minimized by quietly dropping overboard the offending body, thus allowing the vessel of man's evolution to continue to steam majestically forward over the ever calm waters of human credulity.

SECTION VIID

HADAR (Ethiopia)

Investigations carried out by the team headed by D. C. Johanson from 1972–77 in the Afar area of Ethiopia (Fig. 60) resulted in the discovery of a collection of fossil fragments, the main ones being:

(a) a 40% complete skeleton named 'Lucy' (Site 288) (Fig. 62)
(b) the upper and lower fragments of leg bones forming a knee joint (Fig. 63)
(c) small parts of about thirteen individuals collected in one area (Site 333), said to be a family of hominids destroyed by a local 'flash flood'.

All the fossils were dated between 2.8–3.3 million years and Johanson at first considered they were from two different species of hominids, (i.e. apes in the direct line leading to Homo sapiens). Later, in 1979, however, he classed all these fossils together with the jaws found at Laetolil (by Mary Leakey, Richard's mother), and gave them the name Australopithecus afarensis [167].

These jaws found at Laetolil were dated about 3.6 million years and were claimed to be the earliest evidence of the Homo classification ever found [168]. However, they are all seemingly species of apes' jaws and no human features are claimed for them.

With regard to the Hadar fossils, what exactly has been found?

Various reports have been written describing the discoveries, and a careful reading of the main papers [167, 169, 170, 171] leads me to conclude that all the fossils discovered are only of a variety of ape.

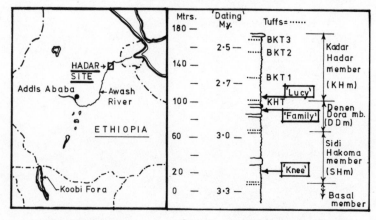

Fig.60. The Hadar
Site location

Fig.61. General stratigraphical
section of Hadar sites

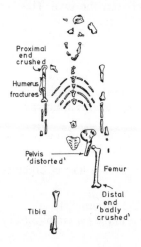

Proximal
end
crushed

Humerus
fractures

Pelvis
'distorted'

Femur

Tibia

Distal
end
'badly
crushed'

Fig.62. 'Lucy's' skeleton

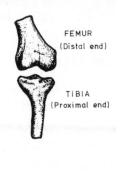

FEMUR
(Distal end)

TIBIA
(Proximal end)

Fig.63. The 'knee joint' fossils

In reading these papers it is noticeable that a fair proportion of them is taken up with a minute description of the fossils, with statements such as:

> . . . the head is slightly retroflexed with only minor tibial torsion; and the intercondyloid eminence is prominent with well developed intercondyloid fossae. [170]

> Two pedal navicular bones . . . exhibit extensive cuboideonavicular facets and the pedal phalanges are highly curved. [167]

Many similar quotations could be given which would only be understood by experts in that field. Whether such lengthy detailed descriptions are really necessary is debatable, for only occasionally is any conclusion drawn from them. These descriptions, although detailed, are too indefinite for interested experts to work from, and they would have to obtain accurate measurements from plaster casts. They do, however, perform one important function which is to give an air of scientific erudition to the paper, for without them the meagreness of the evidence and the speculative nature of the conclusions would become more obvious, even to the general reader. In such prestigious scientific journals as *Nature* and *Science*, the highly technical expertise of specialists in the fields of atomic physics, biochemistry and similar advanced work is very clearly seen. The desire of those working in the very speculative field of palaeo-anthropology to produce equally technical sounding papers is understandable.

The most important question is, did Johanson find apes, or modern men, or a creature half way between the two? This, and other topics of dating, etc., we will now examine.

A. APE CHARACTERISTICS

By far the most frequent reference regarding these fossils is to their ape like nature, as just these few selected quotations indicate:

> The Laetolil and Hadar fossil hominid remains have a distinctive suite of primitive cranial and postcranial characteristics. [24]

> Preserved portions of the adult crania . . . show a host of primitive features. [24]

> The cusps are usually arranged in a simple Y-5 pattern. [24]
> [This is characteristic of ape teeth and refers to the pattern formed by the creases in the top of the large teeth.]

> It has not yet been possible to make satisfactory estimates of cranial capacity on the basis of preserved portions of crania, although pre-liminary observations suggest that it is small, probably within the known range of other Australopithecus species . . . [24]

> In summary, the Hadar and Laetolil remains seem to represent a dis-tinctive early hominid form characterized by . . . a host of primitive dental and cranial characteristics. [24]

Having mentioned many ape-like characteristics, Johanson never-theless makes the quite unjustified comment:

> Although clearly hominid in their dentition, mandibles, cranium, and postcranium, these forms retain hints of a still poorly known Miocene ancestor. [24]

Every fragment described in the papers is classed as 'hominid', (even quite small pieces), but how these could display any human characteristics is difficult to see. One has the impression that any ape-like bone found is classed as 'hominid'. The section E below on 'motivation' also seems to support this.

Comparisons
Several times the fossils are compared with the South African dis-coveries at Kromdraii Taungs, Makapansgat and particularly Swartkrans and Sterkfontein, generally claiming the Hadar fossils are more primitive (i.e. more ape-like!). It is a little surprising to find these old fossils brought back into the limelight particularly as Oxnard showed that they were simply apes and had little relevance to man's supposed evolution. Oxnard's conclusion was fully

supported by Sir Solly Zuckerman after a very careful study of these fossils, as we have set out on p176. Johanson, however, ignores these findings and places Swartkrans homo in the Homo erectus group which is on the direct line to Homo sapiens! (See Fig. 58.)

One other strange comparison is made between an upper jaw found in Hadar and a similar one found in Java. Johanson says:

> These characters as well as other details suggest resemblances with some Homo erectus material, particularly Pithecanthropus IV. [170]

This is the upper jaw shown in Fig. 34 and, comparing the view from below (not illustrated), it is obvious that the jaws are *very* similar. Do we infer from this that the creature classed as Homo erectus, who lived 2.5 million years later (and 5,000 miles away) is the same as Johanson's Australopithecus afarensis? If this were so, it would make nonsense of his carefully constructed tree of human evolution (Fig. 58).

Having shown that the fossils are *very* ape like, we will now consider the more important subject of their few, supposedly human characteristics.

B. 'HUMAN' CHARACTERISTICS

Clearly, if these apes are developing towards Homo sapiens, we would expect to see some human features in evidence. These are so few, however, that one has to read the reports carefully to discover them.

Only three bones are said to show any distinctly human features. These are:

(a) A KNEE JOINT
(b) LUCY'S ARM/LEG RATIO
(c) LUCY'S PELVIS

(a) THE KNEE JOINT
Two leg bone fragments forming a right knee were found at one site (Fig. 63). The actual distance between these bones is not given, but it was assumed that they came from the same individual. In describing the upper bone (femur) the 1976 report says:

> This fragment demonstrates a number of anatomical details which are intimately related to bipedal locomotion: the bicondylar angle is rather high, the lateral lip of the patellar groove is raised and the lateral condyle flattened and elongated. [170]

I could find no evidence in print which proves that this knee joint exhibited bipedalism. The January 1976 issue of the *American Journal of Physical Anthropology* gave abstracts of papers to be presented at the A.G.M. of the American Association of Physical Anthropology in April 1976. On page 188 it gave an abstract of a paper entitled 'Functional implications of the Afar knee joint' by Johanson, Lovejoy, Burstein & Heiple. I can only presume the paper was read. However, I could find no report in any journal and additionally the Natural History Museum had no copy of this paper. As these bones were of one of the very few categories which Johanson claimed to be man-like, surely a paper should have been published to justify his claim. Without this evidence no comment can be made. One is left wondering, however, whether the evidence may have been so frail that it might not have stood up to the close scrutiny to which a published report would have been subjected. Until such evidence is provided, I would consider this claim as 'not proven'.

These knee bones were found in 1973 and Lucy was found in 1974. Both of them were reported in the same article in *Nature* [170]. In this, Johanson makes no claim that Lucy's skeleton showed that she walked upright. Nevertheless, he is so keen to infer this, that he makes a very strange statement. He says:

Previously the 1973 postcranial material has not been assigned to a taxon. It is now clear that it should probably be included in the same category as the AL 288 specimen (Lucy) because of the striking similarity of the proximal tibial fragments in size and morphology as well as the preserved femoral fragments. This is important because: there is now evidence of at least two individuals of a very small hominid in Hadar, and the AL 128 and 129 specimens are situated stratigraphically 80m below the partial skeleton. [170]

The line of reasoning seems to be as follows:
(i)   The two bones of a knee joint were found in a stratum 80m lower than Lucy, the upper bone showing evidence (unquantified) of upright walking.
(ii) The lower bone (tibia)—which possessed no human characteristics—was very similar to Lucy's.
(iii) As the knee bones are 'similar' to Lucy's and found in a deeper stratum, this is held to be sufficient evidence that Lucy walked upright!

What is strange is that the knee bone femur is claimed to show bipedalism, yet this same bone on Lucy is reported:

A complete left femur is associated with the innominate [pelvis] *but the distal portion* [knee end] is badly *crushed*.

Thus the very part of the femur on Lucy's skeleton which ought to show bipedalism is unfortunately crushed!

Such a weak line of argument is far from convincing. Indeed the inference that Lucy walked upright is so obliquely referred to in this passage, that its importance is easily overlooked. In spite of the meagre evidence for Lucy's walking upright, it was this supposed feature which was stressed by some of the more popular writers. Roger Lewin, co-author with Richard Leakey of the book 'Origins' and Science Editor of *New Scientist*, wrote an article on Johanson's report. In this article (whose title misleadingly referred to Lucy as 'near-human'), he said:

> By measuring the size and angle of the limb bones one can see that Lucy walked upright (but probably not achieving the striding gait typical of humans) . . . [172]

From this, the unsuspecting reader would suppose that it was Lucy's bones which had shown these characteristics, instead of one small bone found 80m deeper, and possibly several miles away!

I could find no statement in this particular 1976 report, to which Lewin specifically refers, that Lucy's bones showed that she walked upright. Indeed, this was not claimed until later, and even then was based upon Lucy's *distorted* pelvis—a subject dealt with more fully below. It is not clear whether Lewin's statement was from another source, or whether it is merely an example of 'journalistic licence'.

This publication provides an interesting example of speculation on hominid fossils. We have already noted Johanson's claim that the difference in size of the Laetolil and Hadar jaws is within the normal range for a species, and is probably due to the difference between male and female (sexual dimorphism). In the issue of the *New Scientist* dated 1st February 1979, on p319 is a report of Johanson's 1979 paper [167]. The article comments:

> Judging by the range of size in the *afarensis* specimens, it seems that the males were on average twice as big as the females—this is at least as marked as we see in modern gorillas. Again, if *afarensis* is valid, such a difference in size probably implies that the creatures lived in harems, with a large socially dominant male controlling a number of females.

This statement was based entirely upon a few fossilized bones. Why such speculation is accepted in a publication entitled *New Scientist* is difficult to understand, unless we are witnessing the evolution of a new type of scientist!

(b) ARM/LEG RATIOS

In the article in the *New Scientist* reporting Lucy's discovery [172],

Lucy's arm-to-leg length ratio of 83.9 per cent is said to show she was halfway to becoming human. The reason for this is that the figure for apes is said to be over 100 whilst for man it is around 73. Johanson's report states that this ratio of 83.9 is between the humerus (upper arm bone) and the femur (upper leg bone) saying:

> The right humerus is complete with some crushing of the proximal end. Its total length is estimated at 235mm giving a value of 83.9 for the humeral-femoral index. [170]

Johanson's comment on the ratio is, 'This value is high for modern humans.' [167] Could it perhaps be high enough to be an ape's?

In passing, one cannot but be amused at the way in which Lucy's index is quoted as 83.9. The length of both bones is in any case estimated. The humerus had actually been broken in two places and one end had had 'some crushing'. Moreover, one end of the femur had been 'badly crushed'. To quote the ratio within 0.1% gives this index an air of scientific accuracy which is quite false, and therefore *un*scientific.

One further small error in this article is that Lucy is said to have been buried under 100 metres of sediment, whereas the correct figure is 45m. The figure of 100m is the height of Lucy's stratum *above* the base stratum, this figure appearing on a scale that has clearly been misread (Fig. 61).

I have examined this article in some detail to show the progress of the way in which cautiously worded 'inferences' of original reports (which are themselves based upon much speculation), appear in popular scientific magazines as 'clear indications', finally being quoted in school textbooks as 'scientifically proven'. In spite of this, if any dares to criticize such 'authorities' he is condemned as 'unscientific'. This does raise the question of why such journals as *Nature*, *Science* and the more popular *New Scientist* should lower their otherwise excellent technical standards when it comes to the subject of man's evolution, for it would appear that in this subject at least the wildest speculations are accepted for publication without demur. But in the *Conclusion* of this book, one possible reason why such articles reach the printed page will be considered.

(c) LUCY'S PELVIS
The 1976 reports state:

> The left innominate (pelvis) is complete, although it is somewhat distorted in the pubic region and particularly in the area of sacral articulation . . . The acetabulum is shallow when compared with modern man. [170]

It should be noted in passing that no claim is made that this pelvis shows that Lucy walked upright. Relevant to this, however, is the distortion which the bone is said to possess. It is the *only* bone of Lucy's skeleton which is said to be *distorted*, all others being either badly *broken* into fragments, or quite intact, i.e. the left femur and, according to the report, the right humerus. These two bones, which are long and thin, do not appear to have been distorted. But such distortion might have been expected in view of their shape. In fact the end of the femur and of the humerus were *crushed*. This indicates that they were brittle at the time (as presumably were all the other broken bones) and therefore were unlikely to have been 'distorted'.

This distortion of the pelvis has become important by the time when the 1979 report was written. This report states:

> One of the potentially most significant bones, the A.L. 288-1 in-nominate, is currently being reconstructed. Its morphology is commensurate with a bipedal mode of locomotion. [167]

It is only some five years after its discovery that this distorted bone is regarded as having bipedal characteristics. Even more significant perhaps is its reconstruction now in hand by Johanson and others at Kent State University.

This bone is presumably the only one of its particular kind in existence. So, unless there are clear indentations on the bone, it must be asked how the experts actually *know* it is distorted. Could it not be of the correct shape for this creature? The obverse question to this is how they will know exactly what degree of 'correction' should be applied to this pelvis?

They are clearly convinced that Lucy walked upright. Will the remodelled pelvis 'provide conclusive proof' of this, then to be quoted in our text books as a 'fact'? The results are awaited with interest.

I would suggest that the evidence for upright posture is negligible. Johanson, however, boldy claims:

> Bipedalism appears to have been the *dominant* form of terrestrial locomotion employed by the Hadar and the Laetolil hominids. Morphological features associated with this locomotor mode are clearly manifested in these hominids . . . [167]

Presumably these hominids walked upright much of the time but were quite accustomed to crawling on all fours—a situation as difficult for us to accept mentally as it would be physically for hominids.

The National Geographic caption

There is one final point regarding Lucy's locomotion. Although Johanson made no claim in his first 1976 report in *Nature* that Lucy's skeleton showed that she walked upright, this *was* claimed in his *National Geographic* article which appeared in December 1976 [173]. In the caption to a photo of Lucy's skeleton it says—'The angle of the thigh bone and the flattened surface at its knee joint end . . . proved she walked on two legs.'

As we have seen, the knee joint (distal) end of the femur was 'badly crushed'. How then can it be said that its 'flattened surface' showed that Lucy walked upright?! Such a detail however would not be given in a popular magazine such as this, perhaps to avoid 'confusing' their readers in the presentation of simple 'facts'. Interestingly, in his later report in 1979 [24] Johanson makes no reference to this femur as indicating bipedalism.

Seemingly, in the field of palaeoanthropology, it is not just bones which become distorted with time.

C. THE DROWNED 'FAMILY'

Over 200 fragments were found at two adjacent sites 333 and 333W, which must have come from a minimum of thirteen individuals. How could so many members of the same species have died in the same area? Johanson's answer is simple. He maintains that they were a family of hominids, sheltering in a dried up river bed, which had drowned in a local 'flash flood'.

Johanson reported his discoveries in an article in the *National Geographic Magazine* [173]. To assist the imagination of their readers, the magazine gives a picture of a 2m wall of water approaching a group of hominids who are fleeing from it. A mother runs to pick up a child hominid, whilst all that can be seen of another is two legs protruding from the top of the water.

Can a local flash flood explain why these broken fragments were found buried in no less than 10m (33 ft.) of mudstone? I rather doubt it. Surely, in such a case many of the bones would be kept together by the skin, even if broken, and would therefore be found close together in correct articulation.

To attempt to explain the process by which various fossils were laid down is extremely difficult. What is certain, however, is that very powerful forces must have been at work to have smashed these bones into small pieces and then buried them in mud some 10m thick! This situation of smashed bones buried in great depths of water laid strata, both becoming hardened over a period of time, is very commonplace in geological strata over the whole world. Catastrophic deluges of this size, however, are not generally accepted on the present Uniformitarian Theory of Geology, based as it is on Lyell's 'Principles of Geology'. However, Gould's denunciation of both Lyell's 'science' and integrity has already been given on p87.

Regarding this 'family', there are two aspects of interest. Firstly I could trace no paper which gave a full account of the fossils. Secondly, a *composite* hand, made up from various bones discovered, was said to be very similar to that of humans. The hand bones of an ape *are*, however, like those of humans in any case, so this hardly constitutes proof that the owners of the composite hand were hominids.

Apes or hominids?

Summarizing the above sections, dealing with the various ape and human characteristics displayed by the fossils, it is surely clear that once again only the fragments of various apes have been found. Furthermore, these apes appear to possess no evidence whatever of 'human progress'.

D. GEOLOGY AND DATING

Two reports were made giving datings for the Hadar stratum, the first in May 1976 [169] in *Nature* (the article preceded Johanson's describing the hominid fossils [170]) and another in May 1977 [171].

Naturally one reads these reports in some detail, in order to picture the various strata, sites, levels, etc., before commenting upon them. In searching through these four main reports [167, 169, 170, 171], one serious omission becomes evident, for *not one of them provides a plan showing the precise location of each of the hominid sites*. One plan [169] gives their location but attaches no numbers in order to identify which fossils were found there. Thus on the basis of these four major reports, it is impossible to locate the site for Lucy or for any other fossil!

Such a gross omission is surely inexcusable and could be interpreted as a desire to obscure the evidence, for it makes the formulation of pertinent comments and criticisms upon the facts presented much more difficult.

Potassium Argon dating

Dating of the various strata is mainly by Potassium-Argon dating. These are said to be confirmed by the fossils discovered, by magneto-stratigraphy (the magnetization of the strata) and fission tracks. All of these dating methods warrant more detailed examination. However, here we must concentrate on the Potassium-

Argon method which was the main dating-method used.

The tests were carried out at Case Western Reserve University (where Johanson is an adjunct Professor of Anthropology). The results are reported in the two papers we are considering [169 and 171]. We have already noted the very unreliable basis of Potassium-Argon dating and the diversity of the results which can be obtained. We should now, however, examine the data and reports for internal inconsistencies.

In the 1976 report five tests were made and, regarding their accuracy, it makes the surprising admission:

> Because of the high percentage of atmospheric argon, these determinations are, as yet, relatively imprecise. [169]

Two samples from a basalt stratum, one-third up from the bottom of the strata investigated, gave 2.9 and 3 million years respectively, which correlate closely. However, three samples from the very bottom SHT stratum gave dates of 3.1, 4.1 and 5.3 million years respectively. The report comments:

> Until further experiments, these inconsistent results are not understood. They may result from the presence of excess radiogenic argon in the glass. [169]

In the later 1977 paper it is noticeable that no reference whatsoever is made to these three discordant dates.

Is the admitted unreliability of these results reflected in the summary of the report? No, it is not. Indeed only two paragraphs later it boldly states:

> Thus the Hadar Formation together with its rich fauna and varied geological environments, will permit *precise* palaeoecological and palaeogeographical reconstruction for an important and previously poorly known segment of later Cainozoic hominid evolution. [20]

Strangely, these figures are now considered 'precise' and furthermore would be used outside the immediate locality, for it says:

> The Hadar sequence will be a reference from which stratigraphic and palaeontological studies may be extended into adjacent parts of the west central Afar sedimentary basin. [169]

Clearly, these admittedly dubious figures will now be used to date all other discoveries for many miles around!

Selective reporting

The 1977 paper [171] reports that three tuffs had been 'newly found' above Lucy's level in the KHT member, and labelled BKT1, 2 and 3 (Fig. 61). The report says that the BKT2 layer 'is at present the *most promising* of all the tuffs in the Hadar formation'.

'Promising for what?', it may be asked. Perhaps out of the three tuffs *this is the only one giving dates which can be correlated with those of the basalt flow* lower down.

Having briefly described the other two tuffs, they receive no further mention and no dating tests are reported. Surely tests would have been carried out on all three? Why are only the tests on BKT2 reported?

This bias in the selectivity of 'acceptable results' is an important one on which much space could be devoted and examples provided. In this report, however, there is another statement which could indicate that such selectivity may have been operating, perhaps subconsciously in the minds of the authors. In dealing with the dating of the basalt, it says:

> To be conservative, its 3.0 Myr age should be regarded as a minimum age because a coexisting variety of the flow, which has endured a similar history, has demonstrably lost argon compared to it. [171]

As far as I can see, this 'false' date referred to does not appear in the report and one is left wondering if any other dating tests have been omitted. I have already pointed out that readers of scientific papers and the general public have a right to expect *all* results to be reported, whether they support the writer's conclusions or not.

It is easy to see how such situations can arise. A number of samples are taken from the various strata, both vertically and along their length. Preliminary tests are then run on various specimens. If the anthropologist considers the fossils to be, say, 2–3 million years old, any results wildly different from these figures are rejected out of hand. Others, which are not so far away from the expected figures, may be reported but, if they are too young, they are considered to have 'lost radiogenic Argon'. If, on the other hand, they are too old, they are considered to have 'retained magmatic (subterranean) Argon'. However, those samples yielding acceptable results are then subjected to numerous tests. All of them, of course, show considerable consistency in their datings. This is exactly what would be expected if they were from the same sample or closely adjacent sites. The closeness of these results would then give a spurious air of reliability to the whole dating of a formation.

I am not, of course, for one moment suggesting that this is what occurred in the results presented in these particular reports. I am simply exaggerating the sequence of events to show how under certain circumstances the field could be narrowed down to those results which agree with hominid dating presuppositions. Interestingly, this contention is in fact supported by the Americans themselves. As we have shown on p206, when they criticized the Cambridge datings of the East Rudolf KBS tuff, they said they had obtained 'reproduceable results' to a 'high precision' which were 'not meaningful' in this case being 'an artefact of experimental procedure'! I have also shown (p66) how a first dating for Richard Leakey's '1470' man gave the fantastically high figure of 220 million years, how it was explained away and superseded by a very acceptable, and therefore well publicized, 2.6 million years.

Some light relief

Having brought my reader thus far, it will be obvious that I am making very serious charges against the whole theory of man's evolution from apes. Our views on how man came to exist can have enormous effect upon our whole view of the meaning of life, and I therefore have no desire to trivialize in any way the very factual basis of the evidence I present in this book. Nevertheless, I am conscious that the continuous presentation of facts upon facts may at times make the reading of this book somewhat 'heavy going'. In view of this, a little light relief may not be unwelcome and I give below an article that appeared in 'Punch' magazine on 8th March 1961, which is reproduced by kind permission of the publishers. At that time, Potassium-Argon dating was being used to determine the 'age' of the strata in the Olduvai gorge, where Dr. L. S. B. Leakey was making fossil discoveries. When scientists announce that a stratum is so many millions of years old, it is stated with such confidence that the public accept it as incontrovertible 'fact'. Indeed, the whole subject is surrounded by an aura of sanctity, which the following brilliant skit by B. A. Young should go some way towards dispelling.

More secrets from the past: Oboyoboi Gorge

What may well prove to be the oldest crown cork known to man has been found here by Dr C. J. M. Crikey, the anthropologist. It is thought to be at least 500,000 years old. 'I cannot yet give an exact estimate of its age,' Dr Crikey said, 'but I am sending it back to the museum for radio-cola tests, and these should establish definitely how old it is.'

The finding of the crown cork throws an entirely new light on the use of crown corks by prehistoric man. Until quite recently it was assumed that crown corks had come into use only in comparatively recent times. If the radio-cola tests confirm Dr Crikey's estimates, all previous theories about the use of crown corks will have to be revised.

The cork lining layer had disappeared completely, leaving only the circular metal disc with the characteristic corrugated rim. There is no trace of any inscription having appeared on the crown cork, but X-ray pictures may reveal some kind of prehistoric trade mark under the layer of oxidisation which encrusts the metal at present.

Our Scientific Correspondent writes: The Oboyoboi Gorge, where the prehistoric crown cork was found, is a 300-foot cleft carved out of the surrounding countryside of Tanganyika by the seasonal waters of the Oboyoboi River. The age of any remains found in the bank can be accurately assessed from their height above the level of the river bed, the recently discovered pre-Zinj man, calculated to be 700,000 years old, being at the bottom and Mr Julius Nyerere at the top.

It seems possible that the remote ancestor of man who inhabited the area at the epoch to which the crown cork has been assigned—we may conveniently refer to him as the 'post-Zinj man'—used rudimentary stone tools to fashion crown corks for his crude bottles, probably by cutting a rough circle from a sheet of tin and then laboriously turning up the edges and pressing in the corrugations one at a time. The cork lining would then have been cut from the bark of the giant cork trees that may have flourished there at the time and shaped to fit with the aid of a primitive stone knife.

The radio-cola tests to be applied to the crown cork provide a peculiarly elegant method of measuring the age of any prehistoric object. Cola exists in the form of a number of isotopes. One of these is the radio-active isotope radio-cola. This decays at a rate which is accurately known, throwing off an electron to become stable bitter lemon. By comparing the amount of free radio-cola present in a bottle of cola with the amount theoretically present before the bottle was opened, it is possible to calculate how long the sample has been decaying and so arrive at an accurate estimate of its age.

If the radio-cola tests confirm Dr Crikey's estimate that the crown cork is 500,000 years old, it will be at least 499,950 years older than any other crown cork known to exist.

STOP PRESS: A message from Dr Crikey's camp at Oboyoboi Gorge states that the crown cork found there last week is not prehistoric but was dropped by Armand and Michaela Denis during their visit to the site a year ago. 'The whole thing was a laughable mistake,' Dr Crikey said, 'but it emphasises more than ever the tremendous importance of checking and double-checking all one's calculations.'

D. JOHANSON'S VIEWS

As we have mentioned, Johanson considered that his discoveries were of two separate species. But later he classed them all with the jaws discovered by Mary Leakey and gave them the name Australopithecus afarensis. Fig. 58 gives his version of how man arose from an ape-like ancestor. I have already commented upon the fact that, although based upon the same fossils, Johanson's views are completely different to the speculations of the other experts. Despite this absence of even a reasonable amount of convincing evidence, such diagrams are often confidently published to show 'How Man Evolved' for acceptance by schools and the general public.

Johanson discovered Lucy's ape-like skeleton in November 1974 and said it was dated between 2.6 and 3.3 million years old. Leakey, however, had discovered the very human like 1470 skull two years earlier in stratum which Leakey estimated was 2.9 million years old. Here were two fossils jockeying for the prestigious title of 'The First Evidence of Man', so sought after by palaeoanthropologists. One of the contenders had to be dislodged by some means. As we have seen, the KBS tuff from which Leakey derived his date was retested by four scientists from the University of California, who after several attempts eventually obtained from specially selected minute grains a date of 1.82 million years, which was much lower than the original 2.6 million years.

This lower date for the 1470 skull enabled Johanson and T. D. White to present their view of man's emergence, as shown in Fig. 58, in which Lucy is classed with Homo habilis at about 2 million years ago.

I have already raised the question as to why the scientists at California University should go to the considerable trouble of retesting the KBS tuff. It is perhaps significant that White himself is assistant professor in the Department of Anthropology at California University. Was it perhaps suggested to the geochronologists in the University that the KBS tuff was probably less than 2.6 million years old? It would certainly explain their reason for retesting, which was 'Because of the great interest in the dating . . .' Johanson would, of course, be *very* interested if 1470 could be shown to be younger than 2.9 million years!

The 'Row'
Johanson's claim that the Hadar and Laetolil fossils should be classified as Australopithecus afarensis did not go unchallenged. Both Mary and Richard Leakey did not accept his views. The *International Herald Tribune* reports—'"I think Don [Johanson] was right first time", Richard said, . . . "No way," Johanson said in a separate interview. "The entire range of variation is represented at the 333 site . . ." "To support his challenge, Leakey also said his colleagues had discovered some new fossils in Kenya that were of similar age to Johanson's fossils but that they did not resemble the newly named species" . . . "Leakey declined to discuss the new fossils in detail until he had published a formal report in a scientific journal. In an interview however he said they consisted of *eight*

isolated teeth." "The material I've got is *very insignificant,* but there's enough to challenge Don with", he said, "It gives me the right to offer my opinion."' [174]

Thus the scene is set for a big 'row' between these two rivals. To watch these 'experts' sparring over a few bone fragments hardly merits any serious comment. Such vaporous wranglings do, however, serve an important function in keeping man's ape ancestry well before the public eye.

E. MOTIVATION

The word 'science' is very much a 'trigger' word. To the general public it tends to conjure up immediately a picture of a white coated professor setting up delicate experiments and making incredibly accurate measurements. It is often supposed that when he has all the results before him, he considers them impersonally, sees a pattern or a cause, from which he proposes a theory. When it is corroborated by many other experiments it becomes a law, adding to mankind's knowledge and progress.

As most scientists admit, however, the reality is often far different. Theories can be proposed, attacked and defended with a personal vehemence little realized by most. And academic 'long knives' are notoriously sharp!

Indeed, actual falsification of results in order to give the 'required' answers is apparently more widespread than we may think. This was a subject much discussed in the national Press, which was very revealing. *

We find that a world famous sociologist had completely fabricated one set of results. This had also been the case with another scientist who had been working on living cells. A survey showed that nothing was done to 80% of those who were found to have 'massaged' or 'biased' their results. Some had even been promoted. In the field of psychology, out of 32 replies to a questionnaire, no less than 21 said that the data on which they had based their recent papers was missing, lost, unavailable or accidentally destroyed! [American Psychologist v17p657]. Even Mendel's experiments, so frequently quoted by books on the theory of evolution, have been found to have given him results that were 'too good to be true' by very large odds against [*Annals of Science* vlp115].

Guardian 25th November 1976, *Daily Telegraph* 25th and 26th February 1977, *Sunday Times* 24th October 1976, *Nature* 26th February 1977 v265p764, *New Scientist* 25th December 1969 v44pp642-3, 7th November 1974 v64pp436-7, 17th June 1976 v70p652, 2nd September 1976 v71pp481-3, 25th November 1976 v72pp466-9.

I mention all this merely to show how personal and emotional some scientists can be in their particular subject. Perhaps ambition is the main spur in some of these instances. Such falsifications are unlikely to have any bearing on the very recent fossil discoveries we are considering, for it is likely that the discoveries, measurements and descriptions, as they are reported, are comparatively accurate. My main contention is with the inferences drawn from them, rather than the actual data themselves.

Emotion

It may be thought that digging up the petrified bones of animals which died thousands of years ago would be the most boring and unemotional activity imaginable. Yet even here, human emotions enter in. Johanson gives an account, in the *National Geographic Magazine* [173], of his feelings whilst searching for fossils. It is this organization (which Hillaby observes is 'colourful in all senses of the word' [155]), which produces the magazine which also provides Johanson and Leakey with considerable financial assistance for their expeditions.

Johanson's account certainly gives the impression that the atmosphere is very highly charged, as the following extract shows:

> As we walked, I glanced over my shoulder—and there on the ground I saw a fragment of an arm bone.
> 'Look at that right there,' I said to Tom.
> [Tom Gray, a postgraduate student. His initial reaction is interesting.]
> 'An arm bone of a monkey?' Tom guessed.
> [Johanson is now however emotionally involved—]
> My pulse was quickening. Although the bone was very small, it lacked the characteristic bony flange of the comparable anatomical portion of a monkey. Suddenly I found myself saying, 'It's a hominid!' . . . We looked up the slope. There, incredibly, lay a multitude of bone fragments . . . Tom and I yelled, hugged each other, and danced, mad as any Englishman in the midday sun.

Little room here it seems for a cautious, dispassionate examination of the fossils to ensure their precise origin!

This tendency to see hominid (part-human) characteristics in almost any ape bone found appears to be endemic amongst fossil hunters. With this in mind, an unintended interpretation could be put upon a reply to the question of why no stone tools had been found. The answer was—'We haven't looked for tools yet, *and we tend to find only what we look for.*'

A strange link

Before researching for the first edition of this book, I was well aware of Teilhard de Chardin's involvement with Piltdown and Pekin man, and was therefore surprised to find he was instrumental in the later discoveries in Java, and furthermore wielded considerable financial control of excavations in East Africa. My surprise was even greater on discovering that he had visited the Afar area in Ethiopia.

The occasion was in 1928 when returning to China from France. He spent some two months in Ethiopia in the company of Henry de Monfreid, a notorious gun-runner, drug-smuggler and companion of slave-traders, whom Teilhard had met several times in Boule's laboratory [175p102]. It is difficult to establish his exact movements, but he was certainly in the Southern area of the Afar depression and explored this remote and inhospitable area in sufficient detail to write 'at least two useful little memoranda on Ethiopia and Somaliland' [30p150].

One would hesitate to draw any conclusions, but simply note the coincidence that it was to this very region that his compatriot, the French expert Maurice Taieb, should take Johanson in 1972 as a likely field for hominid discoveries.

CONCLUSION

In this section, I have attempted to sift through the main reports of the expedition to ascertain precisely what was found, in an effort to disentangle the facts from a great deal of fantasy. It is my consideration that all the fossils discovered so far in Hadar are simply those of various apes, whose supposed human characteristics do not bear even superficial examination.

Johanson has been criticized for his slowness in publishing the results of his discoveries. Perhaps the reason may lie in the meagreness of the evidence they provide. When one considers the vast expenditure over several years on this expedition, the final result is a collection of apes' bones which can only be described as 'pitiful'!

SECTION VIIE

THE LAETOLIL FOOTPRINTS

After L. S. B. Leakey's death in 1972, his wife, Mary, continued searching the Olduvai gorge, but concentrated mainly on sites at Laetolil, some 30 km (19m) further South. As we have briefly mentioned, a few jaws were found and classified as Homo erectus. Of more interest, however, was the discovery of many fossilized footprints of animals and, even more important, of some walking 'hominids', all in strata dated 3.6–3.75 million years old.

The footprints were found at seven sites, mostly at two different stratigraphic levels. Certain conditions at the time when the strata were laid down resulted in the footprint impressions becoming hardened and retaining much of their detail. A wide variety of bird and animal tracks was found, many of them identical to existing species. The tracks were first noticed as early as 1976 and studied in 1977. At what stage the 'hominid' tracks were recognized is not clear, but no public announcement was made of their existence until 24th February 1978, when Mary Leakey reported six prints [176]. Further prints were discovered and were reported in *Nature* on 22nd March 1979 [177].

When they were eventually presented in the mass media, the 'ape-like' nature of the individuals was stressed, and the public was assured that they were 'small brained' creatures who had just learnt to walk upright. A picture often accompanied such articles showing two of them viewed from behind, in the process of making the tracks. But surprisingly they looked remarkably human! [178].

The report in *Nature* by Mary Leakey and R. L. Hay also minimized the importance of the hominid tracks. In a written report covering six pages, only 13% of the writing and three pictures are devoted to the 'hominid' tracks. Even then, they are described along with other ape tracks all under the heading 'Primates'.

Three tracks are reported. At site A, one track was 1.5m (5 ft.) long and consisted of five prints, with a stride of 31cm (12 ins), each print being 15.5cm (6.1 ins) long by 10.5m (4.1 ins) wide.

At site G, two parallel tracks, 23.5m (77 ft.) long, were found 25cms (9.8 ins) apart. In view of the difference in the condition of the tracks, they must have been made at separate times. Trail 1 consisted of 22 prints with a stride of 38.7cm (15.2 ins), each print being 18.5 x 8.8cm (7.3 x 3.5 ins). This smaller individual appears to have paused and made a half turn to the left before continuing in the original direction.

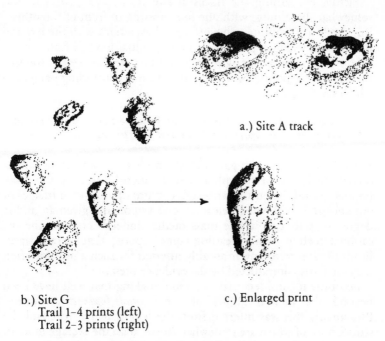

a.) Site A track

b.) Site G
    Trail 1–4 prints (left)
    Trail 2–3 prints (right)

c.) Enlarged print

Fig.64. The Laetolil footprints

Trail 2 had 12 prints, each 21.5 x 10cm (8.5 x 3.9 ins) and the stride was 47.2cm (18.6 ins). All the diagrams of these tracks appearing in the report are illustrated in Fig. 64. It is the description of the prints, however, which provide the most interest. In what follows, it should be remembered that in an ape's hind foot, the big toe is 'opposable' (like the human thumb) in order to facilitate the grasping of branches. This tendency of the toe to stick out is clearly visible in their tracks, one of them being pictured in the report. Describing the hominid prints, however, it states:

> Unlike the cercopithecoid prints, the longest digit is the great toe, *situated as in the human foot* . . . Note that the longitudinal arch of the foot is well developed *and resembles that of modern man*, and the *great toe is parallel to the other toes* . . .'

In the article in the *National Geographic Magazine*, a foot print expert said, 'They looked so modern, so human . . .' [178].
   There is no suggestion here that the toe is in a position halfway between man and ape, and the report seems to accept that the prints are fully human in shape. It does, however, make two claims that the individuals were 'primitive'.

Firstly, concerning the tracks at site A, it says: 'The gait was somewhat shambling, with one foot crossing in front of the other.' But surely a shambling gait would produce a track with the left and right prints widely separated as the individual lurched from side to side, not in almost a straight line, as they were discovered. Indeed, this view is supported by the report itself in a concluding paragraph which says:

> . . . it is immediately evident that the Pliocene hominids at Laetolil had achieved a fully *upright, bipedal and free striding gait* . . .

Thus the claim that the gait was 'shambling' is completely contradicted. Inclusion of this phrase, so frequently used by the more popular pseudo-scientific writers to conjure up cave-man images of our ancestors, will nevertheless be seized upon and given an undue degree of publicity in the mass media. Indeed, one has the occasional feeling, whilst reading some reports, that certain significant phrases were unwarrantably inserted for such a use, for often they are flatly contradicted by the evidence presented.

Secondly it considers that '. . . tool-making may well have been beyond the mental ability of these *small-brained* creatures.' Presumably this was inferred from the length of the feet and the stride, both of which are somewhat shorter than the average modern man. As we have previously emphasized, brain capacity is no indication of the mental ability of its possessor. Furthermore, tracks of similar size to those found at Laetolil would be made by the various races of pygmies around the world, who are fully Homo sapiens.

I would consider that the tracks were made, not by a small-brained hominid, but by a man (or woman) of short stature. As can be seen from some of the passages I have quoted, the tracks give the immediate impression of having been made by human beings. One is therefore left wondering whether this may have been a contributory factor in the subsequent minimizing of their importance.

The Paluxy River tracks

This discovery of man-made tracks at Laetolil is not isolated, however. There is evidence of many tracks being found in the bed of the Paluxy River in Glen Rose, Texas. What makes these of particular importance is that they are in a *Cretaceous* formation, i.e. dated about 100 million years. Furthermore, they appear beside those of long extinct dinosaurs! The bed of the Paluxy River is a soft limestone, and prints may be eroded fairly quickly, whilst during flooding, the course of the river often covers some areas and exposes others.

Fig.65. The large human footprints

from the Paluxy river

The limestone bed contains many tracks of dinosaurs and parties are taken on tours to view them. That human footprints have also appeared from time to time seems to have been an accepted fact by the local inhabitants for decades.

Rumours of these human tracks apparently reached the ears of Roland T. Bird of the Department of Vertebrate Palaeontology of the American Natural History Museum, who investigated the area and wrote an article in *Natural History* in May 1939 [179].

What is clear from his account is his complete rejection of the possibility that human footprints could occur in Cretaceous rocks. He first inspected two slabs in a trader's store containing giant footprints some 15 inches (38cm) long but dismissed them as forgeries (Fig. 65). Hearing that they came from the same place where dinosaur tracks were found, he eventually asked a local farmer in Glen Rose about the 'mystery' tracks. The farmer replied casually, 'Oh, you mean the *man tracks*. Why sure, there used to be a whole trail of them up above the fourth crossing, before the river washed them out.'

The farmer had cut some out of the river in times past, but the effort was hardly worth their low selling price. The farmer took Bird to see the only print still visible, and Bird described it as '. . . the outline of a foot . . . some thing about 15 inches long with a curious elongated heel.' He admits that the mud had originally been very soft, and that the rock had preserved this 'element of softness' (i.e. had retained an accurate and detailed impression?). Nevertheless he claims it 'lacked definition on which to base conclusions' and states that, 'apparently it had been made by some hitherto unknown dinosaur or reptile'! It is strange that an expert palaeontologist should say that a print which was at least human-like *may* have been made by an unknown reptile. This suggests to me that he was strongly biased against accepting the most obvious inference from the evidence before him.

Bird made many enquiries in the area about what he preferred to call 'mystery tracks', which he continues to claim were made by this 'reptile' with the 'curiously elongated heel'. But he found their existence was such common knowledge with the local people that he found himself also referring to the 'man tracks'. The rest of his article describes giant sauropod prints which he found, but no further reference is made to these 'mystery' tracks.

It is clear from the article that Bird would, under no circumstances, accept the possibility that human beings, whether giant or normal, could have lived at the same time as dinosaurs. It is indeed unfortunate that Bird did not pursue his investigations further, for the evidence was nevertheless lying there and he would have found ample evidence to support this contention.

The Film evidence

This very convincing evidence is contained not in an article but in a film entitled 'Footprints in Stone'.* The makers of the film cleared an area of the bed of the river and found several long tracks of dinosaurs, men and giants criss-crossing the area. The prints in the hardened strata are clear and well preserved, showing much detail. Impressions of individual toes are frequent and on some it is clear they were made by a man who was running. Some of the human prints lay halfway across those of a dinosaur. Furthermore, in order to prove conclusively that the tracks could not have been faked, an excavator was hired to remove a large bank. The tracks were found to continue unbroken beneath it.

One of the most interesting parts of the film was the reactions of a visiting group of geologists when confronted with the tracks. Their puzzlement and sheer disbelief was obvious whilst their comments were faltering and non-commital. Here was very clear and obvious proof to any unbiased person that men and dinosaurs were contemporaneous. Yet these experienced geologists reacted in a most evasive manner, not because of the inadequacy of the evidence they had examined at first hand, but simply because of their preconceptions. To have accepted this evidence would have completely shattered the credibility of the painstakingly constructed geological column which has been a dogma of faith for experts of many generations. Had any of these visiting geologists agreed that the inference of the tracks was obvious, they would have been open to ridicule by their professional colleagues. Furthermore, to have held such 'heretical' views would have called into question their suitability to be retained in the senior positions they occupied in the scientific world. With such possible outcomes in mind, their evasiveness can be understood. Indeed geologists are not the only experts who are aware of possible repercussions on their career

---

*Films for Christ Ass., Elmwood, Illinois, U.S.A. or Light & Life Films, 42 Fountainhall Road., Edinburgh, Scotland, EH9 2LW.

prospects, should they hold views which differ fundamentally from their professional colleagues.

We have here considered only one subject where the evidence completely contradicts the standard geological column, but many others could be given. None, however, appear in the secular press. For it is certain that such evidence, even when submitted by accredited experts, is always rejected on very unsatisfactory grounds by scientific periodicals (be they prestigious or popular). This may be ascribed to the 'bias' of the editors concerned. But it is such a universal phenomenon that I would question whether it may go deeper than this. This is an important subject to which I will briefly refer in the conclusion.

APPENDIX VIII

THE NATURAL HISTORY MUSEUM'S EXHIBITION 'MAN'S PLACE IN EVOLUTION'

In 1980 the Natural History Museum mounted a permanent exhibition entitled 'Man's place in evolution' and published an accompanying book with the same title.

The exhibition is in nine bays, in the first of which we are told that 'Man is an animal', and the second shows how he is also 'a mammal, a primate and an ape'.

Bay 3. The chimpanzee and gorilla are displayed, but it is admitted that man's relationship to them is undecided.

Bay 4. Rampithecus had flat molar teeth and the 'reconstructed muzzle' was short. This 'suggests' he was related to man.

Bay 5. Australopithecines—a display of various skulls and a full height reconstruction of Sterkfontein woman, who possesses a pronounced (prognathic) muzzle like a chimpanzee. Yet the book says 'Study her carefully. You can see that she has a short muzzle like a human being . . .'! Reconstructions show that the Australopithecines walked upright—in flat contradiction of Sir Solly Zuckerman's findings.

Bay 6. The Habilines (Homo habilis)—this is a most surprising display, as *Leakey's '1470 Man' is almost ignored.* One large photograph of the skull is on a separate introductory board to the section which is entitled 'Man's Fossil Relations' and no classification is given. *The display case of Homo habilines completely ignores it!* In order to bolster their meagre collection of Habiline fossils, Leakey's skull No. 1813 is included. Yet in two articles in 1976 he classed this as an Australopithecine!

Bay 7. Homo erectus. This is the weakest link in the chain, with Pekin man, Java man and Chellean man (Fig. 51) being used. A 'reconstructed' model of a Pekin site hearth of one foot thickness (300mm) ignores the fact that 24 ft. (7m) of ash were actually found.

Bay 8 deals with the Neanderthals.

Bay 9 summarizes the facts presented and is notable for the final branching diagram (Cladogram) of man's evolution, for *not one of the animals or fossils in the exhibition is shown on the line of man's evolution, only as branches from each other.* Thus although there is the admission that they have not a single fossil which is directly ancestral to man, this is done in such a way that few would notice.

240

This exhibition will be seen by many thousands of people, and as it is designed for young schoolchildren, its effects will be far reaching. In this appendix I have very briefly criticized only the factual evicence it presents. I examine in another work* the questions and answers that are put to the visitor, for these are loaded in such a way that they amount to little more than propaganda for the myth that man evolved from animals.

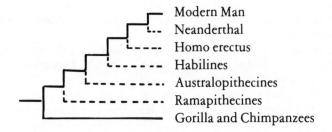

Modern Man
Neanderthal
Homo erectus
Habilines
Australopithecines
Ramapithecines
Gorilla and Chimpanzees

The Natural History Museum's Cladogram
of "Man's Place in Evolution"

*The Rise of the Evolution Fraud (see rear pages)

CONCLUSION

Within the compass of this book, I have examined the circumstances surrounding the discovery of the most important ape-men fossils, reviewed the type of evidence provided, compared differing views of man's history, and shown how *Homo sapiens* has been discovered in strata much deeper than those of his supposed ancestors.

Finally, I would specifically point out one aspect, which is apparent throughout this book, namely the meagre fossil evidence for the ape-men links. There are numerous *complete* skeletons in the earth's strata, both of *Homo sapiens* and of animals, including dinosaurs, apes and monkeys.

But the fossil links between man and the animals consist only of fragments of jaws, some broken skull pieces, part of a foot, etc., no complete skeleton or even a reasonable proportion of one ever having been discovered.

The speculation and generalizations drawn from the fossil evidence seem to follow an inverse law. Where it is very fragmentary, sweeping claims can be made regarding the position and importance of the 'hominid'. Where more fossil bones have been discovered, opinions become more conservative, for extravagant claims could be refuted from the available evidence, and whether the fossils are from an ape or a human becomes more obvious. The very fragmentary nature of the evidence supporting the existence of ape-men is sometimes admitted by the experts, but it is nevertheless held to be 'convincing' and 'irrefutable'.

I would venture to contradict such opinions. On the basis of the evidence provided, I suggest that it is very *un*convincing, and that the case for such links is 'not proven', despite extensive searching of the earth's surface for over one hundred years. This lack of fossil evidence is so embarrassing that the subject is now carefully avoided. For example, the book entitled 'Evolution' is published by the British Natural History Museum (with Routledge & Kegan Paul) and is written by Colin Patterson who is on the Museum staff. From this we may assume it represents the latest official view on the subject, replacing, as it does, their earlier editions. When we turn to the section headed 'Evolution and Man', the opening sentences are:

> In this concluding chapter I am not concerned with the historical story of how our species evolved. Accounts of evolution rely heavily on fossils, and the number of different stories is almost as great as the number of fossils.

There is not a single mention of any of the old favourites—Pekin man, Java man etc.—and the whole section deals only with the genetic similarities between men and apes.

The Museum's exhibition 'Man's Place in Evolution' presents a number of fossils as evidence for man's evolution, but again only refers to their 'relationship' to man as we have seen in Appendix VIII. Indeed the increasing use of 'Cladograms' allows them to deceptively avoid the issue that they have no fossils in the direct line of man's evolution.

One very important aspect of the stream of programmes, articles and references to evolution which are carried by the mass media is that it is very much a one way communication—from the experts to the general public. This method of communication does not allow the asking of awkward questions, or the challenging of the facts presented. With the growing interest in the subject by a number of people who have studied the evidence against evolution in some detail, it is interesting that few experts are willing to debate the subject formally. Perhaps they have heard of the situation in America, where the subject is being vented freely, of the increasing reluctance of experts to enter into debate. I have personally issued a challenge to debate the subject on more than one occasion, but as yet have received no response.

Reviews of 'Ape-Men—Fact or Fallacy?'
This question of the inadequacy of the fossil evidence is alluded to in a review of the first edition of *Ape-Men* which appeared in 'Antiquity' (November 1978) by Richard Burleigh of the British Natural History Museum.

In this review one phrase occurs which required reading several times before its significance was appreciated. The phrase in question was:

> . . . whilst much of the strength of the fossil evidence lies in its essential rarity.

How, one must ask, can the strength of any evidence be due to its rarity? From this it would appear that when the fossil evidence is sparse, the proof is *more* convincing! Pronouncements such as this are redolent of George Orwell's *1984* 'Newspeak'.

In this review, *Ape-Men* was criticized so heavily that it is surprising that the editor should have wasted space on such a poor book. One noticeable feature of this review is its failure to point out a single error of fact. Had one been found, one can be sure that it would have been magnified out of all proportion to its importance, in order to throw doubt on the accuracy of the whole book.

This review was the only one to appear in the secular Press. Yet *Ape-Men* has certainly provoked considerable interest, receiving many warm reviews in Christian periodicals of a wide range of denominations. However apart from these, it has generally been met with a 'barrier of silence'. Sir Solly Zuckerman complained in his book, *Beyond the Ivory Tower*, that his papers on the Australopithecines were ignored. Indeed, many manuscripts are not accepted by publishers if they are critical of the 'established view' in certain subjects. It may be thought that I am taking a jaundiced view. However, the fact that there is a close-knit relationship between a number of influential top scientists and those who control the information-media is one about which the general public is completely unaware, and the importance of this fact is grossly underestimated.

I would refer to one incident in which 'scientific' forces were rapidly mobilized in order to prevent the publication of a well-researched series of books, calling into question the basic assumptions held by scientists in more than one subject.

The suppression of Velikovsky's views
In the field of astronomy and the chronology of the races of man, Immanuel Velikovsky has written several well documented books (*Ages in Chaos, Worlds in Collision, Earth in Upheaval*), which completely contradict the 'established record of events' and the present 'Uniformitarian' views of geologists and scientists. It is an open question regarding the correctness or otherwise of some of Velikovsky's theories. However, the concerted pressure by many scientific bodies brought to bear upon Macmillans, when they were about to publish his works in 1950, is most revealingly documented in 'The Velikovsky Affair' [180]. Macmillans were threatened with a ban on the sale of their textbooks in many universities, and scientists were refusing to see their representatives. In the face of this obviously orchestrated opposition, Macmillans capitulated and passed the rights over to a much smaller publisher. The author, de Grazia, comments:

> The most readily available economic instrument of the scientific establishment is the 'boycott'. It is well-known but not sufficiently appreciated that the leaders of the scientific field wield a triple influence over publishers. They are authors or sponsors of the leading works in the field. They influence opinion about books; this in turn affects purchasing. And they and their subordinates and followers in other colleges purchase an important part of the books and materials sold in the field and used as texts and required reading. When a publisher's contact men find the doors to the mighty suddenly closed to them, this is more than pressure—it can be a mortal blow. The establishment

moved with speed and vigor to block professional support for Velikovsky's book and to boycott it and its publisher. [180]

Velikovsky met the Chairman of Macmillans, who said:

Academic circles are not isolated groups; they are united in local organizations, or in professional associations that are incorporated or represented in larger national organizations . . . In this way the academic pressure may become widespread. [180]

Thus we see that in certain fields the scientific world is far from possessing the openminded, enquiring attitude it so strongly professes. Indeed, I would suggest that there are certain subjects, of which palaeoanthropology is a prime example, which have no right to be called sciences, but only pseudo-sciences. Such fields of apparent knowledge are sustained by what amounts to propaganda, whilst contradictory facts are suppressed. With all this in mind, it will become evident why I have been very circumspect in the writing of this book.

Robert Ardrey is one writer who laments this suppression of dissenting voices. He himself is fully convinced of man's evolution, having written extensively on the subject. He holds the view that man progressed due to his innate, aggressive instincts, and bitterly complains that this interpretation of evolution is suppressed by those who say that man is simply a product of his environment. He contends that they have control of many of the education and scientific appointments and states:

. . . the three sciences central to human understanding—psychology, anthropology and sociology—successfully and continually lie to themselves, lie to each other, lie to their students, and lie to the public at large . . . [181p12]

With such outspoken condemnation, little further comment is called for.

The alternative rejected

I consider that the present day idea that man evolved from the apes is based upon inadequate evidence which has been wilfully misconstrued in order to support the theory, and all undertaken in the name of 'science'.

If man has not come from the apes, the only reasonable alternative is that he was created. However, the implications of such a view are unacceptable to many. Irrespective of any emotional protestations to the contrary, I would contend that such objections are fundamentally *theological* (albeit subconscious) and not scientific. The basic objection is the refusal to acknowledge the existence of an *all* powerful God who is well able to create Man, should He so wish. Those who do object to this view have no alternative but to cling to a theory which can only be sustained by such devious methods as I have outlined in this book.

Thus, in this day and age, as in many spheres of life, the real truth is suppressed. But not for ever, for most assuredly the day will come when all truth will be revealed to mankind in such a fashion that no-one will be able to deny it.

BIBLIOGRAPHY

BOOKS

1 Ager, D. V. 1973. *The Nature of the Stratigraphical Record*, New York—Wiley & Sons.
2 Barnett, S. A. (Ed.). 1958. *A Century of Darwin*, Heinemann.
3 De Beer, G. 1964. *An Atlas of Evolution*, Nelson.
4 Boule, M. & Vallois, F. 1957. *Fossil Men*, Dryden Press (English translation).
5 Broderick, A. H. 1971. *Man and His Ancestors*, Hutchinson & Co.
6 Carrington, R. 1963. *A Million Years of Man*, Weidenfeld & Nicholson.
7 Clark, W. Le Gros. 1964. *The Fossil Evidence for Human Evolution*, University of Chicago Press.
8 Clark, W. Le Gros. 1970. *History of the Primates* (10th edition), British Museum (Natural History).
9 Cole, S. 1975. *Leakey's Luck*, Collins.
10 Collins, D. 1976. *The Human Revolution*, The Phaidon Press.
11 Constable, G. 1973. *The Neanderthalers*, Time-Life Books (Series on 'The Emergence of Man').
12 Cuénot, C. 1958. *Teilhard de Chardin*, Burns & Oates (English translation 1965).
13 Day, M. 1965. *Guide to Fossil Man*, Cassell.
14 Goodall, V. (Ed.). 1975. *The Quest for Man*, Phaidon Press.
15 Huxley, J. (Ed.). 1954. *Evolution as a Process*, Allen & Unwin.
16 Keith, A. 1925 ed. *The Antiquity of Man*, Williams & Norgate.
17 Kenny, M. J. 1966. *Teach Yourself Evolution*, English University Press.
18 Koenigswald, G. H. R. von. 1956. *Meeting Prehistoric Man*, Thames & Hudson.
19 Kroeber, A. L. (Ed.). 1953. *Anthropology Today*, University of Chicago Press.
20 Kurth, G. (Ed.). 1968. *Evolution und Hominisation*, Stuttgart.
21 Leakey, L. S. B. 1953 ed. *Adam's Ancestors*, Methuen.
22 Leakey, L. S. B. 1970. *Unveiling Man's Origin*, Methuen.
23 Lyell, C. 1863. *Geological Evidence of the Antiquity of Man*.
24 Millar, R. 1972. *The Piltdown Men*, Gollancz.
25 Moore, R. 1962. *Man, Time and Fossils*, Cape.
26 Oakley, K. P. 1969. *Frameworks for Dating Fossil Man*, Weidenfeld & Nicholson.
27 O'Connell, Rev. Patrick. 1969. *Science of Today and the Problem of Genesis*.
28 Shapiro, H. L. 1976. *Pekin Man*, Allen & Unwin.
29 Speaight, R. 1967. *Teilhard de Chardin—a Biography*, Collins.
30 Teilhard de Chardin, P. 1962. *Letters from a Traveller*, Collins.
31 Teilhard de Chardin, P. 1965. *The Appearance of Man*, Collins.
32 Vere, F. 1955. *The Piltdown Fantasy*, Cassell.
33 Vere, F. 1959. *Lessons of Piltdown*, E.P.M.
34 Washburn, S. L. (Ed.). 1964. *Classification and Human Evolution*, Methuen.
35 Weidenreich, F. 1965. *Apes, Giants and Man*, University of Chicago Press.
36 Weiner, J. S. 1955. *The Piltdown Forgery*, Oxford University Press.
37 Wendt, H. 1972. *From Ape to Adam*, Thames & Hudson.
38 Woodward, A. S. 1948. *The Earliest Englishman*, Watts & Co.
39 Zeuner, F. E. 1958. *Dating the Past* (4th edition), Methuen & Co.

SECTION I—PILTDOWN

40 1913. Dawson, C. & Woodward, A. S. 'On the discovery of a Palaeolithic human skull and mandible in a flint bearing gravel at Piltdown', *Quarterly Journal*, Geol. Soc., London, vol.69, pp. 117–51. (Report of the meeting held 18th December 1912.)

41 1914. Dawson, C. & Woodward, A. S. 'Supplementary note on the discovery of a Paleolithic human skull and mandible at Piltdown', *Quarterly Journal*, Geol. Soc., London, vol.70, pp.82–93. (Report of the meeting held 17th December 1913.)

42 1915. Dawson, C. & Woodward, A. S. 'On a bone implement from Piltdown, Sussex', *Quarterly Journal*, Geol. Soc., London, vol.71, p.144. (Report of the meeting held 2nd December 1914.)

43 1917. Woodward, A. S. 'Fourth note on the Piltdown gravel with evidence of a second skull of Eoanthropus dawsoni', *Quarterly Journal*, Geol. Soc., London, vol.73, pt.I, pp.1–10.

44 1950. Oakley, K. P. & Hoskins, C. R. 'New evidence on the antiquity of Piltdown man', *Nature*, 11th March, vol.165, pp.379–82.

45 1953. Weiner, J. S., Oakley, K. P. & Le Gros Clark, W. E. 'The solution of the Piltdown problem', *Bulletin*, British Museum (Natural History), Geol.2, No.3, pp.139–46.

46 1955. Weiner, J. S., Oakley, K. P. & Le Gros Clark, W. E. 'Further contributions to the solution of the Piltdown problem', *Bulletin*, British Museum (Natural History), Geol.2, no.6, pp.228–88.

47 1970. 'Ariadne' (Comment on Piltdown hoax), *New Scientist*, 10th December, vol.48, p.471.

48 1971. Head, J. 'Piltdown mystery', *New Scientist*, 14th January, vol.49, p.86.

49 1976. Oakley, K. P. *Antiquity*, vol.L, no.197 (March), pp.9–13.

SECTION II—APE-MEN 'EVIDENCE'

50 1940. Hansen, S. 'Varvity in Danish and Scanian late-glacial deposits', Danmark's Geol. Undersøgelse (2), vol.63.

51 1959. Reed, C. A. 'Animal domestication in prehistoric Near East', *Science*, vol.130, 1630.

52 1968. Funkhouser, J. G. & Naughton, J. J. 'Radiogenic helium and argon in ultra-mafic inclusions from Hawaii', *Journal of Geophysical Research*, 15th July, vol.73, no.14, pp.4601–7.

53 1969. Pilbeam, D. 'Newly recognized mandible of Ramapithecus', *Nature*, 14th June, vol.222, pp.1093–4.

54 1970. Leakey, L. S. B. 'Newly' recognized mandible of Ramapithecus', *Nature*, 10th January, vol.225, pp.199–200.

55 1970. Pilbeam, D. 'Gigantopithecus and the origins of hominidae', *Nature*, 7th February, vol.225, pp.516–19.

56 1972. Eckhardt, R. B. 'Population genetics and human origins', *Scientific American*, v.226, pp.94–103.

57 1976. Fleming, S. 'The first 33 million years', *New Scientist*, 1st July, v.71, pp.6–8.

58 1977. Simons, E. L. 'Ramapithecus', *Scientific American*, May, vol.236, no.5, pp.28–35.

SECTION III—EARLY HOMO SAPIENS

59 1880. Whitney, J. D. 'The auriferous gravels of the Sierra Nevada of California, *Memorandum*, Museum Harvard College, vol.VI, no.1 (1st part), pp.258–88, Section V. Human remains and works of art in the auriferous gravel series.

60 1899. Holmes, W. H. 'A review of the evidence relating to the auriferous gravel men in California', Report of the Smithsonian Institute, Washington, pp.419–72.

61 1912. Hughes, T. McK. 'Discovery of human remains; obliteration of traces of interment'. *Geological Magazine*, December (5), vol.9, pp.187–8.

62 1924. Merriam, J. C. 'Present status of investigations concerning the antiquity of man in California', *Science*, 4th July, vol.LX, no.1540, p.1.

63 1948. Oakley, K. P. 'Fluorine and the relative dating of bones' *Advancement of Science*, vol.4, no.16, pp.336–7.

64 1949. Oakley, K. P. & Montagu, M. F. A. 'A reconsideration of the Galley Hill skeleton', *Bulletin*, British Museum (N.H.), Geol., vol.1, no.2, pp.27–46.

65 1961. Barker, H. & Mackey, J. 'British Museum Natural Radiocarbon Measurements III', *Radiocarbon*, vol.3, pp.39–45.

66 1964. Oakley, K. P. 'The problem of man's antiquity', *Bulletin*, British Museum (N.H.), Geol.9, no.5, pp.85–161.

67 1967. Shotton, F. W. 'The problems and contributions of methods of absolute dating within the Pleistocene period', *Quarterly Journal*, Geol. Soc., vol.122, pp.356–83.

68 1975. Gould, S. J. 'Catastrophies and steady state earth, *Natural History*, February, vol.LXXX, no.2..

SECTION IV—PEKIN MAN

(References marked with * are included in a symposium of Teilhard de Chardin's works in English entitled, *The Appearance of Man*, reference 31 above.)

69 1927. Black, D. 'On a lower hominid tooth from the Choukoutien deposit., *Geol. Survey of China* (Pal. sin.), Series D, vol.7, section 1.

70 1929. Pei, W. C. 'An account of the discovery of an adult Sinanthropus skull in the Choukoutien deposit', *Bull. Geo. Soc. China*, vol.8, p.203.

71 1929. Black, D. 'Preliminary note on additional Sinanthropus material discovered in Choukoutien during 1928', *Bull. Geol. Soc. China*, vol.8.

72 1929. Black D. 'Preliminary notice of the discovery of an adult Sinanthropus skull, *Bull. Geol. Soc. China*, vol.8, p.207.

73 1929. Boule, M. 'Le Sinanthropus', *L'Anthropologie*, vol. 39, pp.455–60.

74 1930. Black, D. 'Notice of the recovery of a second adult Sinanthropus skull specimen', *Bull. Geol. Soc. China*, vol.9, no.2.

75 1930. Teilhard de Chardin, P. & Young, C. C. 'Preliminary report on the Choukoutien fossiliferous deposit', *Bull. Geol. Soc. China*, vol.8, no. 3, pp.173–202.

76 *1930. Teilhard de Chardin, P. 'Sinanthropus pekinensis', *Revue des Questions Scientifiques* (July).

77 1930. Black, D. 'Interim report on the skull of Sinanthropus', *Bull. Geol. Soc. China*, vol.9.

78 1931. Smith, G. E. 'The discovery of primitive man in China', *Antiquity*, March, vol.5, no.17, pp.20–36.

79 1931. Pei, W. C. 'Notice of the discovery of quartz and other stone artefacts . . . at Choukoutien', *Bull. Geol. Soc. China*, vol.11, pp.109–39.

80 1931. Black, D. 'On an adolescent skull of Sinanthropus pekinensis', *Geol. Survey of China* (Pal. sin.), Series D, vol.7, no.2.

81 1931. Teilhard de Chardin, P. 'Le "Sinanthropus" de Pekin', *L'Anthropologie*, vol.41, pp.1–11.

82 1931. Vaufrey, R. (Review of Black's final publication on the skull Sinanthropus found in 1929), *L'Anthropologie*, vol.41, pp.557–62. (Reference 80 above.)

83 1931. Black, D. 'Evidence of the use of fire by Sinanthropus', *Bull. Geol. Soc. Chima*, vol.XI, no.2.

84 1932. Breuil, H. 'Le feu et l'industrie lithique et osseuse à Choukoutien' (The fire and stone and bone industry at Choukoutien), *Bull. Geol. Soc. China*, vol.XI, no.2. Report of meeting of 3rd November 1931 in Pekin.)

85 1932. Breuil, H. 'Le feu et l'industrie de pierre et d'os dans le gisement du "Sinanthropus" à Choukoutien' (The fire and the industry of stone and bone in the layer of Sinanthropus at Choukoutien), *L'Anthropologie*, vol.42, pp.1–17.

86 1932. Teilhard de Chardin, P. & Pei, W. C. 'The lithic industry of the Sinanthropus deposits in Choukoutien', *Bull. Geol. Soc. China*, vol.11, pp.315–58.

87 1932. Vaufrey, R. ('Review of Teilhard and Pei's article on the lithic industry of Sinanthropus'), *L'Anthropologie*, vol.43, p.113. (Reference 79 above.)

88 1933. Black, D., Teilhard, P., Pei, W. C. & Young, C. C. 'Fossil man in China', *Memoir of the Geol. Survey of China*, Series A, no.11 (May).

89 *1934. Teilhard de Chardin, P. 'The prehistoric excavation of Pekin', *Revue des Questions Scientifiques*, vol.25.

90 1934. Pei, W. C. 'A preliminary report on the late Palaeolithic cave of Choukoutien', *Bull. Geol. Soc. China*, vol.13, no.3 (September).

91 1935. Teilhard de Chardin, P. 'Les récents progrès de la préhistoire en Chine', *L'Anthropologie*, vol.45, pp.735–40.

92   1935. Breuil, H. 'L'état actuel sur les industries paléolithiques de Choukoutien', *L'Anthropologie*, vol.45, pp.740–6.

93   1935. Weidenreich, F. 'The Sinanthropus population of Choukoutien', *Bull. Geol. Soc. China*, vol.14, no.4.

94   1936. Weidenreich, F. 'Observations on the form and proportions of endocranial casts of Sinanthropus pekinensis', *Geol. Survey of China* (Pal. sin.), Series D, vol.VII, section 4.

95   1936. Weidenreich, F. 'The mandible of Sinanthropus pekinensis', *Geol. Survey of China* (Pal. sin.), Series D, vol.VII, fasc.3.

96   1937. Boule, M. 'Le Sinanthrope', *L'Anthropologie*, vol.XLVII, pp.1–22.

97   *1937. Teilhard de Chardin, P. 'The discovery of Sinanthropus', *Etudes* (July).

98   1939. Pei, W. C. 'The upper cave industry of Choukoutien', *Geol. Survey of China* (Pal. sin.). Whole series 120. New series D, no. 9 (December).

99   1939. Weidenreich, F. 'On the earliest representation of modern mankind recovered on the soil of East Asia, *Pekin Natural History Bulletin* 13, pp.161–74.

100   1943. Weidenreich, F. 'Skull of Sinanthropus pekinensis', *Geol. Survey of China* (Pal. sin.). Whole series 127. New Series D, no.10, pp.1–484.

101   *1943. Teilhard de Chardin, P. 'Fossil men. Recent discoveries and present-day problems'—Pekin.

SECTION V—JAVA MAN

102   1911. Keith, A. 'The problems of Pithecanthropus', *Nature*, 13th July, vol.87, no.2176.

103   1924. Dubois, E. 'On the principal characters of the cranium and brain, the mandible and the teeth of Pithecanthropus erectus', *Proc. Ac. Sci. Amsterdam*, vol.27, pp.265–78 and 459–64.

104   1932. Dubois, E. 'The distinct organization of Pithecanthropus of which the femur bears evidence, now confirmed from other individuals of the described species', *Proc. Ac. Sci. Amsterdam*, vol.35 (2), pp.716–22.

105   1934. Dubois, E. 'New evidence for the distinct organization of Pithecanthropus,' *Proc. Ac. Sci. Amsterdam*, vol.37 (1), pp.139–45.

106   1938. Koenigswald, G. H. R. von. 'Ein neuer Pithecanthropus', Schädel. *Proc. Ac. Sci. Amsterdam*, vol.41, pp.185–92.

107   1938. Weidenreich, F. 'Pithecanthropus and Sinanthropus', *Nature*, 26th February, vol.141, p.378. 'News and views', p.361.

108   1938. Dubois, E. 'On the fossil human skull recently described and attributed to Pithecanthropus erectus by G. H. R. von Koenigswald', *Proc. Ac. Sci. Amsterdam*, vol.41 (1), pp.380–6.

109   1938. Koenigswald, G. H. R. von & Weidenreich, F., 'Discovery of an additional Pithecanthropus skull', *Nature*, 15th October, vol.142, no.3598, p.715.

110   1939. Koenigswald, G. H. R. von & Weidenreich, F., 'The relationship between Pithecanthropus and Sinanthropus', *Nature*, 2nd December, vol.144, pp.926–9.

111   1940. Dubois, E. 'The fossil remains discovered in Java by Dr. von Koenigswald and attributed by him to Pithecanthropus erectus, in reality remains of Homo wadjakensis', *Proc. Ac. Sci. Amsterdam*, vol.43, pp.494–6, 842–51, 1268–75.

112   1945. Weidenreich, F. 'Giant early man from Java', *Anthrop. paper American Museum* 40, pt.1, pp.1–134.

113   1970. Simons, E. L. & Ettel, P. C. 'Gigantopithecus', *Scientific American*, January, vol.222, no.1, pp.76–85.

114   1970. Pilbeam, D. R. 'Gigantopithecus and the origins of hominidae', *Nature*, 7th February, vol.225, pp.516–18.

SECTION VI—NEANDERTHAL MAN

115   1957. Straus, W. & Cave, A. J. E. 'Palaeontology and the posture of Neanderthal man', *Quarterly Review of Biology*, December, vol.32, pp.348–63.

116   1964. Weiner, J. S. & Campbell, B. 'The taxonomic status of the Swanscombe skull', Royal Anthropological Institute occasional paper no.20, pp.175–209.

117 1970. Ivanhoe, F. 'Was Virchow right about Neanderthal?', *Nature*, 8th August, pp.577–9, vol.227.
118 1971. Wright, D. J. M. 'Syphilis and Neanderthal man', *Nature*, 5th February, vol.229, p.409.
119 1971. Wolpoff, M. H. 'Is Vertesszöllos II an occipital of European Homo erectus?', *Nature*, 20th August, vol.232, p.567.
120 1973. Ottaway, J. H. 'Virchow—an appreciation', *Antiquity*, vol.47, p.106.

SECTION VIIA—SOUTH AFRICA

121 1925. Dart, R. A. 'A note on Makapansgat—a site of early human occupation', *S. African Journal Science*, vol.22, p.454.
122 1925. Dart, R. A. 'Australopithecus africanus: the man-ape of South Africa', *Nature*, 7th February 1925, vol.115, pp.195–9.
123 1936. Broom, R. 'A new fossil anthropoid skull from S. Africa', *Nature*, 19th September, vol.138, pp.486–9.
124 1938. Broom, R. 'The Pleistocene anthropoid apes of S. Africa', *Nature*, 27th August, vol.142, pp.377–9.
125 1948. Dart, R. A. 'The Makapansgat proto-human Australopithecus prometheus', *Am. J. Phys. Anthrop.*, September, New Series, vol.6, no.3, pp.259–83.
126 1949. Broom, R. 'Another new type of fossil ape man', *Nature*, 8th January, vol.163, p.57.
127 1949. Broom, R. & Robinson, J. T. 'A new type of fossil man', *Nature*, 20th August, vol.164, pp.322–3.
128 1949. Dart, R. A. 'The predatory implemental technique of Australopithecus', *Am. J. Phys. Anthrop.*, March, New series, vol.7, no.1, pp.1–38.
129 1954. Oakley, K. P. 'Dating the australopithecene sites', *Am. J. Phys. Anthrop.*, March, New series, vol.12, no.1, pp.9–28.
130 1954. Oakley, K. P. 'Evidence of fire in South African cave deposits', *Nature*, 7th August, vol.174, pp.261–2.
131 1956. Oakley, K. P. 'Fire as a palaeolithic tool and weapon', *Proc. Prehistoric Soc.*, July, New series, vol.21, pp.36–48.
132 1956. Wells, L. H. & Cooke, H. B. S. 'Fossil bovidae from the limeworks quarry, Makapansgat, Potgietersus', *Palaeontologia Africana*, vol.4, p.1.
133 1957. Dart, R. A. 'The osteodontokeratic culture of Australopithecus prometheus', *Transvaal Mus. Mem.*, vol.10, pp.1–105.
134 1958. Brain, C. K. 'The Transvaal ape-man bearing cave deposits', *Transvaal Mus. Mem.*, September, no.11.
135 1914. Reck, H. 'Erste vorläufige Mitteilung über den Fund eines fossilen Menschenskelets usw' ('First preliminary notice of the discovery of a fossil skeleton of a man'), *Sitzungober Gesellschaft, Nature Freunde*, Berlin, no.3, pp.81–95.

SECTION VIIB—OLDUVAI GORGE

136 1933. 'Early human remains in E. Africa'. Report of conference at Cambridge, *Man*, April, vol.33, pp.65–8 and *Nature*, 1st April, vol.131, pp.477–8.
137 1935. Boswell, P. G. H. 'Human remains from Kanam and Kanjera', *Nature*, 9th March, vol.135, p.371.
138 1935. Keith, A. (Review of Leakey's 'The Stone Age races of Kenya'), *Nature*, 2nd February, 2nd vol.135, pp.163–4.
139 1936. Leakey, L. S. B. 'Fossil human remains from Kanam and·Kanjera', *Nature*, 10th October, vol.138, p.643.
140 1951. Leakey, L. S. B. *The Olduvai Gorge*, Cambridge University Press.
141 1959. Leakey, L. S. B. 'A new fossil skull from Olduvai', *Nature*, 15th August, vol.184, pp.491–3.
142 1959. Flint, R. F. 'On the basis of Pleistocene correlation in East Africa', *Geol. Magazine*, 7th August, vol.96, pp.265–84.
143 1960. Oakley, K. P. 'The Kanam jaw', *Nature*, 26th March, vol.185, pp.945–6.
144 1960. Tobias, P. V. 'The Kanam jaw', *Nature*, 26th March, vol.185, pp.946–7.

145 1960. Leakey, L. S. B. 'Recent discoveries at Olduvai gorge', *Nature*, 17th December, vol.188, pp.1050-2.

146 1961. Leakey, L. S. B. 'New finds at Olduvai gorge', *Nature*, 25th February, vol.189, pp.649-50.

147 1964. Leakey, L. S. B., Tobias, P. V. & Napier, J. R. 'A new species of the genus homo from Olduvai gorge', *Nature*, 4th April, vol.202, pp.7-9.

148 1964. Leakey, L. S. B. & Leakey, M. D. 'Recent discoveries of fossil hominids in Tanganyika at Olduvai and near Lake Natron', *Nature*, 4th April, vol.202, pp.5-7.

149 1965. Leakey, L. S. B. *et al.*, *The Olduvai Gorge 1951-1961*, vols.1-3, Cambridge University Press.

150 ' 1974. Protsch, R. 'Age and position of Olduvai hominid I', *J. Human Evol.*, September, vol.3, no.5, pp.379-85.

SECTION VIIC— EAST RUDOLF

151 1973. Innes, H. 'Young man and old bones', *Daily Telegraph Magazine*, 23rd November, no.473.

152 Leakey, R. E. & Lewin, R. *Origins*, MacDonald & Janes, London 1977.

153 1973. Leakey, R. 'Evidence for an advanced Plio-Pleistocene hominid from E. Rudolf, Kenya', *Nature*, 13th April, vol.242, pp.447-450.

154 1973. Leakey, R. 'Skull 1470'. *Nat. Geog. Mag.*, June, vol.143, no.6, pp.819-29.

155 1972. Hillaby, J. 'Dem ole bones', '*New Scientist*, 21st December, vol.56, no.825.

156 1974. Leakey, R. 'Further evidence of Lower Pleistocene hominids from East Rudolf 1973', *Nature*, 19th April, vol.248, pp.653-56.

157 1978. Leakey, M. G. & Leakey, R. E. 'Koobi Fora research project', vol.1, *Clarendon Press*.

158 1976. Leakey, R. 'New hominid fossils from the Koobi Fora formation in Northern Kenya', *Nature*, 17th June, vol.261, pp.574-6.

159 1970. Fitch, F. J. & Miller, J. A. 'Radioisotopic age determinations of Lake Rudolf artefact site', *Nature*, 18th April, vol.226, pp.226-8.

160 1974. Fitch, F. J. *et al.*, 'Dating of rocks at East Rudolf', *Nature*, 20th September, vol.251, pp.213-15.

161 1975. Curtis, G. H. *et al.*, 'Age of KBS tuff in Koobi Fora formation', *Nature*, 4th December, vol.258, pp.395-7.

162 1973. Bowen, B. E. & Vondra, C. F. 'Stratigraphical relationships of the Plio-Pleistocene deposits, East Rudolf', *Nature*, 6th April, vol.242, pp.391-3.

163 1976. Leakey, R. E. F. & Walker, A. C. 'Australopithecus, Homo erectus and the single species hypothesis', *Nature*, 17th June, vol.261, pp.572-4.

164 1973. Tobias, P. V. 'Implications of the new age estimate of the early S. African hominids', *Nature*, 9th November, vol.246, p.80.

165 1972. Thorne, A. G. & Macumber, P. G. 'Discoveries of late Pleistocene man at Kow Swamp, Australia', *Nature*, 11th August, vol.238, pp.316-19.

166 *The Times*, 9th March, 1976.

SECTION VIID—HADAR

167 1979. Johanson, D. C. & White, T. D. 'A systematic assessment of early African hominids', *Science*, 26th January, vol.203, no.4378, pp.321-30.

168 1976. Leakey, M. D. *et al.*, 'Fossil hominids from the Laetolil beds', *Nature*, 5th August, vol.262, pp.460-6.

169 1976. Taieb, M., Johanson, D. C. & Aronson, J. L. *et al.*, 'Geological and palaeontological background of Hadar hominid site Afar, Ethiopia', *Nature*, 25th March, vol.260, pp.289-93.

170 1976. Johanson, D. C. & Taieb, M. 'Plio-Pleistocene hominid discoveries in Hadar, Ethiopia', *Nature*, 25th March, vol.260, pp.293-7.

171 1977. Aronson, J. L., Johanson, D. C. *et al.*, 'New geochronologic and paleomagnetic data for the hominid-bearing Hadar formation of Ethiopia', *Nature*, 26th May, vol.267, pp.323-7.

172 1976. Lewin, R. 'The most complete three million year old near-human found in Ethiopia', *New Scientist*, 8th April, vol.170, p.72.
173 1976. 'Ethiopia yields first "family" of early man', *Nat. Geog. Mag.*, December, vol.150, no.6, pp.790–811.
174 1979. *International Herald Tribune*, 20th February, p.5.
175 de Monfreid, H. *Pearls, Arms and Hashish*, Coward-McCann, Inc., N.Y., 1930.

SECTION VIIE—LAETOLIL

176 1978. *New Scientist*, 23rd February, vol.77, no.1091, p.483.
177 1979. Leakey, M. D. & Hay, R. L. 'Footprints in the Laetolil beds', *Nature*, 22nd March, vol.278, pp.317–23.
178 1979. Leakey, M. D. 'Footprints in the ashes of time', *Nat. Geog. Mag.*, April, vol.155, no.4, pp.446–57.
179 1939. Bird, R. T. 'Thunder in his footsepes', *Natural History Magazine*, pp.254–61.

CONCLUSION

180 de Grazia, A. *The Velikovsky affair*, Sedgwick & Jackson, 1966.
181 Ardrey, R. *The Social contract*, Collins, 1970.

INDEX

REVIEWS OF THE FIRST EDITION

English Churchman. 'This is a most learned, factual and highly-documented treatise on the subject of the findings, during the last two centuries, of certain ape-like fossil fragments from which scientists have deduced that man is descended directly from the apes.

The author exposes with pitiless logic and documentation the "last-word" theories of scientists, geologists and anthropologists, consequent upon the discoveries of such things as the "Piltdown Man", exposing many of them as frauds and hoaxes—which in the case of the Piltdown findings is now universally admitted.

This is a book of absorbing interest, especially to Christian teachers of Science and R.E., since any Secondary schoolboy will tell you glibly that "Man is descended from monkeys—Science has proved it." Mr. Bowden's exposures are quite unanswerable, . . .'

International Catholic Priests Association. 'This is one of the most important works for years on the ape-men fossils, and it shines a bright light on four aspects. Firstly, the author shows that the ape-men fossils are dubious in the extreme. Secondly, he shows that evolutionists have concealed or minimized fossils of real men as ancient as these of their supposed ancestors, the ape-men. Thirdly, the ape-men have not been "discovered" by a huge army of scientists, but rather by a tiny group, numbered almost in single figures, travelling from hoax to hoax. Lastly, many will conclude from this work that right in the centre of this group was none other than Teilhard de Chardin . . . This book is written by a clear thinker with a scientific approach who has long studied the original books and papers, weighed one account against another, and has now given us the results in a condensed yet clear way. Everyone should have this book and make sure that their public library also has it.'

Evangelical Times. 'In places it reads like a detective story . . . Indeed one is left with the inescapable impression that the trail of suspicion goes beyond Piltdown . . . [a book] which will be worth adding to your collection.'

Evangelical Action (Australia). '. . . Although written in a scholarly and technical manner, "Ape-men, Fact or Fallacy" is, nevertheless, quite easily understood by the non-technical reader and I recommend it to all those who, like myself, have to provide answers to evolutionary questions.'

Prophetic Witness (Review by Dr. F. A. Tatford). '. . . This is an important book, covering the whole ground of fossil evidence for evolution, and it cannot be ignored. We commend it to our readers.

Fellowship (Review by Duane T. Gish, Ph.D.—Associate Director, Institute for Creation Research, California). 'Anyone interested in the fossil evidence for the ancestry of man should have a copy of Malcolm Bowden's book . . .'

By the same author—

"The Rise of the Evolution Fraud"

Synopsis

Uniformitarian Theory—amateur status of geology easily overthrown by Charles Lyell's 'Principles of Geology'—Professor S. J. Gould's denunciation of Lyell's 'cunning' and false arguments.

Evolution proposed from time of Greek philosophers.

Darwin's 'Beagle' voyage—Darwin a *Creationist* throughout and for nine months after his return. His *failure* to recognize variation of species on Galapagos Islands.

Anecdotal collection of 'facts' and third rate quality of instruments.

Critical review of devious arguments used by Darwin in 'Origin of Species'—reception of 'origin' and reasons for its acceptance. His appeal to the pride and ambition of his readers.

Theory used to ridicule Church leaders. Used as justification for extreme Right and Left political views.

A study of Darwin the man—the recent evidence supporting Lady Hope's account of his return to the Christian faith. Darwin's harsh childhood.

Charles Lyell—the real power that influenced Darwin—his long term aim of destroying the 'Mosaic account' of Creation.

Review of present day barriers to antievolutionary evidence in the mass media.

Philosophy of evolution. Fundamental logical self contradictions in Rationalist/Evolutionist's arguments. Evolution shown to be a pseudo-science.

The present day results of acceptance of the theory.

The theological reasons for the balance between Evolution and Creation.

The real spiritual issues.

Sovereign Publications, Box 88, Bromley, Kent, BR2 9PF.